Published in Great Britain by
Camden Miniature Steam Services,
13 High Street, Rode, Nr. Bath,
Somerset. BA3 6NZ

Original Copyright 1921
by D. Van Nostrand Company
New York

Reprinted 1993
© Camden Miniature Steam Services

ISBN 0 9519367 1 9

British Library Cataloguing - in - Publication Data.
A catalogue record for this book is available
from the British Library.

WARNING
This book is from an era when workers were less safety conscious than
today, so be careful where appropriate. "Camden" is merely passing on
information. Safety is your responsibility.

We stock one of the widest selections of technical and transportation books
to be found. For a copy of our Booklist write to us at the above address.

Printed and bound by Wessex Press Design & Print Ltd., Graphic House,
55-57 Woodcock Industrial Estate, Warminster, Wiltshire BA12 9DX
Telephone: 0985 215515 Fax: 0985 219043

Pacific Type Locomotive, No. 1737, Pennsylvania Railroad Company

LOCOMOTIVE VALVES

AND

VALVE GEARS

WITH A SPECIAL TREATISE ON VALVE SETTING

AN EXPLANATION OF THE CONSTRUCTION AND ACTION OF THE PLAIN
SLIDE VALVE, THE PISTON VALVE AND THE GEARS WHICH
OPERATE THEM, AS APPLIED TO LOCOMOTIVES

BY

JACOB H. YODER, B.S., M.E.,

*Supervisor, Apprentices, Pa. R. R. Co., Altoona, Pa.;
Member Nat. Assoc. Corporation Training; Associate A.S.M.E.*

AND

GEORGE B. WHAREN, B.S., M.E.,

*Formerly Instructor, Mechanical Engineering, University of Pennsylvania;
Associate Mem. A. S. M. E.; Formerly Machinist Apprentice
Lehigh Valley Railroad Co.; Instructor of Apprentices,
American Locomotive Co. and Pennsylvania Railroad Co.*

SECOND PRINTING—CORRECTED

NEW YORK
D. VAN NOSTRAND COMPANY
EIGHT WARREN STREET
1921

PREFACE

This book has been prepared to meet a general desire among railroad shop men to acquaint themselves thoroughly with the valves and valve gears applied to the modern locomotive and to master the principles of valve motion as a preparation to valve setting. Many men possessing sufficient knowledge of valves and valve gears to enable them to do valve setting have unfortunately guarded this information and kept it from others. Valve motion and valve setting have always appeared to many shop men as more or less of a mystery. It is the aim of this book to enable all those interested in this important subject to acquire a first hand knowledge of it. The material has been compiled largely from notes used in the instruction of apprentices of the Pennsylvania Railroad Company, and from knowledge gained by the authors in practical shop experience. As far as possible, all technical discussions have been avoided and the material arranged so as to present the underlying principles as plain facts. This book is intended not as a technical treatise on the subject, but rather as a practical reference book of valuable information applicable to the everyday work of the average mechanic employed in railroad shops. For the apprentice learning a trade it furnishes information on valves and valve gears that can otherwise be obtained only by laborious work and considerable reading of books not bearing directly on this subject. The book will serve the engineman or fireman desiring to broaden his knowledge of the principles of this subject. Written primarily for the shop man, it contains much information of interest to the draftsman and the designing engineer engaged in locomotive work.

In preparing this book the authors acknowledge indebtedness to Mr. J. T. Wallis, General Superintendent of Motive Power, Pennsylvania Railroad Company, for permitting the use of notes, photographs, drawings, etc. The authors are also indebted to the Baldwin

v

Locomotive Works, the American Locomotive Company and the Pilliod Company, for furnishing valuable material. They are especially grateful to Mr. E. W. Hughes, Instructor of Apprentices, Pennsylvania Railroad Company, and to Mr. J. W. L. Hale, Agent, Massachusetts State Educational Department, Boston, Mass., for carefully reading the proofs and for their many valuable suggestions.

J. H. Y.
G. B. W.

ALTOONA, PA., May 1st, 1917.

CONTENTS

CHAPTER I

PAGE

LOCOMOTIVE VALVES AND VALVE GEARS.............. 1

Locomotive Valves. Common D Slide Valve. Valve Events. Description of the Slide Valve and its Seat. Special Designs of Slide Valves. Balancing the Slide Valve. The Piston Valve. The Universal Valve Chest. Piston Valve for Balanced Compound Locomotives.

CHAPTER II

THE STEPHENSON VALVE GEAR... 35

Relative Crank-pin and Piston Positions for the Different Valve Events at Full Forward Gear. Relative Crank-pin and Piston Positions for the Different Valve Events at the Running Cut-off Position. Relation between Motion of Crank-pin and Motion of Piston. Errors of the Link Motion. A Study of the Valve Gear Parts as they Affect Conditions at the Valve. Effect of Raising and Lowering the Link. The Position of Eccentrics, Relative to the Crank-pin.

CHAPTER III

THE WALSCHAERT VALVE GEAR... 96

Introduction. Construction and Development. Description of Parts. Operating Part of the Gear. Relative Crank-pin and Piston Positions for Different Valve Events at Full Forward Gear. Relative Crank-pin and Piston Positions for Different Valve Events at Short Cut-off Position. Effect of Raising and Lowering the Link-block. Distortions of the Walschaert Valve Gear. Lay-out of Walschaert Gear.

CHAPTER IV

BAKER LOCOMOTIVE VALVE GEAR... 172
SOUTHERN LOCOMOTIVE VALVE GEAR... 190
THE JOY VALVE GEAR.. 194
THE YOUNG LOCOMOTIVE VALVE, VALVE GEAR, AND REVERSE GEAR............. 196
THE GOOCH STATIONARY LINK.. 198
THE ALLEN VALVE GEAR.. 199

CONTENTS

CHAPTER V

EFFECTS OF ALTERING THE VALVE AND ITS EVENTS............................ 200

CHAPTER VI

LOCOMOTIVE VALVE SETTING.. 211
Stephenson Gear. Walschaert Gear. Mallet Valve Gears. Baker Valve Gear. Rules for Valve Setting.

CHAPTER VII

SUMMARY.. 250

APPENDIX... 255
The Steam Engine Indicator and Indicator Diagram. The Indicator Diagram. Application of the Diagram. Horse Power of Locomotives. Tractive Force of the Single Expansion Locomotive. Tractive Force of Two-cylinder Compound Locomotives. Tractive Force of Mallet Articulated Compound Locomotives Classification of Locomotives.

INDEX, , , , , ,   , , , , , , , ...269

LIST OF ILLUSTRATIONS

Pennsylvania Pacific Type Locomotive, No. 1737 ....*Frontispiece*

FIG.   PAGE

1. John Bull Engine. xvi
2. Common " D " Slide Valve. 2
3. Sectional Diagram of Valve, etc. 3
4. Steam Action: Piston moving on its backward stroke. 3
5. Steam Action: Piston Moving on its Forward Stroke. 3
6. Valve without Lap. 4
7. Valve without Lap Moved to Right. 4
8. Valve with Lap. 6
9. Valve with Lap at Cut-off. 6
10. Valve with Exhaust Lap 7
11. Valve with Exhaust Clearance. 7
12. Slide Valve, three Views. 9
13. Slide Valve Seat. 10
14. Slide Valve and Seat in Section. 11
15. Allen Valve. 12
16. Allen Valve Admitting Steam. 12
17. Mallet Compound Locomotive, Norfolk & Western. 13
18. Detail Allen Valve, Norfolk & Western. 13
19. Wilson Valve (Opening Position). 14
20. Wilson Valve, (Wide Open Position). 14
21. Wilson Valve (Exhaust Opening Position) 15
22. American Double Disc Balance. 16
23. American Single Disc Balance. 16
24. Wilson Balanced Valve (Section). 18
25. Wilson Balanced Valve (End View). 19
26. Piston Valve and Bushing. 21
27. Piston Valve in Steam Chest. 21
28. Piston Valve. 22
29. Pacific Type Locomotive. 23
30. P. R. R. Piston Valve with Extended Valve Stem. 24
31. Piston Valve showing Steam Edges, etc., Inside Admission. 25
32. Piston Valve Outside Admission. 26
33. Piston Valve Bushing. 27
34. Detail of Ring. 28
35. Allen Piston Valve. 29
36. Universal Valve Chest, Inside Steampipes. 30
37. Universal Valve Chest, Outside Steampipes. 30
38. Compound Piston Valve. 32

FIG.   PAGE

39. Compound Piston Valve and Cylinders.............................. 32
40. Baldwin Balanced Compound Locomotive............................ 33
41. Names of Parts of Stephenson Gear............................... 36
42. Eccentric Shown as Crank....................................... 37
43. Collar on Axle (No Ecc.)....................................... 37
44. Eccentric (Proper) Center Offset............................... 37
45. Three Positions of eccentric and blades........................ 38
46. Backing and Forward Eccentrics................................. 39
47. Eccentric Strap and Blade...................................... 40
48. Link and Link Block... 41
49. Link Radius... 42
50. Link, Link Block, and Bridle.................................. 42
51. Transmission Bar.. 44
52. Locomotive (No Transmission Bar).............................. 44
53. Rocker Arm and Transmission Bar............................... 45
54. Direct Motion, Stephenson Gear, Piston Valve.................. 46
55. Valve Stem, Yoke, and Key..................................... 47
56. Valve Yoke Entering Steam Chest............................... 47
57. Valve Stem with Sliding Block................................. 47
58. Lift Shaft and Lift Spring.................................... 48
59. Reach Rod. View A, Round—View B, Flat......................... 49
60. Reverse Lever and Quadrant.................................... 51
61. Showing Dead Centers.. 52
62 to 69 inclusive. Diagrams Crank Pin Positions for Valve Events.........53, 55, 56
70, 71. Diagrams Showing Valve Events and Crank Pin Positions.................. 58
72. Diagram showing Relation between Motion of Crank Pin and Piston........... 61
73. Scotch Yoke.. 64
74. Main Rod Center Line of Cylinder on Center Line of Axles.................. 64
75. Main Rod Center Line of Cylinder above Center Line of Axles............... 64
76. Calculation of Angularity..................................... 65
77. Dead Centers not on Diameter.................................. 66
78. Stephenson Link.. 67
79. Angularity of Main Rod (Errors).............................. 68
80. Errors of Link and Main Rod Backward Stroke.................. 69
81. Errors of Link and Main Rod Forward Stroke................... 69
82. Combined Effect of Main Rod Errors........................... 70
83. True Position and Location of Stud for Main Rod Error........ 70
84. Action of Lever Effect of Offset............................. 70
85. Changing Angle of Eccentric Rod.............................. 72
86. Changing Angle of Eccentric Rod.............................. 72
87. Changing Angle of Eccentric Rod.............................. 72
88. Changing Angle of Eccentric Rod.............................. 72
89. Amount of Offset for Main Rod and Eccentric Rod (Errors)..... 74
90. Link with Backset of Eccentric Pin (Error)................... 75
91. Combined Effect of Eccentric Rod and Backset Errors.......... 76
92. True Position of Stud.. 76
93. Layout for Backset of Stud................................... 77
94. Slip of Link Block, Stephenson Gear.......................... 78
95. Change in Valve Travel....................................... 79

FIG.   PAGE

96. Change in Valve Travel.. 79
97. Bent Rocker Arm.. 81
98. Effect on Lead of Hooking Up Lever..................................... 83
99. Effect on Lead of Hooking Up Lever..................................... 83
100. Effect on Lead of Hooking Up Lever..................................... 84
101. Effect on Lead of Hooking Up Lever..................................... 84
102. Effect of Long and Short Eccentric Rods................................ 85
103. Reversibility of Link.. 85
104. Eccentric Set with Center Line of Motion.............................. 86
105. Eccentric Set with Crank Pin.. 86
106. Eccentric Set with Center Line of Motion double Cast Eccentrics....... 86
107. 4-4-2 Type, P. R.R. Co... 87
108. Plain Valve Single Eccentric, no Rocker............................... 88
109. Plain Valve Single Eccentric, Rocker Arm.............................. 88
110. Relative Eccentric and Crank Pin Position............................. 89
111. Relative Eccentric and Crank Pin Position............................. 89
112. Group of Diagram Showing Eccentric and Crank Pin Positions........... 90
113. Open and Crossed Eccentric Rods...................................... 91
114. Outside Admission Piston Valve and Indirect Stephenson Gear.......... 92
115. Four Cylinder Compound Stephenson Gear............................... 93
116. Wheel and Crank on Axle, Compound Engine............................. 94
117. Simplest Form of Walschaert Gear..................................... 97
118. Link Applied, Walschaert Gear.. 98
119. Valve with Lap and Lead.. 99
120. Lap and Lead Lever... 100
121. General Arrangement of Parts, Inside Admission....................... 102
122. General Arrangement of Parts, Outside Admission...................... 103
123. Eccentric Crank and Rod.. 104
124. Eccentric Crank.. 105
125. Eccentric Crank on Center of Axle.................................... 105
126. Eccentric Crank away from Center of Axle............................. 105
127. Eccentric Rod.. 106
128. Eccentric Link and Radius Rod.. 107
129. Eccentric and Link with Light Saddle.........................108 and 109
130. Radius Rod... 110
131. Valve Stem Crosshead Radius Rod, etc................................. 111
132. E6s Valve Gear, Application of Walschaert Valve Gear................. 111
133. E6s Lap and Lead Lever... 112
134. Crosshead and Guide.. 113
135. Cylinder and Steam Chest... 113
136. Cylinder and Piston Valve.. 113
137. P. and R. Engine, Class P-2-B, Atlantic Type (Double Hanger)......... 114
138. N. Y., N. H. & H. Engine, Crosshead on Valve Stem (Outside Admission).... 115
139. Connection of Lap and Lever and Valve Stem (Outside)................. 116
140. Connection of Lap and Lever and Valve Stem (Inside)................. 116
141. Union Link... 117
142. Detail of Valve Stem Crosshead (Two Kinds)..................118 and 119
143. Valve Stem Connection to Crosshead.................................. 120
144. Lift Shaft... 121

FIG.　　　　　　　　　　　　　　　　　　　　　　　　　　　　　　　　PAGE
144a.Walschaert Valve Gear in Course of Erection............................. 122
145. Radius Rod Lifter... 122
146. Radius Rod Lifter... 122
147. Mallet Rounding Curve.. 123
148. Mallet Reverse Shaft and Reverse Lever.................................. 124
149. Reach Rod and Slot... 125
150. Screw Reverse.. 126
151. Detail of Screw.. 127
152. Screw Reverse with Bevel Gears.. 127
153. Hydro-pneumatic Reverse Gear.. 128
154. Cross-section of Hydro-pneumatic Reverse................................ 129
155. Four Cylinder Simple Locomotive... 130
156. Application of Ragonnet Reverse Gear.................................... 132
157. Diagram, Ragonnet Reverse Gear... 133
158. Articulated Triple Compound... 134
159. American Locomotive Co. Power Reverse Gear....................135 to 139
160. 2-10-2 Santa Fe Type Locomotive... 141
161. Top of Link Forward Motion.. 143
162. Bottom of Link Forward Motion... 143
163. Outside Admission Full Forward Gear, Relative Position of Parts......... 145
164. Outside Admission, Relative Crank Pin and Piston Position for Valve Events, Full Forward Gear.. 147
165. Inside Admission Relative Crank Pin Piston Position for Valve Events, Full Forward Gear... 149
166. Outside Admission, Relative Crank Pin and Piston Position for Valve Events, at Running Cut-off.. 152
167. Inside Admission, Relative Crank Pin and Piston Position for Valve Events, at Running Cut-off.... 153
168. Effects of Hooking Up on Valve Travel and Direction of Running........... 155
169. Effects of Hooking Up on Lead... 156
170. Backset of Link Foot Pin... 158
171. Link Foot on and Above Center Line of Axle............................. 159
172. Radius Rod Hanger Connection... 160
173. Radius Rod Sliding Block Connection..................................... 161
174. P. & R. Engine, Light Design of Valve Gear............................. 162
175. Engine No. 6000, B. & O., Heavy Design of Valve Gear.................. 162
176. Layout of Walschaert Gear... 165
177. Plot of Walschaert through One Revolution of Crank Pin................. 170
178. Baker Gear Applied to Switcher... 173
179. Marshall Gear... 174
180. Baker Gear Giving Names of Parts....................................... 175
181. Baker Traction Engine Gear.. 176
182. Baker Traction Engine Gear, Line Diagram............................... 176
183. Marshall Gear, Line Diagram... 177
184. Marshall Gear, Line Diagram Full Forward Position...................... 177
185. Marshall Gear, Line Diagram, Full Forward Position..................... 177
186. Marshall Gear, Line Diagram, Full Forward.............................. 178
187. Marshall Gear, Line Diagram, Full Backing Position..................... 178
188. Reversing Principle of Marshall Gear.................................... 179

FIG.   PAGE

189. Effects of Hooking up Marshall Gear.................................... 180
190. Diagram of Baker-Pilliod Gear.. 181
191. Line Diagram Baker Gear (Inside Admission)............................. 181
192. Baker Gear Development... 181
193. Line Diagram of Baker Gear (Outside Admission)......................... 183
194. Bell Crank, Inside Admission Arrangement.............................. 184
195. Bell Crank, Outside Admission Arrangement............................. 184
196. Application of Baker Gear to Pacific Type Locomotive................... 185
197. Baker Gear Inside Admission, Full Forward Motion....................... 186
198. Baker Gear Inside Admission, Mid Motion............................... 186
199. Baker Gear Inside Admission, Full Backing Motion...................... 186
200. Baker Gear Outside Admission, Full Forward Motion..................... 187
201. Baker Gear Outside Admission, Mid Motion.............................. 187
202. Baker Gear Outside Admission, Full Backing Motion..................... 187
203. Plot of Baker Gear, through One Revolution in Full Forward Motion...... 188
204. 4–8–2 Type Locomotive with Screw Reverse and Baker Gear............... 189
205. 4–6–2 Type Locomotive with Power Reverse and Baker Gear............... 189
205a. Late Design of Baker Gear... 190
206. General Arrangement and Names of Parts, Southern Gear................. 191
207. Eccentric Rod Giving Lap and Lead to Valve............................ 192
208. Southern Gear with Inside Admission Valves............................ 192
209. Southern Gear Applied to Mikado Type Locomotive....................... 193
210. Line Diagram of Joy Valve Gear....................................... 195
211. Joy Valve Gear applied to the Reading Three-Cylinder Engine............ 196
212. Side View of Reading Three-Cylinder Engine............................ 196
213. Arrangement of Cylinders and Valve Gears, Reading Three-Cylinder Engine... 197
214. Application of Young Valve Gear...................................... 197
215. Young Valve.. 198
216. Young Reverse Gear... 198
217. Gooch Link Motion.. 199
218. Allen Valve Gear... 201
219. Valve Diagram for Valve Events....................................... 202
220. Valve Diagram Showing Lead... 3C3
221. Diagram Giving Piston Positions...................................... 204
222. Diagram Showing Positions for Release and Compression................. 205
223. Diagram Showing Complete Valve Events................................ 205
224. Crank Pin Positions for 5-inch Valve Travel.......................... 207
225. Diagram Showing Effects of Shortening Valve Travel................... 208
226. Crank Pin Positions for 3-inch Valve Travel.......................... 209
227. Valve Events with Lap $1\frac{1}{4}$-inch............................ 209
228. Crank Pin Position 3 and 5-inch Valve Travel......................... 212
229. Locating Port Marks, Slide Valve..................................... 212
230. Locating Port Marks, Piston Valve.................................... 214
231. Finding Dead Centers... 214
232. Finding Dead Centers... 214
233. Tram Marks for Lead, Right Valve Stem................................ 216
234. Tram Marks for Cut-off, Right Valve Stem............................. 219
235. Tram Marks for Cut-off, Left Valve Stem.............................. 219
236. Proportions of Lap and Lead Lever.................................... 223

FIG.   PAGE
237. Tram Marks for Checking Lap and Lead Lever........................... 224
238. Right Valve Stem Tram Marks, Trying Lead............................. 225
239. Left Valve Stem Tram Marks, Trying Lead.............................. 225
240. Walschaert Gear Showing Effect of Altering Eccentric Rod.................. 227
241. Tram Marks Right Valve Stem Lead Equalized........................... 227
242. Tram Marks Left Valve Stem Lead Equalized............................ 228
243. Tram Marks, Right Valve Stem after Altering Radius Rod................. 228
244. Front Port Mark... 229
245. Back Port Mark.. 229
246. Forward Port Lead... 230
247. Lap and Lead Lever Proportions....................................... 230
248. Position of Gear Parts before and after Altering Eccentric Rod............. 232
249. Backward and Forward Motion Tram Marks, Right Valve Stem............. 233
250. Backward and Forward Motion Tram Marks, Right Valve Stem............. 233
251. Tram Marks after Alterations are Made................................. 235
252. Backward and Forward Motion Tram Marks, Left Valve Stem.............. 235
253. Backward and Forward Motion Tram Marks, Left Valve Stem.............. 235
254. Determination of Position of Eccentric Crank (Baker Gear)............. 238
255. Dimensions Used in Adjusting Reach Rod............................... 239
256. Tram Marks for Equalizing Lead....................................... 240
257. Effects of Shortening Eccentric Rod................................... 241
258. Tram Marks after Altering Eccentric Rod.............................. 241
259. Effects of Lengthening Eccentric Rod.................................. 242
260. Rules for Scribing Tram Marks.. 243
261. Right Side Lead.. 243
262. Left Side Lead... 243
263. Rules for Lengthening or Shortening Eccentric Blades.................... 245
264. Proportions of Lap and Lead Lever.................................... 247
265. Crosby Indicator... 255
266. Cross-section of Crosby Indicator..................................... 256
267. Crosby Three-way Indicator Cock...................................... 258
268. Indicator Cards from Both Ends of Cylinder............................ 258
269. Good Indicator Card.. 258
270. Head End Indicator Card.. 259
271. Back End Indicator Card.. 259
272. Diagram of Piping for Three-way Cock................................. 260
273. Scaling M.E.P. from Diagram.. 262
274. Four Cards Right and Left Sides....................................... 264

FIG. 1.—John Bull Engine. Early Application of Slide Valve to a Locomotive. This Engine is Now on Exhibition at the Smithsonian Institution, Washington, D. C.

LOCOMOTIVE VALVES AND VALVE GEARS

CHAPTER I

LOCOMOTIVE VALVES

THE locomotive valve in a crude form was invented by Matthew Murray of Leeds, England, toward the end of the eighteenth century. It was subsequently improved by James Watt. The invention of the long D slide valve which is in use to-day is credited to Murdock, an assistant of Watt's. This valve came into general use with the introduction of the locomotive, although Oliver Evans, of Philadelphia, appeared to have perceived its actual value earlier, for he applied it to engines of his own build years before the locomotive era.

The valve of a locomotive is the device by means of which steam is admitted into the cylinders, and after it has done its work, exhausted from the cylinders into the stack.

All locomotive valves must be capable of bringing about the three following conditions in order to make a locomotive engine work satisfactorily:

First—Live steam must be admitted into only one end of the cylinder at a time.

Secondly—The valve must permit the used steam to escape from one end of the cylinder at least as soon as the live steam is admitted into the other end.

Thirdly—The valve must cover the steam ports so that the live steam cannot escape from the steam chest directly to the exhaust port and thence to the stack.

COMMON D SLIDE VALVE

The manner in which the slide valve causes these conditions to occur by moving back and forth upon its seat may be learned in the following discussion. The amount the valve moves from one extreme position to the other is known as "valve travel."

Fig. 2 shows a reproduction of a locomotive slide valve on its seat. In order to obtain a clearer conception of the valve and its seat, refer to Fig. 3, which shows a sectional diagram of the valve on its seat in the steam chest. This figure brings out the inside construction of the valve as well as the ports through which the passage of steam is controlled by the valve. Steam is admitted from the boiler into the space in the steam chest *outside* of the slide valve so that the *outer* edges of the slide valve and *outer* edges of the steam ports control the flow of live steam into the

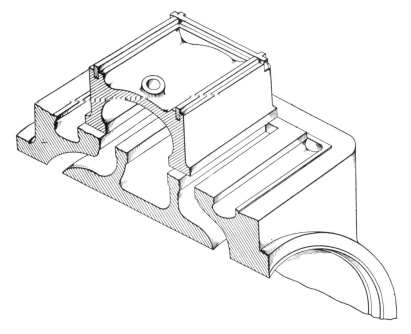

Fig. 2.—Common " **D** " Slide Valve.

cylinder. These edges of the valve and ports are known as the " steam edges." The exhaust port and the exhaust cavity of the slide valve are arranged to control the flow of used steam from the cylinder by the *inner* edges of the steam ports. These edges of the slide valve and steam ports are known as the " exhaust edges."

In Fig. 4 the valve is shown admitting live steam through the front port against the forward side of the piston. The steam forces the piston along its backward stroke as indicated by the arrow. At the same time

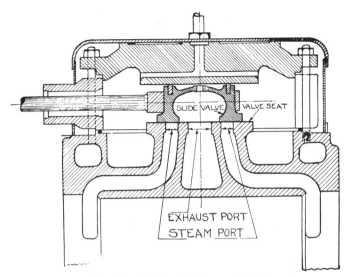

FIG. 3.—Sectional Diagram of Valve, etc.

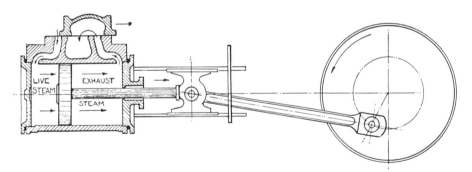

FIG. 4.—Steam Action: Piston Moving on its Backward Stroke.

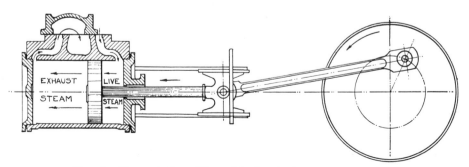

FIG. 5.—Steam Action: Piston Moving on its Forward Stroke.

the back port is uncovered making a passage for the used steam back of the piston to escape into the exhaust port and thence to the stack.

Again, Fig. 5 shows the same condition while the piston is moving along its forward stroke. From these figures it is evident, too, that if live steam were admitted to both sides of the piston at the same time, the pressure would be equal on both sides and there would be no motion imparted to it. Likewise if the exhaust steam were not allowed to escape freely it would have a tendency to hold back the piston.

The valve also forms a wall between the live steam and the exhaust port. It must be so constructed that for all positions of the valve no live steam is permitted to escape from the steam chest directly to the exhaust port and thence to the stack.

Fig. 6 shows a valve that barely closes the ports when in its mid or

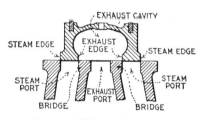

FIG. 6.—Valve without Lap.

central position on the valve seat. (The center of the valve is in line with the center of the seat.)

A slight movement of the valve either way will open a steam port, admitting steam into one end of the cylinder while the other end of the cylinder will be connected with the exhaust port by means of the exhaust cavity of the valve. This condition is seen by reference to Fig. 7, which

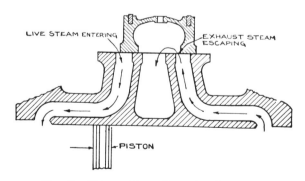

FIG. 7.—Valve without Lap Moved to Right.

shows the same valve moved slightly to the right. The amount the steam edge of the valve uncovers the steam edge of the port is called *port opening*.

Considering one port only, it is also to be noted that the instant the steam edge of the valve closes the port for the admission of steam into the cylinder by passing over the steam edge of the port, the exhaust edge of the valve opens the same port for the exhaust of steam from the cylinder by uncovering the exhaust edge of the port.

A valve made as in Fig. 6 is said to be "line on line," that is, when the valve stands central on its seat the edges of the valve are in line with the edges of the ports. It is evident that, with this valve, steam will be admitted to the cylinder for the entire length of the stroke of the piston, while on the return of the piston the exhaust port will be open for the entire length of the return stroke. In this case the steam pressure in the cylinder during the greater part of the piston stroke remains practically the same as that in the steam chest. At the completion of the stroke of the piston this high-pressure steam is exhausted. The steam at this pressure if allowed to expand is capable of doing work. As the piston moves along its stroke the volume in the cylinder back of the piston increases. With the valve as shown in Fig. 6 (which leaves the port still open), this increased volume will be filled by live steam from the steam chest, so that the steam admitted in the early part of the stroke is not given an opportunity to do work by expanding.

In order to give the steam an opportunity to work by its expansive power as the piston advances along its stroke, the valve must admit live steam into the cylinder during the early part of the piston stroke and then shut off the supply of live steam without opening the exhaust port, thus permitting the steam by its expansive power to force the piston to the end of its stroke. This condition is brought about by extending the steam (or outer) edges of the valve beyond the steam edges of the ports as shown in Fig. 8. In this figure the valve is exactly like that shown in Fig. 6, except that it has added to it the two parts marked L. Each steam edge of the ports is covered by the portion of the valve as indicated between the lines A and B. The amount by which the steam edge of the valve overlaps the steam edge of the port when the valve is in the *middle* of *its travel* is called "steam lap." In the case of the slide valve this is sometimes called "outside lap" or simply "lap." If this distance is three-fourths of an inch on each side (when the valve is in the middle of its travel) the valve will be designated as having *three-fourths inch lap*.

Fig. 9 shows the same valve as in Fig. 8 after it has moved to its extreme left, as indicated by the dotted lines admitting steam through the port *F*, and has returned again to the position shown. In this position the steam edge of the valve is just covering the steam edge of the port and prevents further admission of steam. At the same time the valve

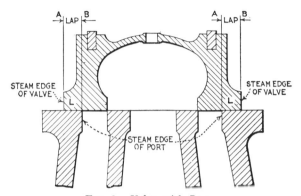

FIG. 8.—Valve with Lap.

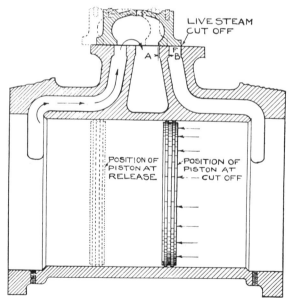

FIG. 9.—Valve with Lap at Cut-off Position.

still covers the exhaust edge of the port *F* by the distance *AB*. It is evident that the steam is confined in the cylinder from the time the valve is moving out of the position shown in Fig. 9 until the exhaust edge of the valve uncovers the exhaust edge of the port. The steam thus confined forces the piston by its expansive power alone. A valve with lap thus causes the steam to be used expansively before it is exhausted.

The valve shown in Fig. 8 is " line on line " with the exhaust ports; that is, when the valve is in the middle of its travel the exhaust edges of

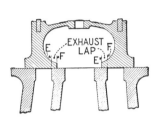

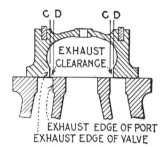

FIG. 10.—Valve with Exhaust Lap.   FIG. 11 —Valve with Exhaust Clearance.

the valve are in line with the exhaust edges of the ports. A valve may be made with "inside" or "exhaust" lap as shown in Fig. 10. "Exhaust lap" is the amount by which the exhaust edge of the valve overlaps the exhaust edge of the steam port when the valve stands in the middle of its travel. In Fig. 10 the "exhaust lap" is represented by the portion of the valve indicated between the lines *E* and *F*.

"Exhaust lap" aids in confining the steam in the cylinder for a longer period than is possible by using steam lap alone. The usual practice, however, in locomotive work is to have the exhaust edges line on line as in Fig. 8, or else have the condition shown in Fig. 11. Here the cavity of the valve is made longer than that shown in Fig. 8, so that the exhaust edges of the valve uncover the exhaust edges of both ports, thereby connecting both steam ports with the exhaust port when the valve is in the middle of its travel. A valve made in this manner is said to have " exhaust clearance." The amount by which the exhaust edge of the valve uncovers the exhaust edge of the steam port when the valve is in the middle of its travel is known as " exhaust clearance." The distance between the lines *C* and *D*, Fig. 11, represents the " exhaust clearance " of the valve.

VALVE EVENTS

As the valve moves back and forth over the valve seat throughout its travel, the various events or changes produced (in the distribution and control of the steam during each stroke of the piston) are designated by the following terms, each of which will be taken up and explained in the order in which it occurs:

1. Admission.
2. Cut-off.
3. Expansion.
4. Release or exhaust.
5. Exhaust closure.
6. Compression.

(1st) **Period of Admission.** Admission begins when the steam edge of the valve uncovers the steam edge of the port and continues until the valve reaches the end of its stroke and returning again passes over the steam edge of the port. It is during admission that steam is taken into the cylinder.

(2d) **Point of Cut-off.** Cut-off occurs when the steam edge of the valve closes the steam port, and thereby prevents the steam from entering the cylinder. After cut-off takes place, the piston must travel the remainder of its uncompleted stroke without receiving steam from the boiler.

(3d) **Period of Expansion.** Expansion takes place from the time cut-off occurs until the valve opens the exhaust. During expansion the steam follows the piston and occupies a larger space and consequently drops in pressure. If no expansion took place the steam would be blown into the exhaust at practically the boiler pressure. During expansion the flow of live steam ceases, hence the earlier the cut-off and the longer the expansion, the longer will the live steam be held back and remain stored for the next stroke.

(4th) **Point of Release or Exhaust.** Release or exhaust occurs when the exhaust edge of the valve uncovers the exhaust edge of the port and discharges the steam into the exhaust port. When the steam has propelled the piston to nearly the end of its stroke, its duty is done and it is important to get rid of it as quickly as possible, as otherwise it will hold back or retard the travel of the piston on its return stroke.

(5th) **Point of Exhaust Closure.** Exhaust closure takes place when the exhaust edge of the valve covers the exhaust edge of the steam port and prevents the steam remaining in the cylinder from escaping into the exhaust port.

(6th) **Period of Compression.** After the exhaust port closes, the steam remaining in the cylinder is confined for a short period and must be forced or " compressed " into the clearance volume (space left in cylinder and port when piston is at the end of its stroke). This causes resistance and is known as compression. It forms a cushion for the piston to strike against and prevents a certain amount of shock, at the same time causing the piston to rebound, giving it speed at the beginning of the stroke when it most requires it.

DESCRIPTION OF SLIDE VALVE AND ITS SEAT

Thus far the events and functions of the slide valve have been taken up and the valve and its seat represented by a section taken through the center line of the valve. In order to get a clear conception of the construction of the valve and its seat, it may be well to study a working draw-

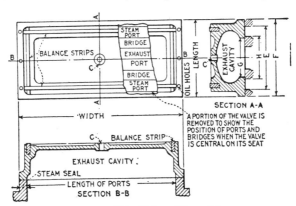

FIG. 12.—Slide Valve, Three Views.

ing of a plain slide valve and its seat as shown in Figs. 12 and 13. Fig. 13 shows a drawing of a valve seat. In order to keep the steam ports from becoming too wide, their length is made as great as possible, usually about equal to the diameter of the cylinder. The width is then made such as to give the proper area through the port and is kept as small as possible in order to avoid excessive valve travel. The width of the bridges is usually made about equal to, or slightly less than, the width of the steam port; while the exhaust port is generally made twice the width of the steam port. The outer edges A, Fig. 13, are made in accordance with the valve design and travel, so that the valve passes slightly beyond the edges A to prevent wearing a shoulder on the valve seat. The corners of both steam ports are finished square in order that the valve will admit and cut off steam along the entire edge of the port at the same instant.

Fig. 12 shows a drawing of the slide valve for the valve seat shown in

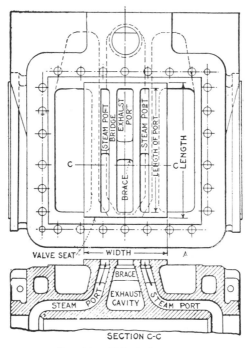

SECTION C-C

FIG. 13.—Slide Valve Seat.

Fig. 13. It is seen that the width of the valve is made larger than the length of the ports, in order that the valve may cover the ends of the ports completely. The amount the valve covers each end of the ports is known as *steam seal*. The section AA, Fig. 12, represents the valve when on the middle of its seat. The length F of the valve or the distance between its steam edges is made equal to the distance E between the outer or steam edges of the steam ports (Fig. 12), plus twice the lap of the valve. The distance G between the exhaust edges of the valve is made equal to the distance H of the valve seat in case the exhaust edges are line on line. The distance *H* on the valve seat is always equal to the width of the exhaust port plus the width of the two bridges. In case the valve has exhaust clearance, the distance *G* of the valve is made equal to the distance *H* of the valve seat plus the exhaust clearance at both ports. When the valve has exhaust lap, the amount of this lap at each port must be *sub-tracted* from the distance *H* of the valve seat in determining the distance *G*.

Fig. 14 shows a sectional view of the slide valve in working order. Here the additional features of the balance strips and the pressure plate are shown. The portion of the top of the valve enclosed by the balance strips, Fig. 12, is known as the " Balanced Area." A steam-tight joint is maintained between the top of the balance strips and the face of

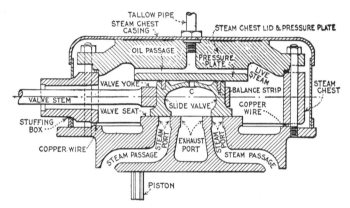

Fig. 14.—Slide Valve and Seat in Section.

the pressure plate, thereby keeping the steam pressure from the area, and materially reducing the pressure of the valve on the valve seat.

The hole at *C* in the top of the valve, Figs. 12 and 14, is to allow any live steam from the steam chest which may leak past the balance strips to escape into the exhaust. This opening to the exhaust port prevents the production on the balanced area of any pressure, due to the steam which may happen to be inside of the balance strips. This would destroy the balancing feature of the valve, cause excessive wear of the valve face and seat, and greatly increase the effort required to reverse the engine.

Any slide valve where the steam pressure is kept from a portion of the top of the valve in any manner is known as a " balanced slide valve." The calculations for this balanced area are explained under the heading of " Balancing the Slide Valve " on page 15.

SPECIAL DESIGNS OF SLIDE VALVES

Among the many designs and modifications of the plain slide valve which have been put on the market, the Allen port and the Wilson types have been used most extensively on American railroads and may be considered as having been designed especially for use on locomotives.

The Allen Valve. The Allen Valve is shown in Figs. 15 and 16. In Fig. 15 the valve is shown in its central position upon the valve seat. This

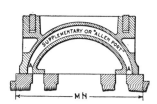

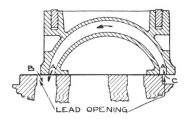

FIG. 15.—Allen Valve.   FIG. 16.—Allen Valve Admitting Steam.

valve has a supplementary port cast through it above the exhaust cavity, indicated by the letters A, A. The valve seat is shortened as shown by the distance MN, Fig. 15, so that when the valve is moved from its central position, opening either steam port (as to the position shown by Fig. 16), the supplementary port AA will register with the end of the seat as shown in this figure, which represents the valve open by a small amount. Live steam enters the port to the left from each side of the valve at the same time. The course of the steam is shown by the arrows, from which it will be seen that the opening at C is added to the usual one at B. The Allen valve is made so that the opening at C through the supplementary port AA is equal to the opening B. In other words the openings at C and B are always equal. Hence the addition of the supplementary port AA gives a double amount of admission, up to the point where the opening at B is equal to the width of the supplementary port AA, so that the total port opening is just twice what it would be with the usual form of valve.

This double admission feature enables the steam to enter the cylinder much more quickly than is possible with the plain slide valve, a condition very favorable to high-speed work. On the other hand, the short seat confines the pressure of the valve on a small area, causing considerable wearing of the parts, and also has the bad effect of causing the edges of

Fig. 17.—Mallet Compound Locomotive using Outside Admission Allen Slide Valves on Low-pressure Cylinders and Inside Admission Piston Valves on the High-pressure Cylinders.

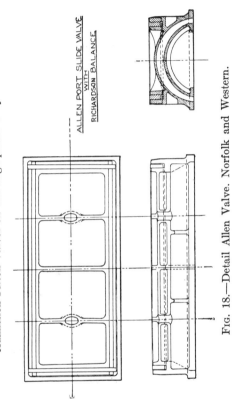

ALLEN PORT SLIDE VALVE
WITH
RICHARDSON BALANCE

Fig. 18.—Detail Allen Valve. Norfolk and Western.

the valve to extend a large amount beyond the edges of the seat, when the valve is in its extreme travel positions.

Fig. 17 shows a photograph of a Mallet compound locomotive using the Allen valve on the front or low-pressure cylinders, while Fig. 18 shows a detail drawing of this valve.

The Wilson Valve. The Wilson valve, manufactured by the American Balanced Valve Company, provides the double admission and also a double exhaust of the steam by casting two supplementary ports at each end of the valve, indicated at *A* and *B* in Fig. 19, one for the admission and one

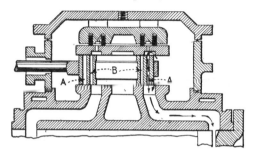

FIG. 19.—Wilson Valve.
Valve in Opening Position.

for the exhaust of the steam. The outer passages, marked *A* at each end, are the ones which give the double admission of steam, while the inner passages, marked *B*, provide for the double exhaust. The course of the

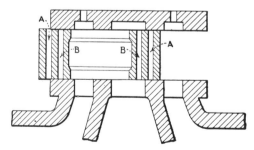

FIG. 20.—Wilson Valve.
Valve in Wide-open Position.

steam during admission is shown by the arrows in Figs. 19 and 20. Fig. 19 represents the valve open by a small amount at one steam port, and Fig. 20 shows the same valve in the extreme left position. Fig. 21 shows the valve when in the position for the beginning of exhaust. The double

exit of the steam from the cylinder is shown by the arrows. The Wilson
valve has the additional advantage for high-speed work of providing,

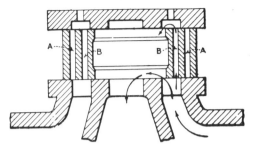

Fig. 21.—Wilson Valve.
Valve in Exhaust Position.

not only a double admission, but also a double exhaust of the steam, a
factor equally important for high piston speeds.

BALANCING THE SLIDE VALVE

With the plain slide valve the steam pressure is allowed to act upon
the entire area of the back of the valve, producing excessive friction between the face of the valve and its seat.   Such a valve is said to be unbalanced.   That is, because the steam-chest pressure acting upon the top
of the valve is greater than the average steam pressure in the cylinder
acting upon the bottom of the valve, the result is a greater downward
force upon the top. With the modern design of large slide valves, and
the use of high steam pressures, it becomes necessary to have the steam
pressures on the top and bottom of the valve about equal to each other
in order that the valve may be moved easily over its seat.   Equalizing
these pressures is what is meant by balancing a slide valve.   The balancing
effect is accomplished by keeping the live steam in the steam chest from
acting upon a certain area on the back of the valve, known as the " balanced area," with the result of reducing the frictional resistance between
the valve face and its seat.   In order for a slide valve to be balanced, it
is necessary to have the force of the steam pressure acting downward on
top of the valve about equal to steam pressure acting upward on the
bottom of the valve. A perfect equalization of these forces or pressures
for all points of the valve travel is practically impossible, because the
balanced area required at each point of the valve travel is different.   However, an average between the largest and smallest area needed gives good

results and is generally used. In case the balanced area is larger than is necessary, the pressure acting against the bottom of the valve is greater than that acting on the top, so that the valve is said to be "overbalanced." When this area is insufficient, the valve is said to be "underbalanced." There are two common methods of balancing a slide valve, one by the use of rectangular strips, as shown in Figs. 12 and 14, and known as the Richardson balanced slide valve, and the other, or American balanced slide valve, employing circular rings, or discs, either one large ring called the "single disc" or two smaller rings, called the "double disc," as shown in Figs. 22 and 23. By these strips or rings (discs) and a suitable

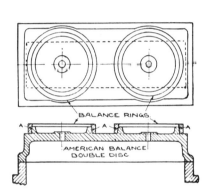

Fig. 22.—American Double-disc Balance.

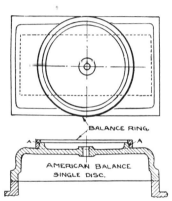

Fig. 23.—American Single-disc Balance.

pressure plate, the steam pressure in the steam chest is kept from a portion of the top of the valve, by means of a steam-tight joint between the top of the strips in the case of the Richardson balance and between the rings or discs in the American balance, and the pressure plate (see Figs. 14, 22 and 23). The area enclosed inside of the strips, from which the steam pressure is withheld, is calculated to give an average balancing effect for all positions of the valve on its seat. The following formulæ have been found to conform to the above condition:

Richardson Balanced Valve. *Area inside of strips equals area of one steam port plus two bridges, plus the exhaust port.*

(To obtain this area *add together* the *widths of one steam port, two bridges and the exhaust port and multiply* this sum by the *length of the ports.*)

American Balanced Valve. (Single Disc.) *Area inside of ring equals the area of one steam port, plus two bridges, plus the exhaust port, plus eight percent.*

Double Disc. *Area inside of rings equals the area of one steam port, plus two bridges, plus the exhaust port, plus fifteen percent.*

Since the double-disc balance has two rings, the area inside of each ring equals one-half of calculated area.

With both forms of balancing (the strips and rings) the wearing parts are the top of the strips and rings, and the bottom of the pressure plate. In order to keep a constant pressure between the strips and pressure plate, suitable leaf springs are placed underneath the strips. In the case of the balancing rings, which are made slightly smaller in diameter than the part over which they fit, a flexible joint or connection between the two ends of the rings enables the latter to be sprung into place and to exert an inward pressure against the tapered portions at *A*, Figs. 22 and 23. This causes the rings to press upward against the pressure plate.

Balancing the Allen Slide Valve. Either the Richardson or the American balance may be employed with the Allen valve. The "balanced area" necessary for the Allen valve is determined by the use of the formula for the type of balancing desired; then from the area as calculated by this formula *subtract* the area of *one side* of the Allen or *supplementary* port.

Balancing the Wilson Valve. An important feature in balancing a slide valve may be seen by examining the Wilson valve, designed to meet the requirements of high steam pressure. With the various methods of balancing locomotive slide valves which have been taken up, the balanced area was calculated to give an average balancing effect for all positions of the valve. With such a valve there are points in the valve travel at which the valve is "underbalanced" and other points where it is "overbalanced." With the use of high-pressure steam, these unbalanced conditions at various positions of the valve on its seat have been unsatisfactory, and an effort is made toward more perfect design of a balanced slide valve in which the valve is practically perfectly balanced in all positions. This result is obtained by providing the largest possible balanced area on the back of the valve when in its central position and then diminishing this area by admitting steam into a portion of this area for those positions of the valve on its seat which require less balanced area. To demonstrate this, refer to Fig. 24, showing a sectional view of a Wilson valve in its central position on its seat. This is its heaviest position; that is, if there were no balance on the valve, it would be subjected to pressure on its back equal to the entire area on the valve face. The area enclosed between the strips and having the dimensions shown by *A* and *C*, Figs. 24 and 25,

respectively, prevents the steam from exerting a pressure on the back
of the valve according to the number of square inches contained in this
area. This balanced area is as large as it is possible to take off the valve
while in its central position, and yet not permit the valve to leave its seat,
due to the pressure underneath. In this case the valve is balanced in its

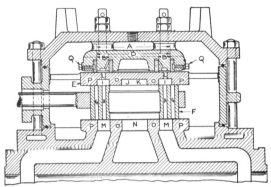

Cross-section of Valve Complete in Chest.

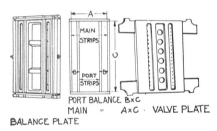

FIG. 24.—Wilson Balanced Valve (Section)

Descriptive References.

A × *C*. Main Balance (by outside strips).	*J*. Pocket in Valve Plate to Equal Exhaust Port.
B × *C*. Port Balance (by one inside strip).	*K*. Relief Holes in Valve Plate.
D. Balance Pressure Plate.	*L*. Ports to Port Balance Area.
E. Valve Plate, or Second Valve Seat.	*M*. Steam Ports.
F. Main Valve, both Faces alike.	*N*. Exhaust Ports.
G. Double Admission Ports.	*O*. Bridges in Seat and Valve Plate.
H. Double Exhaust Ports.	*P*. Outer Edge of Valve Seats.
I. Pockets in Valve Plate Corresponding in Length and Width with Steam Ports.	

heaviest position with the largest balance possible, still to maintain a steam-
tight joint at the faces of the valve. In referring to Fig. 19, page 14,
which shows the valve moved to the position for the beginning of admission of steam to the cylinder, it is seen that in this position, when the cylinder is full of steam, it exerts an upward pressure on the face of the valve
over an area equal to that of the steam port. If this upward force on the

face of the valve at this position were not counteracted, it would, of course, lift the valve off its seat. Since the valve is fully balanced in its central position, there is a force underneath it creating an upward pressure greater than that acting downward on the back of the valve outside of the balancing strips. The valve would therefore be lifted off its seat. In previous discussions the valves have been left underbalanced in their central positions to prevent their being lifted by port pressure at other positions. In the Wilson valve this upward-acting pressure in the port is counteracted by allowing the steam to get on top of the valve through the valve ports

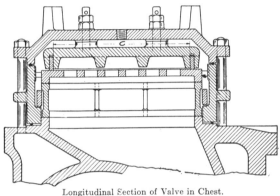

Longitudinal Section of Valve in Chest.

Valve.

FIG. 25.—Wilson Balanced Valve (End View).

Balance Strips cannot fall out. End and Port Strips are held in their grooves by the Main Strips, which are held in by screws Q, Fig. 24. The valve, being of the "Gridiron" type, is very light, and, being the only moving part, the reciprocating weight is a minimum.

at G and H, Fig. 24, and the pressure is at all times equal on both faces of the valve. The steam in the ports pressing upward does not affect the valve, but since the valve plate lies loosely on the back of the valve and the steam pressure in the cylinder port passes through the valve to the pocket port in the face of the valve plate shown at L, Fig. 24, it would lift the valve plate from the valve unless it were permitted to pass to the other side of the valve plate to an area equal to that of the steam port. Therefore the smaller area shown by the dimensions B and C, Figs. 24 and 25, is inclosed in the back of the valve plate and is always open to the steam pressure in the steam port. It will now be clear that when the valve is unbalanced by pressure in the steam port the valve plate is simultaneously unbalanced by the same pressure entering the area $B \times C$. There is one such area over each steam port; each acts with its own port only.

Fig. 20 shows the valve in extreme position of overtraveling its seat. In the common balanced valve this exposed area is just as important as that area of the valve face exposed to the steam port pressure. In the Wilson valve the overtravel is entirely neutralized by the valve traveling out from the upper seat at the same time and to the same extent that it travels over the lower seat, and therefore the overtravel has no effect upon the balancing of this valve. It should be remembered that the seat is so proportioned that the valve will travel to the edge of the seat at the least possible cut-off at which the engine can work. With this proportion of seat it is permissible to use as great a valve travel as possible and at the same time maintain a uniform frictional contact of the valve and seat. The one change in the balanced area and the balancing of the valve at overtravel meet the full requirements of the valve at all of the different points of its travel.

THE PISTON VALVE

The manner in which the piston valve causes the different valve events to occur as mentioned in the fundamental requirements on page 1 may be learned from the following discussion.

A common design of piston valve and bushing is shown in Fig. 26. This construction is of cast iron and represents one of the designs which is extensively used by the Baldwin Locomotive Works.

Fig. 27 shows the piston valve in position in the steam chest, while Fig. 28 shows a cut of a piston valve and cylinder as used on an American or 4–4–0 type of locomotive, arranged for use with the Stephenson valve motion. From these figures it may be seen that piston valves are in reality round or cylindrical slide valves, the ends of which form a wall between the inner and outer portions of the valve and separate the live steam from the exhaust steam.

The piston valve must be so constructed that for all positions of the valve no live steam is permitted to escape from the steam chest directly to the exhaust port, but is allowed to escape from the cylinder only after it has propelled the piston for at least the greater part of its stroke.

Since the development of the locomotive has involved both larger cylinders and higher steam pressures with the addition of superheated steam, the piston valve has to a large extent superseded the plain D slide valve, the former giving the necessary increase in port areas, and being

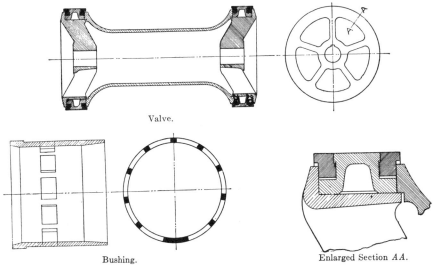

Valve.

Bushing.   Enlarged Section *AA*.

FIG. 26.—Piston Valve and Bushing.

12-in. Piston Valve and Bushing.

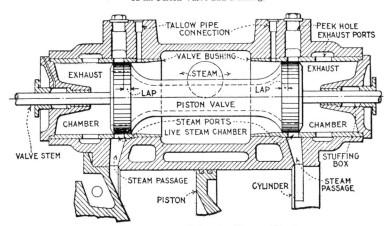

FIG. 27.—Piston Valve in Steam Chest.

Section through cylinder and steam chest with the valve in mid-position.

so perfectly balanced as to reduce friction to a minimum as compared with the unbalanced slide valve or even with the balanced slide valves. In this connection it is the extensive use of superheated steam in recent years that makes piston valves the standard type for the modern locomotive, since this type of valve offers less difficulty in lubricating than the common D slide valve. The relative arrangement of cylinder and piston valve as applied to the modern design of locomotive, using the Walschaert valve gear and superheated steam, is shown by the photograph of the Pacific type locomotive in Fig. 29.

The steam pressure exerted upon the piston valve is equal in all directions. However, the valve, by continuously riding on the bottom of the valve bushing, would cause unequal wear on this bushing. To avoid this condition the valve stem is extended through the front steam-chest head

Fig. 28.—Piston Valve and Cylinder.

and provided with a packing similar to that placed at the back head, so that the valve is carried on the valve stem and valve-stem extension. This construction is shown in Fig. 30, which represents the standard valve adopted by the Pennsylvania Railroad Company. Formerly piston valves were made of cast iron with suitable packing rings provided at the ends. The present tendency in locomotive design is to use light reciprocating parts, and in this connection Fig. 30 shows a recent design of piston valve which is extremely light and yet amply strong. The central portion of this valve is made of a piece of seamless steel tubing, at each end of which is welded a piece of boiler plate, which has previously been formed into the desired shape in a press. The ends of this valve are made of drop-

FIG. 29.—Pacific Type Locomotive Equipped with Inside Admission Piston Valves Using Superheated Steam.

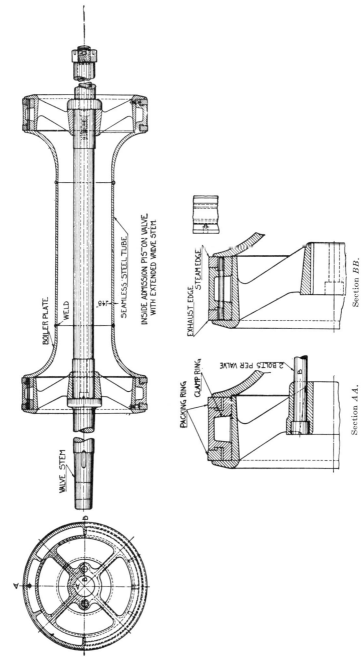

BOILER PLATE

WELD

SEAMLESS STEEL TUBE.

INSIDE ADMISSION PISTON VALVE WITH EXTENDED VALVE STEM.

VALVE STEM

PACKING RING

CLAMP RING

2 BOLTS PER VALVE

Section AA.

EXHAUST EDGE

STEAM EDGE

Section BB.

FIG. 30.—Piston Valve with Extended Valve Stem.   As used by the Pennsylvania Railroad.

forged steel and are held together by means of two bolts. These ends are keyed to the valve stem as shown in Fig. 30 and carry the packing rings which will be explained in detail later on.

Piston valves may be either " inside " admission or " outside " admission. With the *inside* admission piston valve, the inside edges of the valve and the inside edges of the steam ports control the admission of live steam into the cylinders and are known as " steam edges," as shown in Fig. 31. In this case the live steam entirely envelops the central portion of the valve. The outside edges of the valve and the outside edges of the steam ports are then the " exhaust edges " because they control the exit of the exhaust steam from the cylinders. The ends of the valve are in communication with each other from the fact that the piston valve is hollow. It is evident that any unequal exhaust pressure at the two ports will immediately be equalized. It is evident, too, that the pressure of the

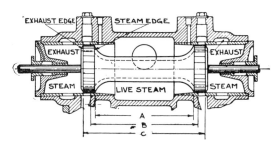

FIG. 31.—Inside Admission Piston Valve showing Steam Edges, etc.

live steam upon the valve is equal in all directions. Furthermore, the inside admission type of piston valve enables the steam passages to be made very short, direct, and of large cross-section. It is seen also that the valve-stem stuffing boxes at each end are subjected only to the exhaust pressure.

Since the *steam lap* of a valve is the amount by which the *steam edges* of the valve overlap the *steam edges* of the ports when the valve is in the center of its travel, it is seen from Fig. 31 that the steam lap for the inside admission piston valve is measured from the *inside edges* of the steam ports to the *inside edges* of the valve, while the exhaust lap, being the amount by which the exhaust edges of the valve overlap the exhaust edges of the steam ports when the valve is in the middle of its travel, is measured between the *outside edges* of the valve and the *outside edges* of the steam ports.

Exhaust clearance is the amount by which the exhaust edge of the valve uncovers the exhaust edge of the steam port when the valve is in the middle of its travel, and is the distance measured between the outside or exhaust edge of the valve and the outside or exhaust edge of the steam port. For the " inside admission " valve, the distance A, Fig. 31, between the two steam edges of the valve must be equal to the distance B between the steam edges of the ports minus the sum of the steam laps.

The distance C, Fig. 31, between the exhaust edges of the valve must be made equal to the distance B plus the width of both ports plus the exhaust laps. In case of exhaust clearance, this distance is made equal to the distance B plus the width of the steam ports *minus* the exhaust clearances. Sometimes piston valves are made so that the exhaust edges of the valve are " line on line " with the exhaust edges of the steam ports. In this case there is neither exhaust lap nor exhaust clearance and the distance C, Fig. 31, for the inside admission piston valve is made equal to distance B plus the widths of both steam ports.

With the " outside admission " piston valve, Fig. 32, the outside edges

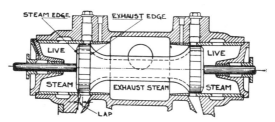

FIG. 32.—Piston Valve, Outside Admission.

of the valve and steam ports are the steam edges and control the admission of live steam to the cylinder, while the inside edges of the valve and steam ports are the exhaust edges and control the release of steam from the cylinder.

As the piston valve moves back and forth in the valve chamber throughout its travel, the various events, or changes, thus produced in the distribution and control of the steam during each stroke of the piston are just the same as those described in the case of the plain D slide valve on page 8, and are known by the same terms, thus: Admission, Cut-off, Expansion, Release, Exhaust Closure, and Compression.

The valve seat for the piston valve is cylindrical in shape and is made in the form of bushings which are pressed into the steam chest, one at each end. Fig. 33 shows a valve bushing as used on a modern locomotive. The openings *A*, in the bushing, form the steam ports and communicate with the steam passages which extend entirely around the bushing as seen in Fig. 33. The openings *B* form the exhaust ports and communicate with the exhaust passages made in the casting which leads from the exhaust chamber to the stack. The parts of the bushing left between the

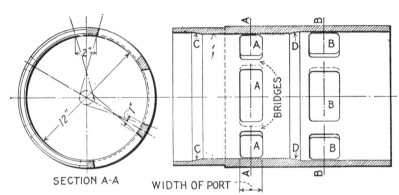

SECTION A-A   WIDTH OF PORT

openings *A* are called the bridges and are designed to give sufficient bearing surface to prevent the packing rings of the valve from springing out and catching in the port. These bridges are usually from three-quarters to one or one and one-half inches in width, with the exception of the one placed in the bottom of the bushing, which is made wider, usually about two or three inches.

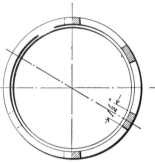

SECTION B-B

Fig. 33.—Piston Valve Bushing.

The width of the steam port is equal to the lengthwise dimension of the opening *A*, of the bushing, as indicated in Fig. 33. The length of the port is equal to the inside circumference of the bushing minus the sum of the widths of the bridges. The valve bushing is counterbored at *C* in Fig. 33 to enable the valve to be inserted and removed with greater ease. The tapered surfaces at *C* and *D* automatically press the packing rings together when the valve is being put in place.

Heretofore the terms "steam edges" and "exhaust edges" of the piston valve have been used without stating how or by what means these edges are formed. These edges are formed by means of packing rings (or valve rings). The object of packing rings is to maintain a steam-tight joint between the ends of the valve and the valve bushing. They are the only parts of the valve that touch the bushing all the way around, and consequently the edges of the rings control the distribution of the steam. With the inside admission piston valve the inner edges of the *inside* packing rings form the steam edges of the valve, while the outer edges of the *outside* packing rings form the exhaust edges of the valve as indicated in Fig. 31.

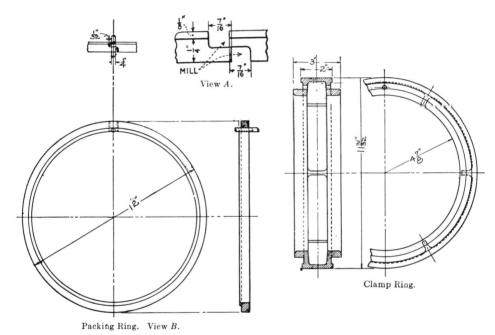

View *A*.

Clamp Ring.

Packing Ring.   View *B*.

Fɪɢ. 34.—Detail of Ring.

Fig. 34 shows a detail of a recent design of *packing ring* as used on the valve shown in Fig. 30. As mentioned previously, the packing rings form a wall and maintain a steam-tight joint between the valve and bushing. This is accomplished by having the rings exert an outward pressure against the inner walls of the valve bushing. In order that this pressure be sufficient, the outside diameter of these rings is usually made about one and one-half percent larger than the bore of the valve bushing, and after removing a portion of the rings as shown in view *A*, Fig. 34, the ends thus formed are sprung together as shown in view *B*, which enables them to be placed in the bushing. Sections AA and BB, Fig. 30, show two sectional views of the valve end with packing rings in place. This construction is made up of two packing rings and a clamp ring. The valve ends are made in a separate piece which enables the packing rings to be readily assembled as may be seen from a study of Figs. 30 and 34. Section AA, Fig. 30, is a view showing the hole through the bolt B of the valve end, while Section BB shows a view through the pin which holds the packing rings from turning around on the valve.

The clamp ring is made of one piece of cast iron and turned to an outside diameter about one-thirty-second of an inch less than the bore of the bushing, so that the packing rings alone bear against the wall of the bushing. In Section AA, Fig. 30, it is seen that the packing rings have a small lip which fits into a recess in the clamp ring. This construction, while enabling the packing rings to spring outward and exert a pressure against the valve bushing at all times, prevents the packing rings from springing out far enough to catch on the ends of the bushings when the valve is being put into place or removed for repairs. If one of the rings becomes broken, this construction also prevents any part of the broken ring from dropping out and catching in the port or causing trouble in removing the valve.

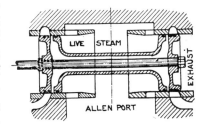

Fig. 35.—Allen Piston Valve.

The Piston Valve with Allen Port. The Allen Port has been applied to piston valves, as illustrated by Fig. 35, which probably needs no further explanation.

THE UNIVERSAL VALVE CHEST

The Universal Valve chest is a practical piston valve arrangement for application to existing slide valve cylinders designed to replace the slide valve steam chest without changing the cylinder or steam chest joint. Figs. 36 and 37 show the universal valve chest applied on an old outside admission slide valve seat. The piston valve used must, therefore, be of the outside admission type. By referring to Fig. 37, a general idea of the construction of the universal valve chest applied to a locomotive having outside steam pipes may be had. This device may be arranged for either inside or outside steam pipes as may be desired. The valve

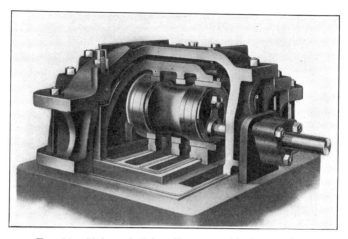

FIG. 36.—Universal Valve Chest. Inside Steam Pipes.

PARTS FURNISHED BY MANUFACTURER

Steam Chests
Valve Chambers ⎱ Assembled
Valve Bushings ⎰
Valves Complete
Joint Wires, Chest ⎱ to be Soldered in Place
Joint Wires, Valve Chamber ⎰

Holding Down Screws
Screw Caps
Bushing Set Screws
Steam Chest Plugs
Peep Hole Plugs
Valve Stems

PARTS FURNISHED BY R. R. Co.

Steam Chest Casings
Steam Pipe Joint Piece
Valve Chamber Studs

Steam Chest Studs
Oil Stud

LABOR BY R. R. Co.

Offsetting Valve Rod
Shifting Eccentrics to Suit Valve Setting

Tapping Valve Seat for Valve Chamber Studs
Fitting Valve Chamber to Valve Seat

FIG. 37.—Universal Valve Chest. Outside Steam Pipes.

For Outside Steam Pipes, A piston valve arrangement applied to existing slide valve cylinders. It renders possible the use of superheated steam without the necessity of applying new cylinders.

chamber consists of an independent steam chest with separate steam and exhaust port joint-wires susceptible of adjustment from the outside of the steam chest, and is secured in a steam-tight position by studs and by the steam chest pressure which is exerted over a large portion of its area. In order that the alignment of the valve stem may suit the existing gear, the valve stem is connected below the center of the valve and is provided with a quarter-inch vertical adjustment.

The diameters of the piston valves for these universal steam chests are made in accordance with the existing slide valve ports. The present practice is to use an eight-inch diameter valve with ports up to and including nineteen inches in length; a nine-inch diameter valve with ports from twenty to twenty-two inches in length and a ten-inch valve with ports exceeding twenty-two inches in length.

PISTON VALVE FOR BALANCED COMPOUND LOCOMOTIVES

Another form of piston valve and bushing designed by the Baldwin Locomotive Works that has found extensive use on some of the western roads is shown in Fig. 38. This type has been designed particularly for use on balanced compound locomotives where a single valve actuated by a single valve gear controls the admission and exhaust from both high- and low-pressure cylinders. The application of this valve to the cylinders of a compound locomotive is shown in Fig. 39, which gives a diagram of the steam distribution as controlled by this valve. The live-steam port in this design is centrally located between the ports leading to the high-pressure cylinder, so that steam enters the high-pressure cylinder through the steam port and central external cavity of the valve. The inside edges of the inner rings 6 and 7, Fig. 39, on the valve, control the admission of live steam into the high-pressure cylinder, thereby forming an *inside admission* piston valve for the high-pressure cylinders. The exhaust from the high-pressure cylinders controlled by the outer edges of rings 5 and 8 takes place through the opposite steam port to the interior of the valve, which acts as a receiver. The outer edges of the rings 1, 4, 9, and 12 on the end portions of the valve control the admission of steam to the low-pressure cylinder. The steam passes from the front of the high-pressure cylinder through the valve to the front of the low-pressure cylinder, or from the back of the high-pressure to the back of the low-pressure cylinder. The exhaust from the low-pressure cylinder is controlled by the inner edges

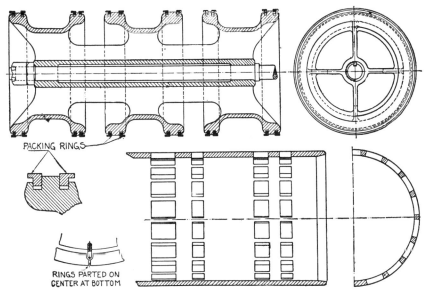

PACKING RINGS

RINGS PARTED ON
CENTER AT BOTTOM

Fɪɢ. 38.—Compound Piston Valve.

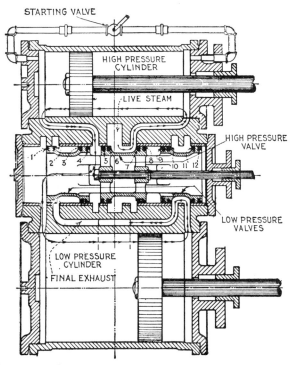

STARTING VALVE

HIGH PRESSURE
CYLINDER

LIVE STEAM

HIGH PRESSURE
VALVE

1   2 3   4   5 6 7   8 9   10 11 12

LOW PRESSURE
VALVES

LOW PRESSURE
CYLINDER

FINAL EXHAUST

Fɪɢ. 39. Compound Piston Valve and Cylinders Showing Steam Distribution.

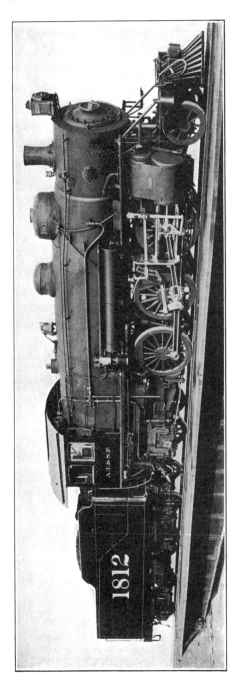

FIG. 40.—Balanced Compound Locomotive Equipped with Compound Piston Valve. Built by the Baldwin Locomotive Works.

of the rings 2, 3, 10, and 11, and takes place through external cavities (under the front and back portion of the valve) which communicate with the final exhaust port. It is seen that this valve, with respect to the low-pressure cylinder, is of the *outside* admission type. The starting valve connects the two live-steam ports of the high-pressure cylinder to allow the steam to pass over the high-pressure piston, thereby using high-pressure steam in the low-pressure cylinder.

Fig. 40 shows the relative arrangement of high- and low-pressure cylinders, and the compound valves as applied by the Baldwin Locomotive Works to a Prairie type locomotive.

CHAPTER II

THE STEPHENSON VALVE GEAR

In the foregoing pages the slide and piston valves, along with the valve events, have been described. It will now be advantageous to take up a study of the parts which cause these events to take place. These parts are usually called the " valve gear " or " valve motion," because they drive, or give motion to, the valve.

The function of a valve gear is, by means of the motion of the engine, to impart a movement to the valve such that it will admit live steam into the cylinder and exhaust the used steam from the cylinder into the atmosphere, in a manner which will cause the steam by its initial pressure and its expansive power to continue to operate the engine.

A valve gear applicable to a locomotive engine must be capable of running the engine in either direction at the will of the operator, or, in other words, it must be *reversible*. This means that the gear must comprise a movable part controlled by the engineman. Devices of all kinds have been invented for this purpose, among the best and most important of which are the various " link motions," the link being the feature in the gear producing the reversibility of the engine.

The Stephenson link motion is a form of valve gear which has had extensive use on locomotives in the United States. Credit for inventing this gear has been given Mr. William Howe of Newcastle, England, who applied the link to locomotives built by Messrs. Robert Stephenson & Co., about the year 1843. Although Stephenson gave Howe the means of applying this invention, Howe failed to perceive its value, and did not patent his idea. Seeing how well it worked, Stephenson paid Howe twenty guineas, or about one hundred and five dollars, for the device, and secured a patent in his own name, since which it has been called the Stephenson link motion.

Fig. 41 illustrates a common application of the Stephenson gear to the Atlantic type of locomotive. The various parts are named, affording the reader an opportunity to become familiar with them and their relative location. It is to be noted that for the usual design of engine there are

35

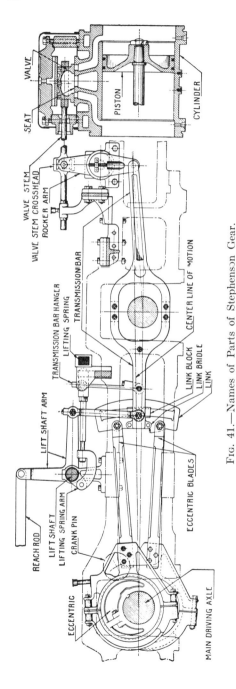

VALVE

PISTON

CYLINDER

SEAT

VALVE STEM

VALVE STEM CROSSHEAD

ROCKER ARM

TRANSMISSION BAR HANGER

LIFTING SPRING

TRANSMISSION BAR

CENTER LINE OF MOTION

LINK BLOCK

LINK BRIDLE

LINK

LIFT SHAFT ARM

ECCENTRIC BLADES

REACH ROD

LIFT SHAFT

LIFTING SPRING ARM

CRANK PIN

ECCENTRIC

MAIN DRIVING AXLE

Fig. 41.—Names of Parts of Stephenson Gear.

two distinct valve gears, one on each side, both operated by one reverse lever and lift shaft.

In the following pages each of the principal parts of the Stephenson valve gear are taken up and described in detail.

The Eccentric. The eccentric as a means of changing the rotary motion of the axle to a reciprocating motion for the link was invented by William Murdock, a Scotch engineer, and patented in the year 1799. The eccentric is made to impart the movement to the valve, and acts as if it were a crank on the end of the axle, as shown in Fig. 42. Since it is impracticable to place a crank in the axle, as would otherwise be required for the Stephenson link, the same effect is produced by placing a band or a collar around the axle.

Fig. 43 shows an axle with a split collar attached, having its center in the center of the axle. It is evident that as the axle revolves, this collar would not give any motion to the valve gear parts, because all points in its outer face move in the same circle, having the same effect as putting the eccentric strap directly on the axle itself. In order to impart motion to the valve gear, it is necessary to move the center of the collar away from the center of the axle to which it is attached, as shown in Fig. 44. Such an arrangement is called an " eccentric."

The outside diameter of the eccentric is largely determined by the diameter of the axle to which it is attached, and must always be made large enough, so that after all boring and turning operations are completed sufficient metal is left at the small part to give ample strength and to prevent the eccentric strap from touching the axle.

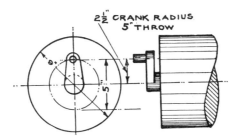

FIG. 42. Eccentric Shown as Crank.

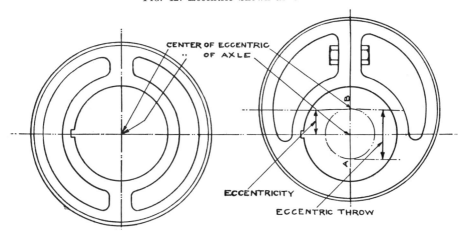

FIG. 43.—Collar on Axle (no Eccentric).   FIG. 44.—Eccentric (Proper) Center Offset.

The distance the center of the eccentric is offset from the center of the axle is called the " eccentricity," and is equal to one-half the *throw* of the eccentric or to one-half the amount which the eccentric moves the eccentric rods, while turning through one complete revolution, as indicated by the diameter of the circle *AB*, Fig. 44.

Referring to Fig. 44, it is seen that as the axle revolves, the center of the eccentric *B* describes a circle *AB*; and it is also evident that the surface of the eccentric does not move in the same circle as was the case in Fig. 43, where the center of the collar and that of the axle were the same.

The effect of the eccentricity is to give motion to the eccentric rods and the entire gear, as may be seen by studying Fig. 45. View *A*, Fig. 45, shows the center of the eccentric directly above the center of the axle while view *B*, Fig. 45, shows the position of the parts after the axle has made one-quarter turn in the direction indicated by the arrow. Here the center of the eccentric is directly to the right of the center of the axle, and the eccentric rod end, or in other words, the link pin has been moved

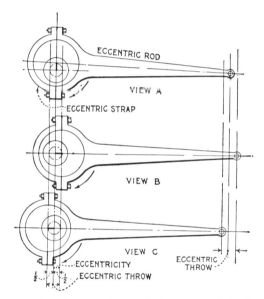

Fig. 45.—Three Positions of Eccentric and Blades.

to its extreme right position. Likewise, after the eccentric has made three-quarters of a turn in the same direction, the eccentric rod and link pin are at the extreme left position, as shown in view *C*. Hence it is seen that as the eccentric rotates the total movement of the eccentric rod is equal to twice the eccentricity. The amount of this total motion imparted to the eccentric rod is called the " throw " of the eccentric.

If a locomotive were to run in one direction only, one eccentric for each valve would be sufficient. However, since both forward and backward running are required of a locomotive, there must be an eccentric for forward running and an eccentric for backward running, to control *each valve.* The eccentric for forward running is known as the "forward eccentric," and the one for backward running, the "backing eccentric."

Fig. 46 shows a common design of both forward and backing eccentrics. Point *F* is the center of the forward eccentric and point *B* the center of

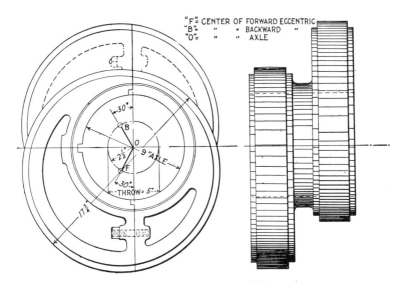

FIG. 46.—Backing and Forward Eccentrics.

the backing eccentric. The distances *OF* and *OB* determine the throw of the eccentrics as explained above. Hereafter the eccentrics will be represented by their outside circles and lines from the center of the axle to the centers of the eccentrics, marking the center of the forward eccentric *F* and that of the backing eccentric *B*.

Eccentric Strap and Rods. The motion produced by the eccentrics is transferred to the link by means of the eccentric straps and eccentric rods or blades. Fig. 47 shows a common type of eccentric strap and blade as used on the Atlantic type of locomotive.

The eccentric strap is made in two pieces, and when bolted together in position envelops the eccentric as indicated in the side view in Fig. 47. The strap is held from sliding sideways off the eccentric by means of the recess turned in the strap to fit over the projection on the face of the eccentric. In order to provide a good wearing surface and reduce friction the inside of the straps are lined with bronze as indicated in Fig. 47. Liners or "shims" are placed between the two parts of the strap and the bronze, turned to give a running fit on the outside of the eccentric. As the bronze wears from use, the shims may be reduced in thickness or replaced by thinner ones to give the proper fit on the eccentric. Sometimes eccentric straps are made entirely of bronze.

The eccentric rod is usually fastened on the strap by means of three bolts. The back end of the rod is fitted accurately into a recess in the eccentric strap, and one of the three bolt holes is usually slotted in order

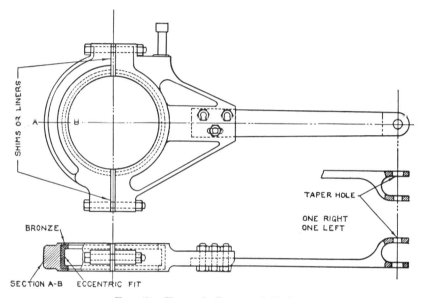

Fig. 47.—Eccentric Strap and Blade.

to adjust the rod and strap to the correct length. After this is done the two remaining holes are drilled, thereby insuring accuracy in length.

The forward end of the rod is forked and provided with a pin known as the link pin or the eccentric blade pin, the ends of which are tapered and fitted tightly into the forked ends of the rods, but this pin is made to turn freely in a bushing pressed into the link. This arrangement confines the wear to the straight part of the link pin and to the bushing in the link.

Link and Link Block. The *link* is the part of the Stephenson gear which enables the engineman, through the medium of the reverse lever and lift shaft, by raising and lowering the link, to determine the direction of running of the engine, and the amount of valve travel suitable for different speeds, as will be explained later. A common type of link and block is shown in Fig. 48. The forward eccentric rod is always connected to the *top* of the link and the backing eccentric rod to the *bottom* of the link. Hence the link block works in the upper half of the link slot for forward running and in the lower half of the link slot for backward running. The link is moved over the link block by means of the reverse lever; lowering it for the forward motion and raising it past the center for the backward motion. The position of the link over the link block determines

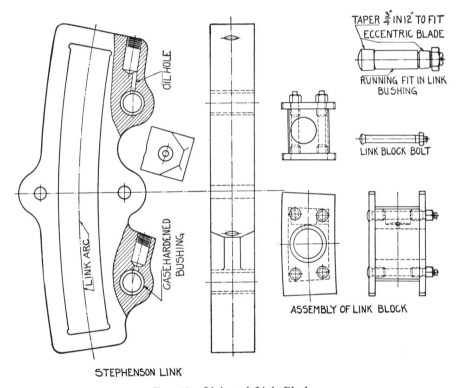

STEPHENSON LINK

FIG. 48.—Link and Link Block.

which eccentric is used to impart motion to the valve. In fact, for most positions of the link the combined effect of both eccentrics gives motion to the valve.

The link slot is curved, forming an arc of a circle known as the link arc. The radius of the link arc is measured from the center of the link slot to the center of the main axle (the axle carrying the eccentrics), when the link and eccentrics are in one position only, namely: when the two

eccentrics are turned towards the link and make equal angles with the
center line of motion (see page 86, Fig. 104), and with the link in the

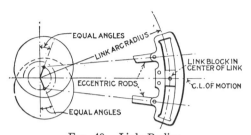

FIG. 49.—Link Radius.
Eccentrics Turned toward Link, Making Equal Angles with Center Line of Motion.

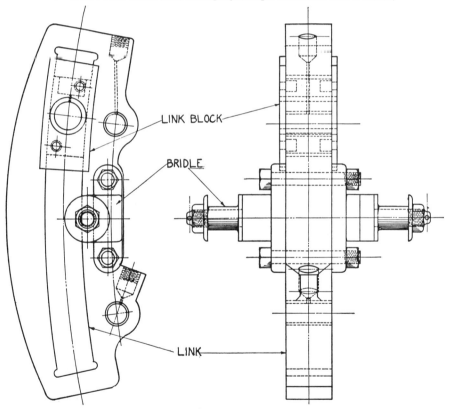

FIG. 50.—Link, Link Block, and Bridle.

position to have the center of the link block at the center of the link, as
shown in Fig. 49.

The link saddle or bridle is attached to the link to provide a means of support, and is designed to enable the link to be raised or lowered over the link block and transmission bar. With the modern heavy links two bridles are required, one on each side of the link, as shown in Fig. 50.

The link is supported by means of link hangers, the lower ends of which are attached to the link bridle studs on each side of the link and the upper ends to the lift shaft arm; see Fig. 41.

The link block affords a means for connecting the back end of the transmission bar to the link, which transmits the movement of the eccentrics through the link to the transmission bar and at the same time allows the link to be moved in a vertical direction without any interference.

Transmission Bar. The transmission bar is the member of the gear which connects the link block and rocker arm, transmitting the motion of the former directly to the lower end of the rocker arm. A common design found on an Atlantic type locomotive is shown in Fig. 51. The forward end of this bar is supported by the rocker arm; while the back end, being attached to the link block, which fits loosely in the link slot, requires some support which will permit of the movement imparted by the link through the link block, and still be strong enough to hold firmly the bar and link block in position relative to the link. For this purpose a hanger is employed, having its upper end pivoted to the frame of the locomotive as shown in Fig. 41.

The length of the transmission bar hanger determines the position of the link block and is made such that the link block is located half way between the extreme upper and extreme lower positions of the link when the reverse lever is in the center notch. The link block center is usually placed near the horizontal center line of the axles. (See Fig. 41; and for Piston Valve, Direct Motion, Fig. 54.)

In some cases the transmission bar is omitted and the link block is connected directly to the lower end of the rocker arm. The American type passenger locomotive or the 4–4–0 class is the most common design using this form, and is shown in Fig. 52.

The Rocker Arm. The rocker arm is an important member of the Stephenson link motion. The type of the motion is classified with respect to the rocker arm. A Stephenson link motion with a rocker arm is known as an "indirect motion" or "standard gear." When no rocker arm is used the motion is said to be "*direct*."

In the case of an indirect gear the rocker arm transmits the motion of

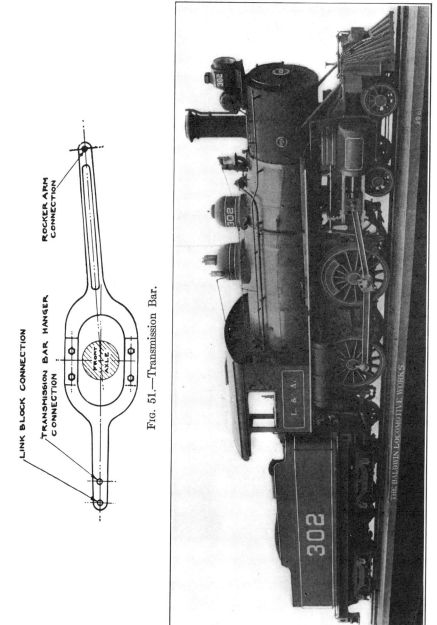

LINK BLOCK CONNECTION

ROCKER ARM CONNECTION

TRANSMISSION BAR HANGER CONNECTION

FRONT AXLE

FIG. 51.—Transmission Bar.

FIG. 52.—American Type Locomotive Equipped with Stephenson Valve Gear without Transmission Bar.

the eccentrics imparted to its lower end C, Fig. 53, view A, by means of the connected gear parts, (eccentric rod; link; link block; and transmission bar) to the valve stem, which is connected to the upper end D of the rocker arm. The rocker arm has two distinct purposes. First, it transfers the motion from the *inside* position of the transmission bar *up* and out or *across* the frame to the valve stem center line, or center line of the steam chest, Fig. 53. Secondly, it *reverses* the *direction of motion* as seen in view A. When the lower end C or link end of the rocker arm is moved forward, the top or valve end D is moved in the opposite direction. This reversing of the direction of motion between the two arms of the rocker arm, when used, gives the name "Indirect," to the gear. The motion of the valve is directly opposite in direction to that of the link block and eccentrics, so that

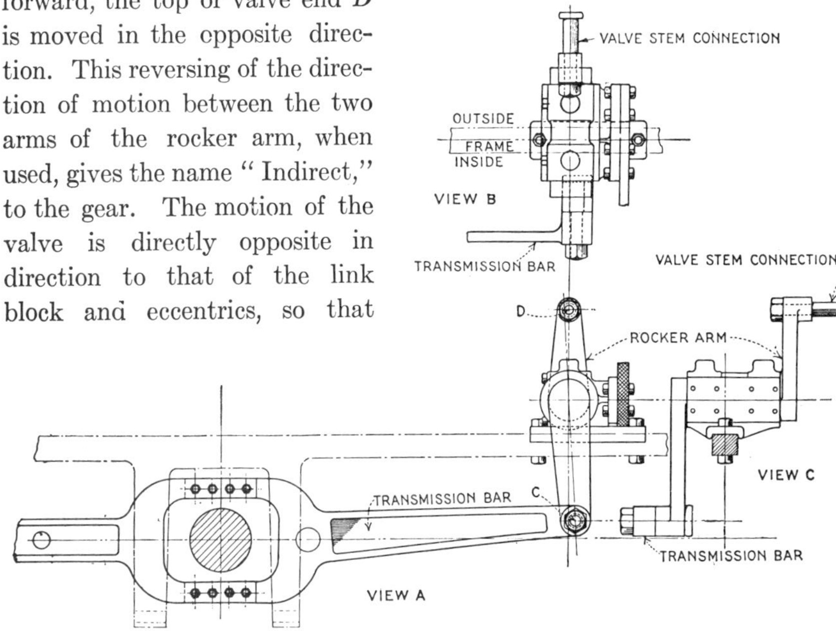

FIG. 53.—Three Views, Rocker Arm and Transmission Bar.

when the eccentrics impart a forward motion to the link, the valve is drawn backward and when the link moves backward the valve is forced ahead. This is an important point in the Stephenson motion, and will be treated in greater detail under "Valve Setting."

The two arms of the rocker arm may or may not be of the same length, and they need not be in the same straight line. One arm is usually bent, either to the front or back, as the case in hand may require. The reason for this bending of the rocker arm and the amount of bending required is treated under the heading of "Relative Motion of Parts," page 50.

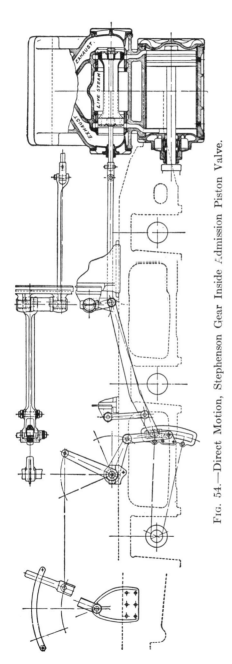

FIG. 54.—Direct Motion, Stephenson Gear Inside Admission Piston Valve.

Direct Valve Motion (Stephenson Gear). The use of the piston valve and the location of the valve chamber in the cylinder saddle permit the use of the direct valve motion, shown in Fig. 54; the central suspension feature in combination with the very direct connections justifies the name. The double-ended rocker has been eliminated, and the motion work being wholly within the frames, the wheels may be spaced and arranged without reference to the rocker arm. In this case the transmission bar connects to a "rocker yoke," both arms of which are on the same side of the center bearing; either the two arms are below the bearing as in Fig. 54, or they may be both above as the design in hand may require.

The Valve Stem and Yoke. The valve stem and yoke impart the motion of the upper end of the rocker arm to the valve (standard gear). The stem is the round part outside of the steam chest and the yoke used in connection with the slide valve forms a means for connection to the valve, so that the latter may move without any "play" or lost motion, and at the same time have freedom of motion up and down to adjust itself on the seat under the influence of the steam pressure.

The yoke and stem are always made in two parts to enable the yoke end to be placed in the steam chest through the stuffing box. The two pieces are fastened together by means of a taper key as shown in Fig. 55. Since the stuffing box hole is cast in the steam chest, a long stem on the end of the yoke would not permit of its assembly in this manner. (See Fig. 56.) When the piston valve is used, the valve stem fastens directly to the valve, thus eliminating the use of the valve yoke.

As the rocker arm moves, the .valve stem pin center will travel in an arc of a circle about the rocker arm pivot or bearing, as a center, and hence causes the back end of the valve stem to be sprung up and down along the path of the arc. This springing is generally of a small amount, and is taken up by the use of a long valve stem. However, when a short valve stem is used, some modification is required to do away with the springing of the stem.

Fig. 57 shows a common means used to connect the rocker arm to the valve stem when the design of the engine and gear requires a short valve stem. If the valve stem is connected to the upper arm of the rocker arm, and if the valve

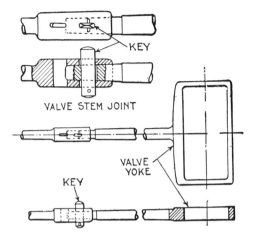

Fig. 55.—Valve Stem, Yoke, and Key.

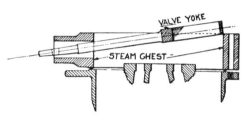

Fig. 56.—Valve Yoke Entering Steam Chest.

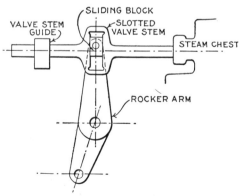

Fig. 57.—Valve Stem with Sliding Block.

stem is comparatively short, the springing effect of the curved path of the center of pin D, Fig. 53, is too great, and causes undue wearing of the valve stem packing. Fig. 57 shows the upper arm of the rocker arm connected to a sliding block which is free to move up and down through a slot in the valve stem. Here there is no " play " or " lost motion " in transmitting the movement of the gear to the valve. Such an arrangement is called a " Scotch yoke," and is usually employed on the Atlantic type of locomotive, where the rocker arm is set ahead of the front driver and requires a short valve stem. With this arrangement a bearing or guide is provided to carry the back end of the valve stem (see Fig. 41, page 36).

Lift Shaft. The lift shaft (sometimes called reverse shaft); reach rod,

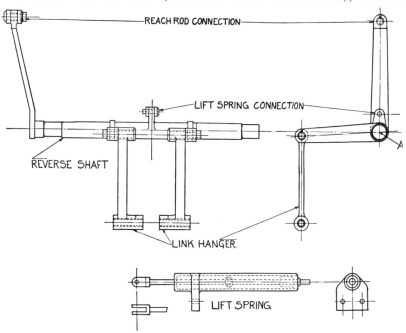

FIG. 58.—Lift Shaft and Lift Spring.

reverse lever and quadrant are the parts of a valve gear which, at the will of the engineman, afford a means of changing the operating conditions of the gear and holding the parts in the desired position for the work in hand.

A common type of lift shaft is shown in Fig. 58. It is pivoted at point A by a bearing at each end, fastened to the engine frame, with one arm on the end at the right side of the engine reaching up for the reach rod connection, and two arms as shown for the link hangers on each side.

Lift Shaft Balancing Spring. The balancing, or lift spring is provided to take the weight of the links from the reverse lever, so as to enable the links to be raised and lowered with greater ease. One end of the spring plunger or rod is attached to a short lever on the lift shaft and the other end is fitted to a suitable holder provided with an adjusting nut for securing the proper tension. In Fig. 58 the balancing spring is shown separate from the lift shaft.

Reach Rod. The reach rod connects the top arm of the lift shaft with the reverse lever and is made of flat bar stock or a round hollow

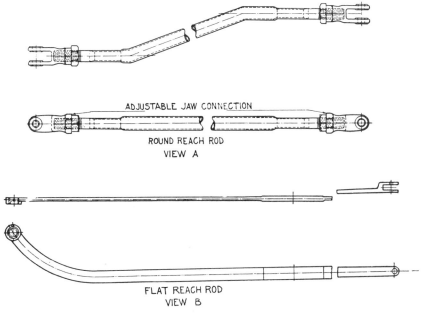

ADJUSTABLE JAW CONNECTION
ROUND REACH ROD
VIEW A

FLAT REACH ROD
VIEW B

FIG. 59.—Reach Rod, View *A*, Round—View *B*, Flat.

material with " adjustable " jaw connections at both ends. In view *B* the flat bar is not as readily adjusted for length as the style shown in view *A*, Fig. 59.

Reverse Lever and Quadrant. The reverse lever is the part by which the engineman controls the condition of action of the valve gear with respect to the direction of running of the locomotive and the position for the speed or working condition at hand. It is shown in Fig. 60 in mid-position or " center-notch." The quadrant affords the means of holding the reverse lever in position for the running conditions at hand. The upper surface is notched and the lever is held in these notches by a latch arrangement.

In order to afford a fine adjustment without making small notches in the quadrant, two latches, A and B, Fig. 60, one on each side of the reverse lever, are provided. The distance between these latches is such that while latch A enters a notch, the other latch B is between the notches as shown in Fig. 60. Hence if latch A is lifted and the lever moved half a notch, latch B drops into a notch and fastens the lever. Both latches are lifted at the same time by the one trigger or latch handle.

The middle position notch is determined by the position of the lever to bring the valve motion in mid gear or the center of link block in the middle of its travel in the link slot. The extreme front and back notches are found by the position of the lever to have the motion in full forward and full backward positions respectively. When these two extreme positions of the reverse lever are determined, pins are placed in the quadrant to act as stops for the lever.

Now that the uses of the different parts of the Stephenson valve gear are known, it will be well to trace the movement of the valve through a complete revolution of the driver, considering one steam port only.

RELATIVE CRANK=PIN AND PISTON POSITIONS FOR THE DIFFFERENT VALVE EVENTS AT FULL FORWARD GEAR

Figs. 62 to 69 inclusive show a series of diagrams representing positions of the crank-pin for different positions of the valve. For the sake of simplicity the valve and cylinder are shown in section, while the parts of the gear are represented by their center lines and center points only. As will be apparent, these sketches are slightly out of proportion; the valve and eccentric throw have been enlarged in order to bring out more clearly the positions of the edges of the valve and the edges of the steam ports. Before referring to these diagrams it may be well to note the meaning of some of the terms which will be used in explaining the diagrams.

Lead. The amount by which the valve opens a steam port for the admission of steam when the piston is at the beginning of the stroke is known as *lead*.

Valve Travel. The distance the valve travels when passing from one extreme position to the other is known as *valve travel*. The amount of this

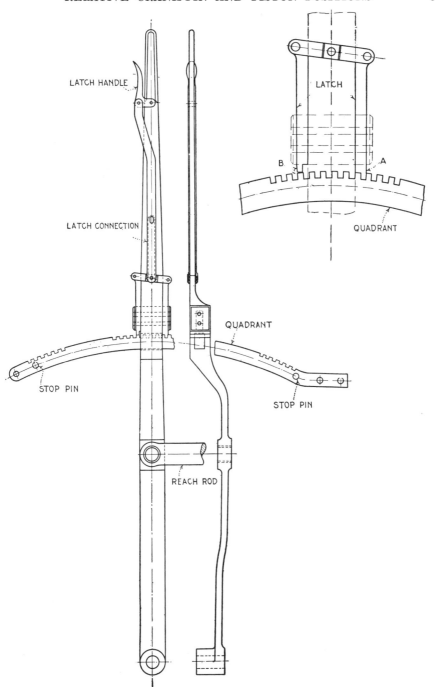

FIG. 60.—Reverse Lever and Quadrant.

travel depends on the position of the reverse lever. The least travel a valve can have in order to have a full port opening must be twice the lap of the valve plus twice the width of the steam port.

Over-travel. The amount by which the steam edge of the valve passes over the exhaust edge of the ports is known as *over-travel.*

Dead Center Position of the Engine. Dead center has reference to the position of the main crank-pin relative to the main rod and piston. An engine is said to be on a dead center *when the center of the main crank-pin is on the straight line drawn through the center of the main driving axle and the center of the crosshead pin.* Or, in other words, an engine is on dead center when the center line of the main rod or that line extended, passes through the center of the main driving axle—see Fig. 61. When

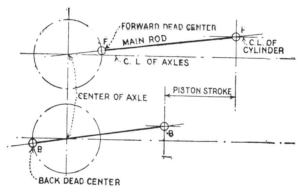

FIG. 61.—Dead Centers.

the crank-pin is on dead center, the piston is in the extreme position of its travel. There are two dead centers for each side of a locomotive, one when the piston is at the extreme forward end of its travel, known as the *forward dead center,* and one when the piston is on its extreme backward position, known as the *back dead center.* The term " dead center " means " no turning " effect received from the piston, which fact is evident from a study of the above discussion and reference to Fig. 61.

In Fig. 62 the valve motion is represented as being in *full forward gear* or with the reverse lever in the extreme forward position (or corner notch). It shows the beginning of the backward stroke or the crank-pin on the forward dead center. In this position there is *lead opening at the front port.* At the beginning of the forward stroke or with the parts in the position shown in Fig. 62, the valve and the piston are traveling in the same direction as indicated by the arrows. With the running gear in this position in order for the engine to move forward, the valve must admit live steam from the steam chest into the cylinder *through the front port.* Hence, it is necessary for the valve to move backward on its seat while the piston is traveling along its backward stroke and the crank-pin is turning through the lower half of its circle. By following this movement through from Fig. 62

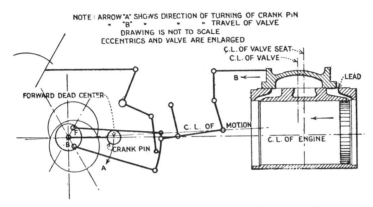

Fig. 62.—Lead Opening at Front Port at beginning of Backward Stroke. Engine in Full Forward Gear.

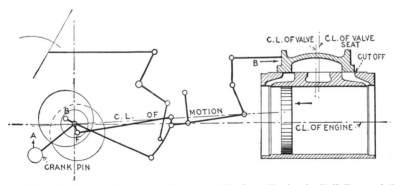

Fig. 63.—Cut-off at Front Port during Backward Stroke. Engine in Full Forward Gear.

to the position shown in Fig. 63, it is seen that the valve will open the front port for admission of steam. This period is called the *period of admission.*

It is seen by referring to Figs. 62 and 63 that the forward eccentric *follows* the crank-pin when moving forward. This is necessary because the rocker arm causes the valve to move in a direction opposite to the direction of motion of the link block and the valve is required to open the front port, therefore, to move backward on its seat, admitting live steam through the front port into the cylinder. As already explained, a valve motion of this kind is known as an *indirect* or the *standard motion*. In a *direct motion* there is no rocker arm and the forward eccentric *leads* or goes in advance of the crank-pin.

Fig. 63 shows the valve at cut-off at the front port. The piston has traveled almost to the back end of its stroke, while the crank-pin is almost on the back dead center. It is seen that at this point the valve and piston are traveling in opposite directions.

From this position until the valve has moved forward on its seat (in the direction shown by the arrow *B* in Fig. 63) the amount necessary to bring it in the position shown in Fig. 64 (or " release ") the face of the valve has kept the front port *closed*. No steam has been admitted or exhausted from the front port. During this time the piston has traveled along its back ward stroke and increased the space in the cylinder, allowing the steam to expand and fill up the larger space. This period is called the *period of expansion*, and occurs between the point of cut-off shown in Fig. 63 and the point of release shown in Fig. 64.

The exhaust of the steam from the cylinder through the front port continues during the entire time that the piston and crank-pin are traveling from their positions of *release*, shown in Fig. 64, to the position of *exhaust closure*, or the one shown in Fig. 65. This period is called *the period of exhaust*, and occurs during the return stroke of the piston while the crank-pin is turning through the upper portion of its path (running forward).

After the crank-pin has traveled on around to the position shown in Fig. 65, the valve has closed the front port and shut off the flow of exhaust steam from the cylinder, giving the *point of exhaust closure*. It is seen that the piston has reversed its direction from that in Fig. 62, and returned to a position almost at the front end of its stroke; while the crank-pin has turned through the upper half of its path to a position a little above the forward dead center. From this position the steam which has remained in the cylinder in front of the piston is squeezed, or compressed (by the advancing piston) into a smaller and smaller space, until the piston reaches the position of its stroke where the valve opens the front port for the admission of steam, or arrives a small distance from its extreme forward travel position with the crank-pin slightly above the forward dead center. This period is called the *period of compression*, and occurs after

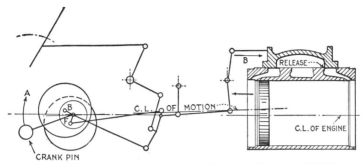

FIG. 64.—Release at Front Port during Backward Stroke. Engine in Full Forward Gear.

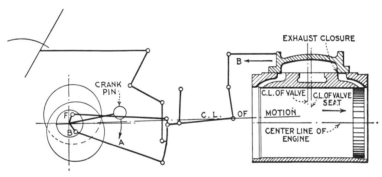

FIG. 65.—Exhaust Closure at Front Port during Forward Stroke of Piston. Engine in Full Forward Gear.

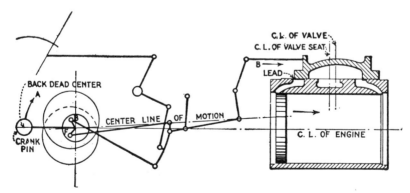

FIG. 66.—Lead Opening at Back Port at Beginning of Forward Stroke. Engine in Full Forward Gear.

exhaust closure takes place, until the valve opens the port for the admission of steam.

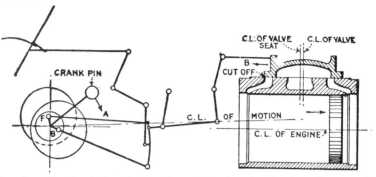

FIG. 67.—Cut-off at Back Port during Forward Stroke. Engine in Full Forward Gear.

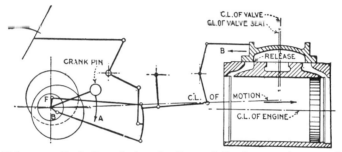

FIG. 68.—Release at Back Port during the Forward Stroke. Engine in Full Forward Gear.

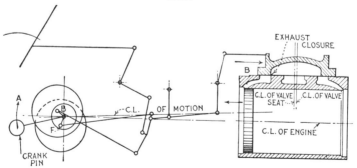

FIG. 69.—Exhaust Closure at Back Port during Backward Stroke. Engine in Full Forward Gear.

Now that the engine has been followed through one complete revolution of the crank-pin giving the complete outline of valve events for the front port it is to be noted that the same operation of the valve and piston with the same valve events has taken place at the back port, and may be observed by referring to Figs. 66, 67, 68, and 69, which illustrate the relative valve, piston, and crank-pin positions for all the valve events at the back port during the *forward* stroke of the piston and its return, when the engine is running *forward* in *full gear.*

RELATIVE CRANK=PIN AND PISTON POSITIONS FOR THE DIFFERENT VALVE EVENTS AT THE RUNNING CUT=OFF POSITION.

The foregoing study has been with the reverse lever in the extreme forward notch of the quadrant, giving the full travel to the valve and known as *full forward gear.* It may be well to observe what effect the changing of the position of the reverse lever will have on the action of the valve. In this connection the diagrams shown in Figs. 70 and 71 will be used.

Fig. 70 shows the relative positions of the crank-pin and piston at the different valve events for one complete revolution of the drivers. These positions are represented by numbers 1, 2, 3, and 4 opposite the crank-pin and piston positions at which each event occurs when the link motion is in the *full forward gear.* It is to be noted that when the crank-pin occupies the positions 1, 2, 3, etc., in its path, the piston is at the corresponding positions 1, 2, 3, etc., of its stroke, as indicated in the right-hand diagrams, Figs. 70 and 71. In the diagrams showing the piston positions let the top line along the piston stroke represent the highest steam pressure at the admission of steam and the bottom line represent the exhaust pressure during the return of the piston.

Referring to Fig. 70 it is seen that for position 1, or the point of admission of steam, the crank-pin is above its forward dead center and the piston is a little back of the exact end of its stroke, showing that the admission occurs before the end of the stroke or before the crank-pin has reached the dead center. This is due to the fact that the valve has *lead.* The valve starts to open the port for admission before the dead center is reached, hence when the crank-pin is on the dead center the valve has the port open for admission an amount equal to the lead. If the valve had no lead, the point of admission would be on the dead center. Hence it is seen that *lead* hastens the point of admission relative to the piston stroke and crank-pin positions.

Position 2, or the point at which the valve cuts off the admission of live steam into the cylinder, occurs after the piston and crank-pin have traveled through about seven-eighths of their entire distance in one direction, or at about seven-eighths stroke. This gives a long period of admission, represented by the distance between positions 1 and 2 in Fig. 70. Here the steam is admitted during almost the entire stroke of the piston; which condition produces a great amount of power, but uses a large quantity of steam.

Position 3, or the point of release, occurs a short distance after the

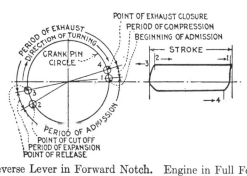

FIG. 70.—Reverse Lever in Forward Notch.   Engine in Full Forward Gear.

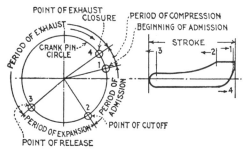

FIG. 71.—Reverse Lever in Notch near Center.   Engine in Running Cut-off Position.

VALVE EVENTS.

No. 1.	Beginning of Admission.	No. 3.	Point of Release.
No. 1 to 2.	Period of Admission.	No. 3 to 4.	Period of Exhaust.
No. 2.	Point of Cut-off.	No. 4.	Point Exhaust Closure.
No. 2 to 3.	Period of Expansion.	No. 4 to 1.	Period of Compression.

point of cut-off (position 2), affording the steam (which is closed up in the cylinder by the valve covering the port) but very little opportunity to expand. Hence the period of expansion between positions 2 and 3 is very short, resulting in a high exhaust pressure and a loss of valuable steam. Hence in full gear there is a large amount of steam taken into the cylinder and exhausted at a high pressure with very little use of its expansive power.

Position 4, or the point of exhaust closure, occurs after the crank-pin and piston have completed their travel in one direction and have returned almost to the end of their travel in the opposite direction. During the time the crank-pin and piston are traveling from position 3, or release, to position 4, or exhaust closure, the steam which has previously been admitted into the cylinder is exhausted through the same steam port at which it was admitted; thence to the exhaust cavity of the valve into the exhaust port, and to the smoke stack.

Between position 4, exhaust closure, and position 1, point of admission, the period of compression occurs. The steam which was in the cylinder when the valve closed the port for the exhaust is confined into the space in the cylinder which is ahead of the piston and below the valve seat. The advancing piston decreases this space and compresses the steam as described above.

Running Cut-off Position. Fig. 71 illustrates the position of the piston and crank-pin for the different valve events, with the reverse lever drawn back in the notch for the cut-off commonly used in the forward motion. This position of the gear is known as the " Running Cut-off Position " for the *forward* motion. The cut-off occurs when the piston has traveled about one-fourth its stroke. By referring to Fig. 71, the position of the crank-pin and piston for the different valve events at the one-quarter cut-off position of the link may be compared with those when the motion is in full gear, shown in Fig. 70.

In the first place, by referring to Fig. 41, it is to be noted that when the reverse lever is drawn backward from its forward notch toward its center notch, the link is raised by means of the lift shaft and arms, thereby causing the link block attached to the transmission bar to work nearer the center of the link. The link block thereby receives a shorter travel from the link; and in turn shortens the valve travel. This short valve travel causes each event of the valve to be *hastened* relative to the piston stroke, with results as will be observed in the following:

In Fig. 71 the valve gives earlier admission of steam by reason of the fact that the position of the crank-pin at the point of admission is still farther above its forward dead center; which condition brings the piston farther back of the forward end of its travel than that shown for full forward gear in Fig. 70. This fact shows that the amount of *lead* has been materially *increased*, as the piston and crank-pin have to travel a greater distance before coming to the dead center after admission takes place. Therefore, the valve will have opened the port a greater amount for the admission of steam, when the crank-pin is on its forward dead center;

hence a greater amount of *lead*. The *increasing lead* as the reverse lever is drawn back to the center in both forward and backward direction of running is an essential feature of the Stephenson link motion and one which will be studied in detail later.

The *cut-off* position is also *earlier* in the stroke than when in full gear, giving a much *shorter period of admission*.

The *release* position is somewhat hastened, but the period of expansion has been materially lengthened.

From the fact that the point of release occurs early in the stroke or at about three-quarter stroke, the steam is allowed to escape and reduces the pressure considerably before the piston starts the return stroke, thereby exhausting the steam as quickly as possible.

The point of exhaust closure, or the beginning of compression, takes place earlier in the return stroke than when in full gear. This gives a longer period for compression, caused by the piston advancing to the end of its stroke through a greater distance after exhaust closure, and hence compressing a larger volume of steam into the same space as in Fig. 70 (or into the cylinder clearance volume). This increases the pressure materially at the end of compression, thereby giving a greater cushion of steam against the piston while passing over the dead center.

The fact that (when running at an early cut-off, as the one-quarter cut-off in Fig. 71) there is a small amount of steam admitted during the short period of admission, and that this volume of steam is used expansively for a greater distance of the piston stroke, affords a very much more economical use of the steam, and therefore, of the fuel, than is possible when running in full gear, as in Fig. 70. The early cut-off makes it possible to obtain higher rates of speed and a lower consumption of steam and fuel than could be maintained at full gear, but at the sacrifice of power.

RELATION BETWEEN MOTION OF CRANK=PIN AND MOTION OF PISTON

It is frequently desired to set a locomotive valve so as to cut off steam when the piston has traveled a certain part of its stroke (as the one-quarter or one-half positions). To illustrate the relations between crank-pin and piston positions, refer to Fig. 72, in which the circumference of the circle *AKBR* (drawn from the center of the axle) with a radius equal to the distance between the center of the axle and the center of the crank-pin, represents the path of the crank-pin. Assume that the motion of the crank-pin is uniform; that is, that it passes through equal spaces in equal periods of time. The direction in which the crank-pin turns is indicated by the arrow marked 1 and the direction in which the piston moves is indicated by the arrow marked 2.

In the diagram the crosshead pin only is shown. It is not necessary to illustrate the piston, because the connection between the crosshead pin and the piston is rigid. Hence, if the motion of one of these is known, the motion of the other is likewise determined, since the motions of both are alike.

The line AB represents the line of motion of the center of the crosshead pin P; and whatever position the crank-pin may occupy, the center

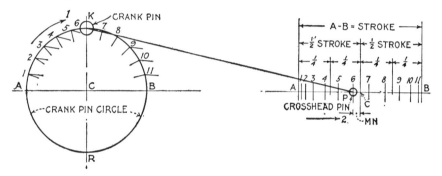

FIG. 72.—Diagram Showing Relation between Motion of Crank-pin and Piston.

Arrow No. 1 Shows Direction of Turning of Crank-pin.
Arrow No. 2 Shows Direction of Motion of Piston.
    Nos. 1, 2, 3, etc., on crank-pin circle are spaced equally and are traveled by the crank-pin in equal periods of time.
    Nos. 1, 2, 3, etc., on the piston stroke show positions of the piston corresponding to the respective positions of the crank-pin. These spaces are *unequal* but all are traveled over by the piston in *equal periods of time.*
    In the sketch the crank-pin is shown on the top quarter K, while the crosshead pin and therefore the piston is back of the middle of its stroke by the distance MN in the figure.

P is always on the line AB. The half circumference AKB is the path of the center of the crank-pin during the forward stroke of the piston (running forward). The point A is the position of the crank-pin center at the beginning of the stroke, and the point B the position of the same at the end of the stroke. The half-circumference AKB is divided into 12 equal parts, although any other number would serve the purpose equally well. The distance between the crank-pin center K and the crosshead pin center P represents the length of the main rod. The distances ACB across the crank-pin path, and ACB of the crosshead pin center line of motion are equal, each representing the piston stroke.

When the crank-pin is at position A of its path, the crosshead pin is at the beginning of its forward stroke, or at point A of its path.   Again, when the crank-pin is at position 1 of its path on the crank-pin circle, the crosshead pin is at position 1 of its path.   In a similar manner the points 2, 3, 4, etc., of the crosshead pin path indicate the various positions of the crosshead pin, and therefore, of the piston when the crank-pin is in the corresponding positions, as 2, 3, 4, etc., of its path.

Notice carefully that the spaces from A to 1, from 1 to 2, etc., of the crank-pin path, along its half circumference AKB, are all *equal*, and the crank-pin moves through each of these spaces in equal periods of time; that is, if it requires one second to move from A to 1, it requires also one second to move from 1 to 2, etc.   The corresponding spaces from A to 1 and from 1 to 2, etc., of the crosshead pin path along the straight line AB are *not equal;* and yet the crosshead pin must move through these spaces in equal periods of time.   If it requires the crosshead pin one second to move from A to 1, it requires also one second for it to move from 1 to 2 of its path.   But this last space is greater than the first, hence it is seen that the crosshead pin, and therefore the piston, has a *variable* or *changing* motion.   Furthermore, it is seen that when the crank-pin is on the top quarter K, the crosshead pin P, and therefore the piston, is back of the center C of its stroke by the distance marked MN in Fig. 72.   This also shows that the crosshead pin (and the piston) have traveled only from A to 6 or less than half the stroke, while the crank-pin has traveled the distance A to 6 on the crank-pin circle, which is one-quarter of a revolution, or one-half the distance it must travel to give a complete stroke to the piston.   On the other hand, while the crank-pin travels from 6 to B on the crank-pin circle, the piston has traveled from 6 to B of its path, which is more than one-half its stroke.   Hence, when the piston is at fifty percent or one-half stroke, the crank-pin is *not* on the exact quarters.

Likewise, when the crank-pin is half way between either dead center and quarter, as at points 9 or 3, the piston is *not* on one-quarter stroke, as is readily apparent in Fig. 72.   Therefore, when setting the valve for cut-off of steam at a certain percent of the piston stroke, it must be set with relation to the *piston travel* and *not* with relation to the position of the *crank-pin*.   For example, if it is desired to set a valve for " one-quarter cut-off " it must be set to cut off steam when the *piston* has traveled one-fourth of its stroke from either end and *not* when the wheel or *crank-pin* is half way between either dead center and the quarter (that is, has made one-eighth of a revolution).   The amount the piston is away from its one-quarter stroke position when the crank-pin is half way between the dead center and the quarter is greater than the distance the piston is off its *central position* when the crank-pin is on its quarter position. These facts are obvious from a study of Fig. 72.

Again, by examining Fig. 72, it is seen that the distance traveled by the piston from positions 5 to 6 is less than the corresponding distance 6 to 7; also the distance traveled from position 4 to 5 is less than the corresponding distance from 7 to 8. It is thus seen that the spaces traveled over by the piston while the crank-pin is turning from point A, the back dead center, to point K, the top quarter, are smaller than the corresponding spaces traveled by the piston when the crank-pin travels from point K on the top quarter to point B, the forward dead center.

That is, space A to 1 is less than space 11 to B;
1 to 2 is less than space 10 to 11;
2 to 3 is less than space 9 to 10;
3 to 4 is less than space 8 to 9;
4 to 5 is less than space 7 to 8;
5 to 6 is less than space 6 to 7.

Sinces spaces A to 1 and 11 to B are very small, their difference in length can scarcely be measured and is always neglected; but spaces 5 to 6 and 6 to 7 are quite large and the difference in length can readily be seen.

It is evident that the piston has not only a changing or variable motion throughout its stroke, but that the motions on the two halves of its stroke are not the same. In other words, the two halves of the stroke are not symmetrical.

This unlike or unsymmetrical motion of the piston on the two halves of its stroke is due to the fact that the main rod is constantly changing its angle with the center line of the engine. This characteristic is usually termed the " Angularity of the Main Rod." The effects of this angularity may be further illustrated by referring to Figs. 73 and 74.

Fig. 73 shows an arrangement of an attachment for the crank-pin and main rod end similar to that used for the rocker arm and valve stem connection on some of the Atlantic type of locomotives where the rocker arm pin is attached to a block or crosshead which slides in a slot in the valve stem (the " Scotch Yoke "). Here the valve stem is allowed to move in a straight horizontal line, and hence does away with any effects produced

by a changing angle. If it were practicable to have such an arrangement for the connection of the crank-pin and main rod as shown in Fig. 73
there would be no angularity, as is evident from a study of Figs. 73 and
74. The latter figure represents the ordinary method used to connect
the crank-pin and main rod end.

At positions 1 in both Figs. 73 and 74, the crank-pin and piston are at
the same position, on the backward dead center. When the crank-pin

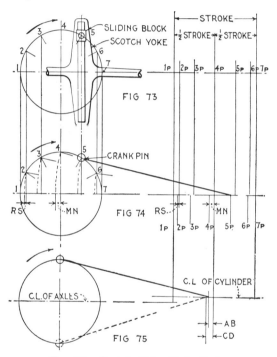

Fig. 73.—Scotch Yoke Main Rod.
Fig. 74.—Main Rod Center Line of Cylinder on Center Line on Axles.
Fig. 75.—Main Rod Center Line of Cylinder above Center Line on Axles.

has turned to position 2, the position of the piston (where there is no
angularity) is shown by point 2P, Fig. 73. Now, since the crank-pin
spaces are equal in both Figs. 73 and 74, the difference in the position of
the piston in the two figures is due to the arrangement of the crank-pin
and main rod end connections. In Fig. 74 the crank-pin end of the main
rod is moved away from the center line of the engine, producing the
" angularity of the main rod," with the effect of drawing *back* the piston

from its position in Fig. 73, where there is no angularity. It is clear
that in Fig. 74 the piston is always *back* of the position it would occupy
if there were no angularity as in Fig. 73. These differences in the position
of the piston are larger toward the center of the piston stroke than at
either end, as is apparent from these figures.

As is usually the case in modern locomotive design (in order to allow
for settling on the springs), the center line of the cylinders is above the
center line of the driving axles, causing the angularity effect to be greater
for the backward stroke, or when the crank-pin is in the lower half of its
path, than during the forward stroke, or when the crank-pin is on the
upper half of the crank-pin path (running forward). This is due to the

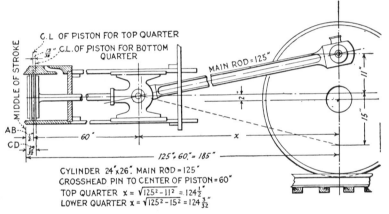

CYLINDER 24″x26″. MAIN ROD = 125″
CROSSHEAD PIN TO CENTER OF PISTON = 60″
TOP QUARTER x = $\sqrt{125^2 - 11^2}$ = 124½″
LOWER QUARTER x = $\sqrt{125^2 - 15^2}$ = 124 3/32″

FIG. 76.—Calculation of Angularity of Main Rod.

fact that the main rod forms a larger angle with the center line of the engine
when the crank-pin is below the center line of the axles, than it does when
the crank-pin is above the center of the axles, as is shown in Fig. 75.
The amount the piston is back of the middle of its stroke, when the crank-
pin is on either quarter, may be calculated. For example, Fig. 76 shows
the crank-pin on the top quarter with such dimensions as may be found
on a Pacific type of locomotive. In this case, the distance from the center
O of the main driving axle to the middle position of the stroke is the
length of the main rod (125 inches) plus 60 inches (the distance from the
crosshead pin to the center of the piston) or a total of 185 inches. The
distance X (when the crank-pin is on the top quarter) is $\sqrt{125^2 - 11^2}$ or
$\sqrt{15625 - 121}$, which equals $\sqrt{15504}$, or 124.51 inches, practically 124½

inches. The amount the piston is back of the middle of the stroke would be $(125+60)-(124\frac{1}{2}+60)$, which equals $\frac{1}{2}$ inch, or AB in Fig. 75 and 76.

When the crank-pin is on the lower quarter, the distance X is $\sqrt{125^2-15^2}$ $=\sqrt{15625-225}$, which equals $\sqrt{15400}$, or $124.09+$ inches (practically $124\frac{3}{32}$ inches), which would give $(125''+60'')-(124\frac{3}{32}''+60'')$, or $\frac{29}{32}$ inches, as the distance CD, Figs. 75 and 76. In this case the difference between distances AB and CD, Figs. 75 and 76, is $\frac{29}{32}''-\frac{1}{2}''$ or $\frac{13}{32}''$.

Raising the center line of the cylinders above the center line of the axles not only produces unequal "angularity of the main rod," but also

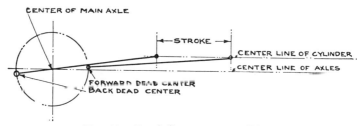

FIG. 77.—Dead Centers not on Diameter.

causes the forward and backward dead centers of the crank-pin to come "undiametrically opposite." That is, the forward and backward dead centers are not diametrically opposite each other when the center line of the cylinders is above the center line of the axles, as is seen from a study of Fig. 77. A line drawn from the extreme travel positions of the cross-head through the center of the main axle will locate the dead centers in Fig. 77, and it is seen that these points cannot be on a diameter.

ERRORS OF THE LINK MOTION

There are three sources of error with the Stephenson link motion as it is applied to locomotives. These tend to make the valve events occur at different points in the stroke of the piston for the two ends of the cylinder. These sources of error, in the order of their importance, are: (1) the off-set of the eccentric blades pin back of the link arc; (2) the angular motion, or angularity of the eccentric blades; and (3) the angular motion, or angularity of the main rod. To a certain extent, the latter two compensate (or off-set) the first; and to complete the compensation the link bridle (or saddle) stud connecting the link with the hanger is set back of the link arc.

Fig. 78 shows the arrangement of saddle and stud with reference to the link arc. This figure also shows the eccentric blade pin holes back of the link arc, which arrangement introduces the error mentioned as first or chief. If the Stephenson link motion were free from this irregular movement imparted to it by the angularity of the main rod and eccentric blades, and the distortional effect of the attachment to the latter to the link back of the link arc, it would give a true or perfect motion to the valve. But, as will be pointed out, some errors do exist which cause the motion

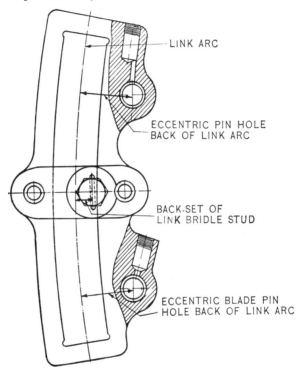

LINK ARC

ECCENTRIC PIN HOLE
BACK OF LINK ARC

BACK-SET OF
LINK BRIDLE STUD

ECCENTRIC BLADE PIN
HOLE BACK OF LINK ARC

FIG. 78.—Stephenson Link.

to be *untrue* or *imperfect* relative to the piston position. It has always been a source of trouble to attempt to change from a sliding motion to one of rotation or from a rotary motion to a sliding motion. These changes of motion are found in the case of the piston and crank-pin and also with the eccentric and link.

First. Errors Due to Angularity of Main Rod. As a matter of convenience a discussion of the effects of the angularity of the main rod on the link motion will be taken up before those of the gear parts are treated.

The angularity of the main rod has already been discussed (page 63) with respect to the motion existing between the piston and crank-pin. As stated on page 64, Fig. 75, the effect of the angularity of the main rod is to bring the piston back of its central point when the crank-pin is on either quarter position.

For the study of the link motion it will be more convenient to change this procedure, and to consider the motion from the movement of the piston and to locate the position of the crank-pin when the piston is in its mid-position. From a study of Fig. 79, it is seen that when the piston is in the center of its stroke, the crank-pin lags behind the quarter position when the engine is running in the forward direction, or when the piston is traveling in the backward direction. This is shown by the distance between points C and B, Fig. 79. During the forward movement of the piston the crank-pin runs ahead of the top quarter position, indicated

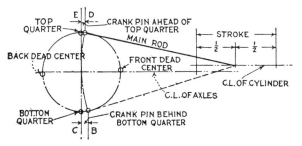

Fig. 79.—Angularity of Main Rod (Errors).

by the distance between points E and D. These errors of the angularity of the main rod exist at all points of the stroke (except the dead center positions) but are at their greatest near the half-stroke and are zero when the crank-pin is on the dead centers. It is then seen that the angularity varies from its smallest to its largest amount while the crank-pin passes from the dead center to about the quarter position, or 90°.

Now, since the eccentrics and links are driven by the motion of the crank-pin through the main axle, it is evident that this error will be introduced into the motion of the link, and hence carried to the valve. Consequently, during the backward movement of the piston, the eccentrics and link will lag behind their true or proper position; and cut-off, release, and compression at the front port will not occur at the desired points, but rather will be found later in the piston stroke. This is true when considering the angular effect of the main rod separately and assuming that the other two sources of error do not exist. Likewise, when the piston is traveling along its forward stroke (forward running of the engine) the crank-pin runs ahead. This will cause the eccentrics and link to be ahead of their true position, and hence the cut-off, release, and compression at the back port occur earlier in the piston stroke than is desired. It is thus seen that the angularity of the main rod itself causes unequal valve events at the two

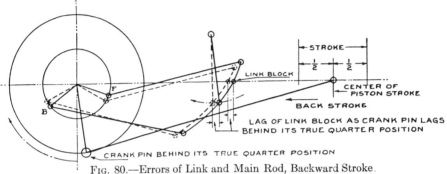

FIG. 80.—Errors of Link and Main Rod, Backward Stroke.

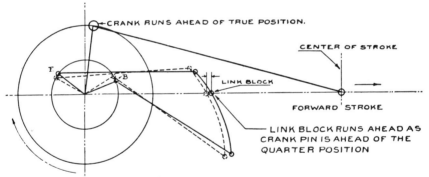

FIG. 81.—Errors of Link and Main Rod, Forward Stroke.

ends of the cylinder; being late in *front* and early *behind*, relative to the position of the piston.

Figs. 80 and 81 show this distortional effect of the angularity of the main rod if it is assumed that the irregularities of the other errors do not exist. The full-line diagram shows the actual position of the eccentrics and link and the dotted-line diagram indicates the position of the gear if no distortion were present. Fig. 80 represents the lag of the gear during the backward movement of the piston when the piston is in the middle of its stroke. Fig. 81 represents the running ahead of the gear during the forward movement of the piston at the middle stroke position of the latter. Here the crank-pin and gear parts *run ahead* of their true positions.

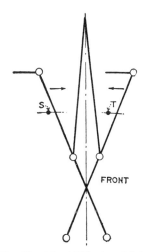

FIG. 82.—Combined Effect of Main Rod Errors.

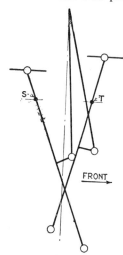

FIG. 83.—True Position and Location of Stud for Main Rod Error.

In order to study the manner of correcting for this distortion of the angularity of the main rod, it will be well to combine the actual or full-

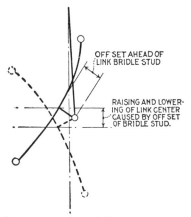

FIG. 84.—Action of Lever Effect of Off-set.

line positions shown in Figs. 80 and 81 into one diagram as in Fig. 82. Here points S and T represent the true position of the link block corresponding to the dotted-line position of Figs. 80 and 81. The arrows on the link show the direction of motion for each position. Here, in accordance with the previous discussion, it is seen that in the front position, the link block is *slow* or *behind* its true point, T, and in the back position it is seen to be *fast* or *ahead* of its true point, S. Now, if the link at its forward position (Fig. 82) were raised over the block, there would be a point on the link which would be made to fall on point T, the true location for the block when the link is in this forward position. Likewise, if the link in its backward position were allowed to drop a little in its arc, it would fall on point *S*, the true position of the block. This raising and lowering of the link is accomplished by attaching the hanger in front of or outside of the link arc, as shown in Fig. 83, by off-setting the saddle stud. This causes a *lever effect*, which, as the link swings about the hanger stud as its center, raises and lowers the link as shown here. A study of Fig. 84 will make this action clear. Hence, to correct for the angularity of the main rod, the link saddle stud must be placed *outside*, or *ahead* of the link arc.

Second: Errors Due to the Angularity of the Eccentric Blades. The action between the eccentrics and link ends is somewhat similar to that between the crank-pin and piston. The principal difference is, that instead of the distortion increasing to its greatest amount near the quarter positions or for about 90° of turning and then decreasing again, the eccentric blade angular effect increases to its greatest amount at about 180° of rotation, or at about twice the amount of turning required to place the crank-pin in the position producing the greatest angularity of the main rod.

This changing angle of the eccentric rod is shown in Figs. 85 to 87, inclusive. In the former, the full lines represent the position of least angle between the eccentric blades and the center line of axles; and in the latter, the full lines represent the greatest angle formed between the blades and center line of axles.

Referring again to Figs. 85 to 87, it will be seen that from the position for the least angle to that of the greatest angle, the crank-pin and eccentrics have turned through one-half of a revolution. A study of these diagrams will make clear the fact that the angular effect varies from the smallest to the largest amount during one-half revolution, or while the crank-pin passes from one dead center to the other, or through 180° of turning.

This changing angle of the eccentric blades causes the movement of the link to be variable, like the variable motion of the crosshead due to the angularity of the main rod as was explained. Considering the crank-pin to be on the forward dead center to start with, the distortion of the link motion produced by the angular motion of the eccentric blades, as the crank-pin and eccentrics make one complete revolution, or 360°, may be observed by studying Figs. 85 to 88 inclusive, which show the position of the gear parts, in quarter turns, for one complete revolution.

Assuming that the errors of the main rod do not exist, the full line diagram of Fig. 85 shows the parts under consideration when the crank-pin is on the forward dead center. The distance xc is the radius of the link arc and point c marks the location of the link arc when its center is on the center of the axle. Point D locates the center of the link for this position. Now Fig. 86 represents the position of the parts when the crankpin and eccentrics have turned through 90° or one-quarter turn. Here

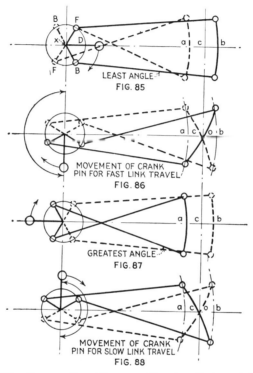

Figs. 85, 86, 87, 88.—Comparative Diagrams Showing Fast and Slow Motion of the Link as Derived from the Eccentrics Due to Changing Angle of Eccentric Rods.

it is seen by the full-line diagram that the link center has moved only a small amount, represented by the distance between points b and o. That is, the link has been moved from point b backward to point o. In Fig. 87, the parts are shown to be advanced through the second quarter of a turn, or one-half of a revolution, making one stroke of the piston. The crank-pin is now on the backward dead center. Here the link center has been moved a much larger amount, or from point o backward to point a, showing very forcibly that the movement of the link during this second quarter of turning has been very much faster than while the crank-pin was turning through the first quarter of a revolution.

Fig. 88 shows the parts as they are located when the crank-pin is on the top quarter, or when the crank-pin and eccentrics have turned through the third quarter of a revolution. Here the center of the link has moved through exactly the same distance as it did while the crank-pin was turning through the second quarter of a revolution, and it has returned to the same position, or point *o*. Now when the crank-pin reached the forward dead center again, one complete revolution will have been made, and referring again to Fig. 85, it is seen that the link has moved from point *o* forward to point *b*, or the position occupied at the beginning.

The facts to be noted in this discussion are: (1) that the slow travel of the link occurs while the crank-pin is turning from the top quarter to the bottom quarter positions (or the fourth and first quarter turns, running forward), and while it is ahead of the vertical center line through the axle. This slow movement of the link is produced by the comparatively small change in the angle of the eccentric blades, these being in the open condition during this time. (2) That the faster travel of the link takes place during the movement of the crank-pin from the bottom to the top quarter positions (or the second and third quarter turns, running forward) and while it is back of the vertical center line of the axle. This comparatively fast movement of the link is caused by the similarly large changes in the angle of the eccentric blades, the latter being in the crossed condition during this time. The angular effect increases as the angle of the blades increases. Here it is seen that the angularity of the eccentric blades, considered separately, causes the link motion to be distorted as follows:

While the crank-pin is turning through the front half of its path and when the piston is traveling in the forward half of its stroke (either direction), the movement of the link is slow or " lagging," and while the crank-pin is turning through the *back* half of its path and when the piston is in the backward half of its stroke (traveling in either direction), that the movement of the link is fast or " hasty." This irregularity in the motion of the link is transferred to the valve. These effects are obviously in the same direction as those due to the angularity of the main rod, and the two add together. Therefore, the angularity of the eccentric blades causes unequal valve events at the two ends of the cylinder, making them *late* in *front* (during slow motion of link) and *early behind* (during fast motion of link) relative to the position of the piston.

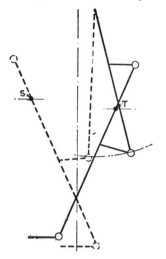

The corrections for the distortion of the motion produced by the angularity of the eccentric blades is, therefore, made in like manner to the corrections for the effects of the angularity of the main rod: by off-setting the link bridle stud ahead or in front of the link arc, and the two amounts of off-set are actually added together. The sum or combined off-set is represented in Fig. 89. Here the amount of off-set is seen to be more than the amount necessary for correcting the effects of the angularity of the main rod alone shown by Fig. 83. (The diagram in Fig. 89 represents approximately the sum of the two off-sets.)

FIG. 89.—Combined Off-set Main Rod and Eccentric Rod Errors.

It is obvious that the error of the angular motion of the eccentric blades is more pronounced with short blades, as the changes in the angle are larger than is the case with long blades, when the angle has a smaller range.

Third: Error Due to the Location of the Eccentric Blade Pins Back of the Link Arc. In the previous discussion, the distortional effects of the location of the eccentric blade pins back of the link arc, and the angularity of the main rod, were assumed not to exist. Now, however, in this present study, it is possible to separate only the error due to the angularity of main rod, so that the movement of the link as affected by the angularity of the eccentric blades and the back-set of the blade pins will be treated together.

The appearance of the link in the form of diagram which has been used is shown in Fig. 90. The back-set of the eccentric blade pins gives to the shape of the diagram the additional line (or lever effect) shown between points *M* and *N*, Fig. 90, and is equal to the distance between the link arc and the center of the eccentric blade pins. This has the effect of increasing the length of the eccentric blades, and also of introducing another angular motion, as is apparent in the figure.

The nature of the combined errors of the eccentric blades, angularity, and the back-set of the blade pins is shown in Fig. 91. One set of diagrams shows the eccentric blades connected to the link on the link arc as in the other cases, and the second set (full lines) shows the " lever " effect of the back-set of the blade pins. The saddle stud is located on the link arc, and and points S and T represent the true positions of the link for a certain cut-off. The diagrams without the effect of the back-set of the blade pins (dotted lines) show the link to be in the same positions relative to the true points S and T as are given in Fig. 82; that is, late in front at T during the forward stroke of the piston, and early at the back point S during the backward stroke of the piston. It is seen that the back-set of the eccentric blade pins makes the lines adjoining the eccentric (representing the eccentric blades) and the extremities of the link, crooked, whereas with these pins located on the link arc, these lines are straight. Consequently the back-set of the eccentric blade pins produces an additional angular motion between the eccentrics and link, with the effect, for the position shown in Fig. 91, that as the angle is increased the link is drawn back nearer the eccentrics than is the case with the link which has the eccentric blade pins located on the link arc. The action is like that of a " knuckle joint," any movement of which must draw the ends closer together.

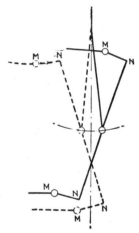

FIG. 90.—Link with Back-set of Eccentric Pin.

Here it is seen that the link with back-set blade pins is moved to the other side of the true points S and T, so that the effect of the back-set pins is just the opposite to that of the angularity of the eccentric blades (also main rod). Also the movement at the *front* is *fast*, and at the *back* is *slow*, just the *reverse* of the previous conditions, or those produced by the angularity of the main rod and eccentric blades. Since the rocker arm reverses the direction of the action of the link, the fast or " hasty " motion in front at T, or a drawing back of the link beyond its true position, forces the " outside admission " slide valve ahead of its true position, quickening the cut-off for the front port during the backward movement of the piston. At the backward position of the link its motion is *slow* or *lagging*, and it is back of its true position. This has the effect of pushing the slide valve ahead, *delaying* the cut-off at the back port, during the forward stroke of the piston.

This effect will be seen to be directly opposite to those produced by
the angularities of the main rod and the eccentric blades and hence the
correction for this error will be necessarily the opposite and the saddle
stud must be moved in the reverse direction; or back of (or inside) the link
arc.   The effect of the back-set of the eccentric blade pins is also great

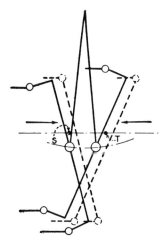

FIG. 91.—Combined Effect of Eccentric
Rod and Back-set Errors.

Dotted Lines Show Link Pins on Link Arc.
Full Lines Show Link Pins Back of Link Arc.

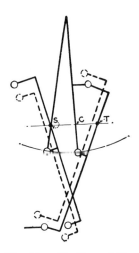

FIG. 92.—True Position of Stud.

Dotted Lines Show Link with Bridle Stud
on Link Arc.   Full Lines Show Bridle Stud
Placed Inside of Link Arc.

enough to over-balance the combined effects of the angularities of the
main rod and eccentric blades, requiring the bridle stud to be placed back
of, or inside of the link arc.

The final position of the bridle stud is determined by the resultant of
all the three errors.   The errors and their corrections are found to be as
follows:

Cause.	Errors in Valve Moment.	Correction by Moving Bridle Stud.
Angularity of main rod	Slow in front and fast in the back	Outside or in front of the link arc
Angularity of eccentric blades	Slow in front and fast in the back	Outside or in front of the link arc
Back-set of eccentric blade pins	Fast in front and slow in the back	Inside or back of the link arc

Fig. 92 shows the bridle stud located back of the link arc, as a result of, first: moving it outside or ahead of the link arc to correct for the angularity of the main rod, then a second movement in the same direction to correct the error of the angularity of the eccentric blades; and then a third movement in the opposite direction and to an extent much greater than the sum of the other two movements, to correct for the back-set of the eccentric blade pins. This brings the location of the bridle stud backward again until it is placed within the link arc, *as is always the case in locomotive practice.*

This movement of the link bridle stud does not completely correct for the existing errors of the Stephenson link motion for all points of cut-off or all positions of the link and reverse lever, but thus far in the design it is the best that can be done, and the result is almost to eliminate these irregularities and to make the motion entirely practicable. Nowadays the amount of off-set necessary for any particular design of locomotive is determined in the drawing room. The bridle is designed to give the de-termined off-set when applied to the link in the shop. The valves may be " squared " in this way for any one travel or position of the link and reverse lever providing for one particular cut-off, for example at one-quarter stroke; but it will not be square for any other cut-off because of the fact that the errors of the motion are not wholly eliminated. This point will be treated in detail under valve setting.

A method which may be used in the drawing room for determining the amount of off-set (or back-set) of the bridle stud which is necessary

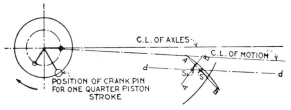

FIG. 93.—Layout for Backset of Stud.

to equalize cut-off at any one desired point of the stroke of the piston is in general as follows: Select the point of cut-off at which it is desired to have the gear perfect, for example, the one-quarter stroke; then locate the positions of the link for this cut-off at both ends, from the relative positions of the eccentrics and reverse lever as shown in Fig. 93. Draw the lines *AB* (for both positions of the link) square with the link arc at the center point. The link is represented in the two positions for equalized cut-off at one-quarter piston stroke and inasmuch as the point of link suspension in locomotive practice is usually at the center of the link, the bridle stud center must be found on the lines AB for each position. It must of course be the same distance from the link arc in each position. Hence, two points, S_1 and S, are located on the lines AB at equal distances from the link arc, and of such a distance or length that a line dd parallel to the center line of motion may be drawn through them. The position of the lift shaft pivot is also determined in the drawing room. This, if not properly located, will produce a slight distortion in the cut-off at both ends of the cylinder. The position of the lift shaft pivot (or center of bearing) is dependent upon the lengths of the lift shaft arms and the link hanger, and the ideal condition is to suspend the hanger in such a manner that for the several elevations of the link the point of the link hanger and lift arm connection will move with the link through the distances determined by the corresponding positions of the link.

Slip of the Link Block. The slip of the link block in the link is the common term applied to the sliding motion of the block in the link slot

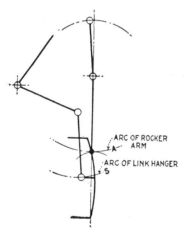

as the parts are in motion, caused by the different paths through which the respective parts move. Fig. 94 shows why the slip exists.

The rocker arm moves in an arc as shown at A. The link, being suspended from the lift shaft by the hanger, swings on the arc S. The necessary sliding or moving of the link block in the link slot is apparent from this diagram. There is also some slip produced as the link oscillates about the link saddle stud as a center. These two motions cause what is termed "slip of the block." It is necessary to make the link slot long enough to take care of this movement or

FIG. 94.—Slip of Link Block, Stephenson Gear.

"slip"; other than this it is of minor importance in the design of the gear, save as it affects the wearing of the surfaces of the link slot at the position where the gear is generally used, namely, the running cut-off position of the forward motion.

A STUDY OF THE VALVE GEAR PARTS AS THEY AFFECT CONDITIONS AT THE VALVE

It is seen from a study of the preceding diagrams showing the action of the link as the crank-pin and eccentrics make one complete revolution,

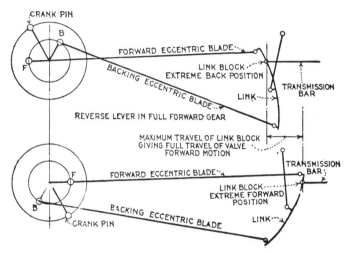

FIG. 95.—Change in Valve Travel.

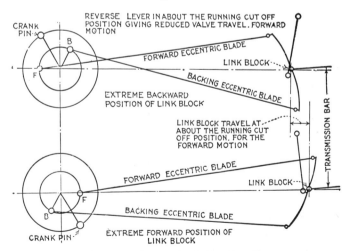

FIG. 96.—Change in Valve Travel.

that the motion of the link, producing practically the entire movement of the valve, is made up of two distinct movements, first, a swinging or oscillating motion about the link bridle stud on the hanger; and secondly, its movement back and forth or swinging on the hanger pin at its connection to the lift shaft arm. It is the former, or oscillating of the link on the saddle stud, which gives the link block a smaller amount of travel as it is made to work near to the center or " mid-gear " position of the link slot.

Hence as the link is raised (for the forward motion) to have the link block work near the center of the link, the valve travel is shortened in accordance with the reduced link block movement.

When the link block is working near the upper end of the link, it receives practically the full throw of the forward eccentric. Thus the link block in turn causes the valve to receive a comparatively larger travel.

To shorten the travel of the valve, it is necessary to cause the travel of the link block to be *shortened*. This is done by lifting the link (for the forward motion) by means of the reverse lever and the lift shaft, causing the link block to work nearer the center of the link and thus receive a shorter motion from the forward eccentric. Hence, to obtain long valve travel, the link block is made to work near the end of the link by lowering the link for the forward motion, and raising it for the backward motion.

By a study of Figs. 95 and 96, page 79, it is seen how, by raising and lowering the link over the link block, a change in the link block travel and consequently the valve travel is brought about.

Rocker Arm. In considering this feature, it may be well to refer back to Fig. 41, page 36, and see what effect the length of the two arms of the rocker arm will have upon the travel of the valve; that is, how the rocker arm may change the travel of the valve from that of the link block. Now if the lower and upper arms of the rocker arm are of equal length it is evident that the horizontal travel of lower and upper pin centers will be equal, but should the upper arm be *shorter* than the lower one, the travel of the upper pin center in the valve stem will be *shorter* than that of the lower pin center and of the link block. Likewise, should the upper arm be *longer* than the lower arm, the travel of the upper pin center at the valve stem will be *greater* than that of the lower pin, and of the link block. Hence, equal arms in the rocker arm will *not* change the length of travel of the valve from that of the link block, while unequal length will alter the valve travel from the link block travel; a shorter top arm *reducing*, and a longer top arm *increasing*, the valve travel from that of the link block.

As mentioned on page 45, the rocker arm is generally bent, or back-set, slightly, and appears as shown in Fig. 97. The amount of bending required is determined in the following manner: When the upper arm of the rocker arm stands midway in its path (usually when it is in a vertical or plumb position) the lower arm is made to be at right angles or 90° to the center line of motion, see Fig. 97. The position of the link block being somewhat lower than the lower end of the rocker arm, it is necessary to bring the lower arm of the rocker arm forward as shown here. It is also necessary to have this 90° condition just described so that the movement of the lower arm or transmission bar pin will swing an equal distance each side of its mid-position. As may be seen from a study of the figure, if the rocker arm were made straight down its lower arm would not move

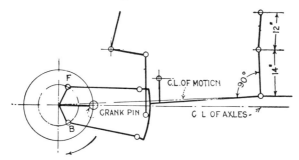

Fig. 97.—Bent Rocker Arm.

an equal amount each way from the center position. Hence, to do away with this inequality a bent rocker arm is used.

In the case of unequal lengths of arms of the rocker, it frequently becomes necessary to determine the amount the rocker arm will change the travel of the valve from that of the link block; or how far the pin center in the lower arm will move for a known travel of the valve and pin center in the upper arm. For instance, in the case of setting a valve, suppose the rocker arm has unequal lengths of arms, the upper arm being twelve inches and the lower arm fourteen inches in length, and it is desired to move the valve one-fourth of an inch. Here the upper pin center moves one-fourth of an inch on an arc with a radius equal to the length of the upper arm, or twelve inches, and it is desired to calculate the distance the lower pin center will swing on a radius of fourteen inches, or the length of the lower arm. The procedure is as follows: multiply the distance the upper arm moves by the length of the lower arm and divide the product by the length of the upper arm. Thus: $\frac{1}{4} \times \frac{14}{12} = 0.291$ inch. To reduce

.291 to a common fraction to the nearest 64th of an inch, multiply the decimal 0.291 by 64 and take the nearest whole number. Thus, 0.291 $\times 64 = 18.624$ sixty-fourths, or $\dfrac{18.624}{64}$. Since the $\dfrac{18.624}{64}$ is over one-half way between $\frac{18}{64}$ inch and $\frac{19}{64}$ inch, take $\frac{19}{64}$ of an inch as the amount (to the nearest 64th) that the lower pin center will move. This is also the *distance* traveled by the link block for a movement of one-fourth inch at the valve.

EFFECTS OF RAISING OR LOWERING THE LINK

First: Valve Travel. By referring again to Figs. 95 and 96 on page 79, it is seen that as the link is raised, the link block works nearer the center of the link; which fact produces a shorter link block travel, as the link works from one extreme position to the other, principally by reason of two distinct motions. first, the motion imparted by the link on the link bridle stud as a center; and secondly, the oscillation (or swinging back and forth) of the link on the link hanger from its attachment to the lift shaft arm as a center. The combined effect of these two motions is shown in the two sketches of Figs. 95 and 96. The former figure shows the link dropped to the extreme forward position, while the latter represents the same conditions when the link is raised to about the running cut-off position. In the upper sketch of Fig. 95 the top of the link is swung back on the bridle stud and the eccentrics have also drawn the entire link back on the link hanger as a radius, so that the link block occupies its extreme backward position. In the lower sketch of Fig. 95 the top of the link is swung forward on the bridle stud and the link is moved forward on the link hanger, so that the link block is in its extreme forward position. Now the horizontal travel of the link block produced by the link in its movement from one extreme position to the other is the motion imparted to the valve through the transmission bar, rocker arm, and valve stem. (In some designs of the Stephenson gear the transmission bar is omitted.) Now as the link is raised over the link block by means of the reverse lever to secure shorter valve travel for increasing the speed of the locomotive, the link block travel is reduced, because of the fact that it is made to work at a point nearer the center of the link, where the horizontal motion from one extreme position of the link to the other is less than at the ends of the link. By referring to Fig. 96, which shows the link block in about the running cut-off position in the link, it is to be noted that while the link (in the two sketches) occupies the same positions as those shown in Fig. 95, the link block movement from one position to the other is not nearly as great as in the former case (Fig. 95). The reason for this shortening of the link block travel is obvious from a study of Figs. 95 and 96. The shorter link block travel results in a correspondingly shorter valve travel. In this manner, the travel of the valve may be changed to suit the conditions under which the engine is working.

Second: Lead. When the crank pin is on a dead center and the link is raised or lowered, a movement of the valve is noticed. Since "lead" is the amount the valve opens the steam port for the admission of steam when the crank is on a dead center, this movement will affect the lead.

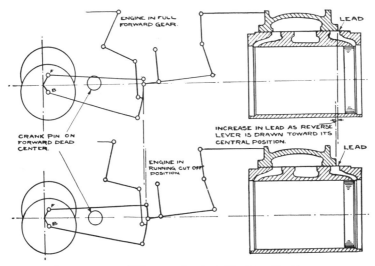

FIGS. 98, 99.—Effect on Lead of Hooking Up Lever.

By studying Figs. 98 and 99 it is seen that the lead increases as the link block is made to work nearer the center of the link when the position of the link is changed by means of the reverse lever. This "variable" or changeable lead is an advantage, since a large lead is desired when running on a short cut-off or when running at high speed; while at low speed an early admission is not necessary; besides it is then undesirable, as it tends unduly to hold back the piston while the crank pin is passing dead center.

The reason for this variable action or changing of the position of the link as the crank-pin and eccentrics revolve may be seen from a study of Fig. 100. Here the crank-pin is shown on the forward dead center, for which position of the crank-pin the forward eccentric is at F and the backing eccentric is at B, the forward eccentric blade being shown by a full line, and the backing eccentric blade by a dotted line. For this position of the crank-pin the valve has opened the port by the amount of the full gear lead. If there were only one eccentric—for example, the forward eccentric at F—and it was also connected to the bottom of the link as

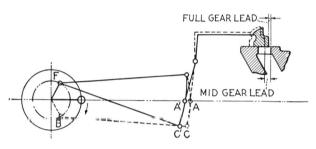

FIG. 100.—Effect on Lead of Hooking Up Lever.

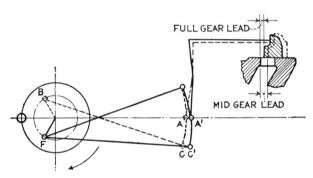

FIG. 101.—Effect on Lead of Hooking Up Lever.

shown by line FC, and the link arc be struck from F as a center, the link might then be moved throughout its range, by the reverse lever, without changing the lead. The lead then would remain constant or the same for all positions of the reverse lever. But since the two eccentrics are connected to the link and since they are connected by equal lengths of blades, the link (by connecting the backing eccentric blade to the bottom) is pushed forward by the amount represented by the distance between points C and C' and the center of the link occupies the position shown at point A and pushes the link block ahead by an amount represented by the distance from A to A'. Hence the rocker arm draws the valve back on its seat and increases the mid-gear lead. This increase will be variable along the link slot. As the link is raised from full gear position to mid-gear position, the lead will increase from its least, or full gear amount, to its greatest, or mid-gear amount.

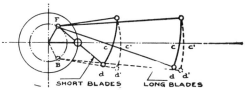

FIG. 102.—Effect of Long and Short Eccentric Rods.

Fig. 101 shows the same condition for the backward dead center position of the crank-pin. The amount that the lead will change from full gear to mid-gear is governed by the length of the eccentric blades. Short blades will increase its amount, while long blades will decrease the amount of change in lead from full to mid-gear. Fig. 102 shows the effect of the length of the eccentric blades upon the variable lead condition.

Third: The Direction of Running. Referring to Fig. 103, when the link is in the position of the forward motion shown by the upper sketch of this figure and the crank-pin is on the lower quarter position, the

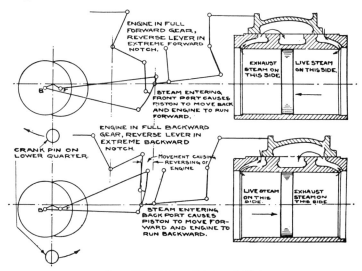

FIG. 103.—Reversibility of Link.

valve is admitting steam to the cylinder through the front port, causing the piston to move backward and the engine to run forward, as is evident from this figure. Now, by raising the link to the position shown by the lower sketch of Fig. 103, it is seen that the link block has been moved backward by the link, so that the valve is admitting steam to the cylinder through the *back* port, causing the piston to move forward in the cylinder and the engine to run backward. It is thus seen that when the link block works in the upper half of the link the engine will run forward, and when placed so the link block works in the lower half of the link the engine will run backward.

THE POSITION OF ECCENTRICS RELATIVE TO THE CRANK=PIN

On pages 37 to 39, inclusive, the eccentrics and their purpose were described, but it remains to determine their positions on the axle to give the desired effect at the valve.

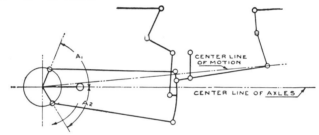

Fig. 104.—Eccentric Set with Center Line of Motion.

Angles A_1 and A_2 are Equal when Measured from Center Line of Motion; and not from Center Line of Axles.

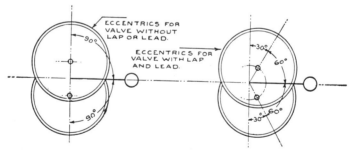

Fig. 105.—Eccentric Set 90°   Fig. 106.—Eccentric Set 60° with Center Line
with Crank-pin.   of Motion—Double Cast Eccentrics.

For a valve without *lap* or *lead*, as shown in Fig. 6, page 4, the eccentrics would be set at 90°, or square with the *center line of motion when the crank-pin is on dead center*. The center line of motion is a line drawn from the center of the main axle through the center of the lower rocker arm pin, as shown in Fig. 104. In case the center of the crank-pin is on the center line of motion when the crank-pin is on dead center, if the valve had no lap or lead, the eccentrics would be set at 90° with the crank pin or each eccentric would be set at equal distances from the crank-pin as shown in Fig. 105.

Since a valve has steam lap and is usually set with lead, the eccentrics must be turned on the axle so as to move the valve from its central position a distance equal to the steam lap plus the lead, when the crank-pin is on dead center. In the common design of valve gears, or indirect motion, as shown in Fig. 41, page 36, the eccentrics are turned *toward* the crank-pin to produce this effect. Fig. 106 shows the eccentrics giving the angles as set on a 4–4–2, or Atlantic type of locomotive, or one as shown in Fig. 107.

In order to make this principle clearer, it may be well to consider a single eccentric moving a plain D slide valve directly, without the use of a link and rocker arm. Referring to Fig. 108, if the valve had no lap and no lead, as in Fig. 6, page 88, the eccentric would be set one-quarter of a turn away from the crank-pin,* and the valve and steam port edge will be line on line. To give the valve lead it must be drawn back on its seat. This is done by

* For simplicity, the crank-pin will be referred to instead of the center line of motion. See page 86, Fig. 104.

Fig. 107.—4–4–2 Atlantic Type Locomotive Equipped with Stephenson Gear and Slide Valve.

moving the eccentric on the axle from position 1 farther away from the crank-pin to position 2, Fig. 108.

Now, referring to Fig. 109, in which a rocker arm has been introduced, it is to be noted that the position of the eccentric is changed from below the crank-pin to a corresponding position above the pin, or from leading the pin to following the pin (running forward). This change is necessary because the rocker arm *reverses* the direction of the valve with relation to the eccentric. This fact is apparent from a comparison of Figs. 108 and 109. However, the same condition exists as before. In order to give lead to the valve the eccentric must be moved away from the quarter, or 90° position from the crank-pin, that is, in this case from position 1 to

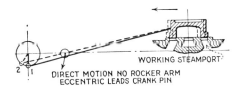

FIG. 108.—Plain Valve Single Eccentric, no Rocker.

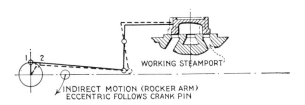

FIG. 109.—Plain Valve Single Eccentric Rocker Arm.

position 2. But it is to be noted also that *with the use of the rocker arm* the eccentric must be moved *toward* the crank-pin to give lead to the valve, whereas without the rocker arm it is moved *away from* the pin.

This reversing is clear from a careful study of the figures. Hence, in the usual design of locomotive valve gear, the eccentrics are moved *toward* the crank-pin to secure the lead. This is the condition for the use of a rocker arm and, of course, with an *indirect* or standard engine.

The amount of angular movement of the eccentric necessary to secure this condition of lead is called the " Angle of Advance," and is determined from the amount of lap the valve has, and the desired lead when in full gear. Knowing these, the eccentrics are moved an amount, and in a direction such as to move the valve an amount equal to the lap plus the lead. The position of the forward eccentric is based upon the lead for the forward motion of running of the engine, and that of the backing eccentric on the condition of the backward position of the gear. As the lead is generally the same for both forward and backward running and as the lap must be the same (being fixed on the one valve) the forward and

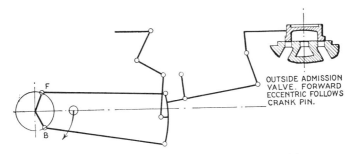

Fig. 110.—Relative Eccentric and Crank-pin Position.

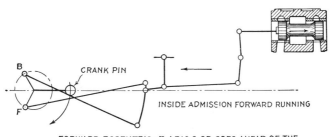

Fig. 111.—Relative Eccentric and Crank-pin Position.

backing eccentric are usually moved the same distance from the *center line of motion.*

From these facts, shown in Figs. 108 and 109, the following rules for *outside admission valves* may be drawn: For standard or indirect engines (rocker arm) the *forward* eccentric always *follows* the crank-pin in its path when running forward.

For the direct engine (no rocker arm) the *forward* eccentric always *leads* or goes ahead of the crank-pin in its path when running forward.

For *inside admission valves* the opposite condition exists. Referring to the following line diagrams these facts may be studied:

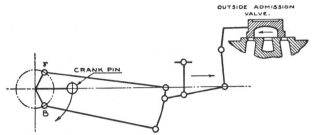

Indirect Motion, Open Blades with Rocker Arm, Usual Design

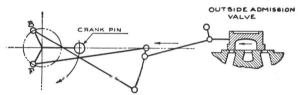

Direct Motion, Crossed Blades, without Rocker Arm, Rare Design.

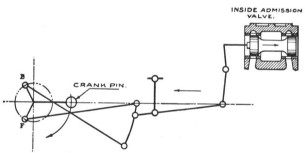

Indirect Motion, Crossed Blades, with Rocker Arm, Rare Design.

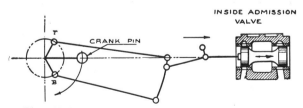

Direct Motion, Open Blades without Rocker Arm, Usual Design.

FIG. 112.—Group of Diagrams showing Eccentric and Crank-pin Positions.

Comparative diagram showing positions of eccentrics relative to crank-pin for steam admission at forward port with outside and inside admission valves with and without rocker arm.

It is seen by referring to Fig. 110 that as the crank-pin turns in the forward direction of running of the locomotive, the forward eccentric will follow the pin, and (for the position shown) will push the link ahead and the rocker arm will draw the valve back, opening the front steam port. Now, if the forward eccentric F were placed on the other side of the crank-pin (so as to lead the pin in its path) it would draw the link back and force the valve ahead. This action would close the front port, and would be contrary to that required for the forward direction of running. Likewise, if the forward eccentric were connected to the bottom of the link and the backing eccentric to the top, this condition would also be the reverse of that required for the forward direction of running.

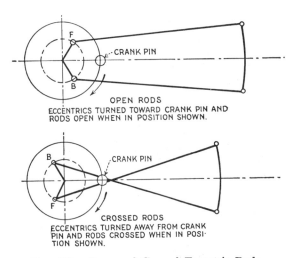

OPEN RODS
ECCENTRICS TURNED TOWARD CRANK PIN AND
RODS OPEN WHEN IN POSITION SHOWN.

CROSSED RODS
ECCENTRICS TURNED AWAY FROM CRANK
PIN AND RODS CROSSED WHEN IN POSI-
TION SHOWN.

FIG. 113.—Open and Crossed Eccentric Rods.

Referring to Fig. 111, which shows an inside admission piston valve, the same condition as was observed for the outside admission slide valve may be noted, but particularly the reversed direction of motion of the forward eccentric. This is seen to be pulling back on the link and forcing the valve ahead, thus causing the front steam port to be opened as it was in the case with the outside admission slide valve. Here it is noted that the forward eccentric must lead the crank-pin to produce forward running of the engine. If the forward eccentric were connected to the bottom of the link and the backing eccentric to the top, it would, as before, destroy the forward direction of running, as also would be true if the positions of the

Fig. 114.—Stephenson Valve Gear and Outside Admission Piston Valve Applied to an American (4–4–0) Type Locomotive by the Pennsylvania Railroad Company.

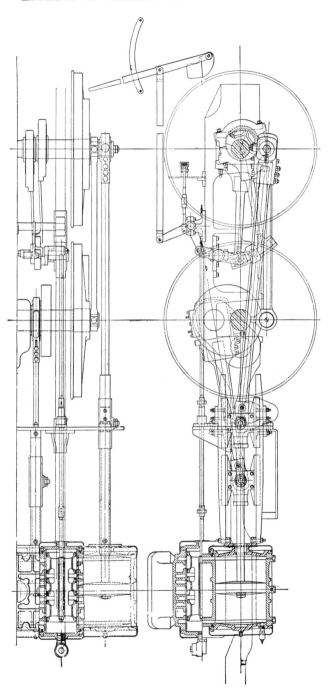

Fig. 115.—Stephenson Gear as Applied to Four-cylinder Compound Locomotive.

two eccentrics relative to the crank-pin were reversed. A study of the diagram shown in Fig. 112 will aid in a clear understanding of these facts.

In order to open the outside admission valve for steam admission at the front port the valve must be drawn back on its seat, and to produce this same condition with an inside admission valve the direction of motion of the valve on its seat must be reversed or the valve must be pushed ahead, instead of being drawn back. This reversing is accomplished by changing

FIG. 116.—Wheel and Crank on Axle, Compound Engine.

the position of the eccentric relative to the crank-pin. The same relation is true for the back port and for both ports with the backward motion.

It is customary, however, to use the design with open eccentric blades, and the rocker arm, with outside admission valves, and the construction without the rocker arm with inside admission valves.

The meaning of open eccentric blades may be seen by referring to Fig. 113. The open eccentric rods are preferred to the crossed rods because the angular effect is less and is therefore more easily overcome. Fig. 114 shows an American or 4–4–0 type locomotive equipped with a piston valve and indirect Stephenson valve gear.

The compound piston valve, Fig. 39, page 32, applied to a Baldwin compound engine, is sometimes operated by an indirect Stephenson gear shown in Fig. 115. Here the outside or low-pressure cylinders are connected to the rear or main axle which carries the eccentrics. The inside or high-pressure cylinders are connected to the front axle with internal cranks as shown in Fig. 116. The indirect gear is used because of the fact that the piston valve with respect to the low-pressure cylinder is arranged for outside admission.

CHAPTER III

THE WALSCHAERT VALVE GEAR

INTRODUCTION

ONE of the most interesting features in recent American locomotive construction is the widespread adoption of the Walschaert valve gear.

Although as old as the Stephenson link motion, it met with little favor in this country for over half a century. To understand the reason for this, and to explain its recent general adoption, requires a review of its development.

In 1844, Egide Walschaerts, at that time chief shop superintendent of the Brussels Southern Railroad, invented the type of valve gear which bears his name. (The final " s " has been dropped in naming the gear.) Because of the fact that the rules of the railroad company did not allow the foreman in the shops to exploit a patent in Belgium, for his own profit, the application for the patent was made by a friend, M. Fischer, of Brussels, Engineer of the State Railroads. The patent was granted by royal decree November 30, 1844, and the mechanism described in the patent resembles the motion which is now in use on many American locomotives.

The Stephenson shifting link motion came into prominence a year earlier, or in 1843. The Walschaert valve gear attracted much attention in Europe and gradually became the accepted type of valve motion by designers there, just as American constructors favored the Stephenson link.

Although there were a number of special cases in which the Walschaert valve gear was applied to locomotives in this country as far back as twenty-five or thirty years ago, it is in comparatively recent years that it has met with any large degree of favor by American designers. However, with the increases in power and weight of the modern locomotive, American designers have turned to the Walschaert valve gear to meet conditions under which it affords certain mechanical advantages and superiority of structural features over the Stephenson link motion.

Rarely in the history of the development of the locomotive in this country has any important improvement, once introduced, been so rapidly accepted as this type of valve motion. Its use is undoubtedly to be permanent, and a clear understanding of its principles and construction is therefore essential for all those who work upon engines equipped with it.

CONSTRUCTION AND DEVELOPMENT

As the Walschaert valve gear, like any other device, is merely a development from a simpler form, it may be well to start with the original form and trace the various steps in its evolution. Fig. 117 represents the simplest form of valve motion; that is, a single eccentric of the return crank form, driving a plain normal valve (without lap or lead) by means of an eccentric rod directly connected to the valve stem.

Assuming that the engine is to run forward, then with the crankpin on the back dead center as shown, the eccentric crank-pin center must be on the top quarter position, in which case the valve will be in its middle or central position, with all the ports closed. With the throttle open,

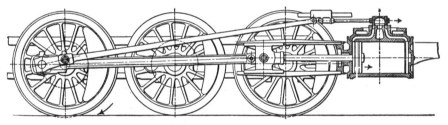

FIG. 117.—Simplest Form of Walschaert Gear Development.

the left-hand engine being connected to the wheel on the other side of the axle with its main crank-pin on the lower quarter, the valve would be in position to admit steam in front of the piston, and would start the engine in the forward direction. The eccentric crank on the right-hand side (the one shown) would then move forward, uncovering the back steam port, and would admit steam behind the piston, so that the engine would continue to run forward. With this gear it is evident that the engine will run in one direction only; that is, in the direction just described. The engine cannot run in the backward direction, since if it were turned backward, the valve would open the forward port, admit steam against the forward side of the piston and keep it from continuing on its forward stroke.

The first thing to do in the development of this simple form of engine valve gear is to provide some suitable means by which it can be made to reverse the direction of running of the locomotive. This can be accomplished by introducing between the eccentric and the valve stem a " beam " or " link," pivoted at its center, so that one end moves with and in the same direction as the eccentric rod, and the other end in exactly the opposite direction. Such a construction is shown in Fig. 118, with the valve stem connected to a radius rod working in the lower end of the link, and the main crank-pin in the upper quarter position as shown in diagram *A*. Here

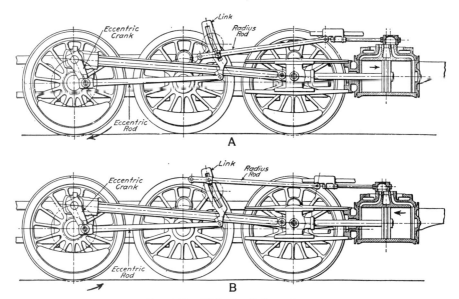

Fig. 118.—Link Applied to Gear.

the eccentric will have moved the valve to its extreme forward position, the back port will be open for the admission of steam behind the piston, and this will cause the engine to run forward. If, however, with the main crank-pin in the same position, the valve stem were connected to the upper end of the link, as shown in diagram *B*, the valve would be moved to its extreme position to the left, or backward position, the *front* port would be open, and steam would be admitted *ahead* of the piston, causing the engine to run *backward*.

With a flexible valve stem, or a radius rod, connected with a block which slides in a curved slot in a link, as shown, and with some suitable mechanism for raising and lowering this block, it is evident that such a gear will reverse the direction of running of the locomotive.

This gear is far from being perfect, as the valve does not close the port for admission of steam until it is in its central position on its seat. With the eccentric only a quarter of a revolution ahead of the main crank-pin, the valve is not centered until the main crank-pin is on the dead center. Consequently, steam will be admitted to the cylinders throughout the entire stroke of the piston. This will cause the engine to use as much steam in working against a light as against a heavy load. In order to govern

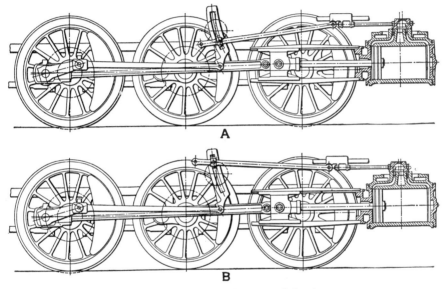

Fig. 119.—Valve with Lap and Lead.

the period of admission of steam, or give a " variable " cut-off, the valve must be redesigned so that it will close the steam port before the former reaches its central or middle position; this is accomplished by giving the valve lap and lead. In other words, the valve and valve motion must be changed so that the valve will be advanced from the central position on the seat a distance equal to the amount of the lap plus the lead, when the main crank-pin is on either dead center position.

This advance of the valve cannot be obtained by any change in the position of the eccentric crank relative to the main crank-pin. The truth of this statement may be seen from the following discussion: Fig. 119

shows the same valve motion as shown in Fig. 118, except that the valve
has steam lap and the eccentric crank has been moved ahead of the crank-
pin a distance greater than *one-quarter* of a revolution. If, then, the
link block is at the bottom of the link, as in position *A* of Fig. 119, the
advance given to the eccentric will move the valve forward for the admission of steam, by a distance equal to the amount of lap plus the lead, and
the engine will run forward. If, on the other hand, the link block is moved
to the upper end of the link, as shown in position *B*, the advance given
to the eccentric crank will have the opposite effect, the front port will

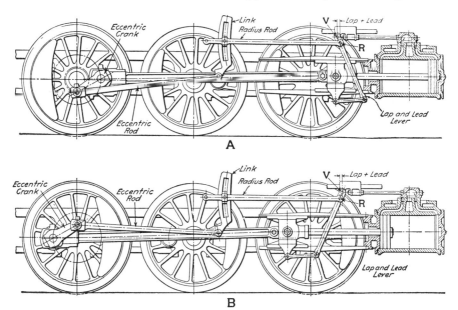

Fig. 120.—Lap and Lead Lever.

still be open, and the reversibility of the direction of running of the engine
will be thus *destroyed*. In order to provide *lap* and *lead*, therefore, in any
gear where there is but *one eccentric*, some means must be employed other
than advancing or receding the eccentric crank-pin relative to the main
crank-pin, if there is to be any method of reversing the direction of running
of the engine.

In the Walschaert valve gear, the motion for providing lap and lead
to the valve is derived from the crosshead by means of a *lap and lead lever*,
or " combination lever." Suppose that the link block is in the center

of the link, as shown in Fig. 120, diagram A; as the center of the link block is in the center of the link support there will be no movement imparted to the radius rod and valve as the link swings back and forth under the action of the eccentric crank. If, then, the radius rod is connected to the lap and lead lever at the point R, with the upper end of the lever connected to the valve stem at V and the lower end of the lever to the crosshead arm by means of a short union link or " lap and lead lever connector," as shown, the lap and lead lever will move the valve back and forth as the lever is caused to swing about point R as a center.

With the main crank pin on the front dead center as shown in position A, Fig. 120, and with the lap and lead lever in the position shown, the valve will have moved back a sufficient distance to uncover the front port. With the main crank-pin on the back dead center, as shown in position B, Fig. 120, the lap and lead lever is inclined in the opposite direction and has moved the valve forward, uncovering the back port. In this manner the Walschaert valve gear derives its lead.

DESCRIPTION OF PARTS

In the foregoing pages the development of the gear has been followed through from its simplest form, showing the reasons for using the various parts. It remains now to make a careful study of the construction and application of the parts taken separately.

The arrangement of the Walschaert valve gear depends largely on the general design of the locomotive. Some of the ordinary forms of construction of the various parts of the gear are illustrated and described in the following pages.

Fig. 121 shows the Walschaert valve gear applied to an Atlantic type locomotive, using an inside admission piston valve. Here the parts are named, affording one the opportunity to become acquainted with the names and locations of the various parts of the gear.

Fig. 122 illustrates the Walschaert valve gear arranged for outside admission slide valves.

The Eccentric Crank. From Fig. 123 it is seen that the eccentric crank is connected to an extension of the main crank-pin, and that this is the part of the gear which takes the motion from the main crank-pin to operate the gear. It is usually fastened rigidly to the main pin by means of a key and binding bolt, as is seen by this illustration. The eccentric

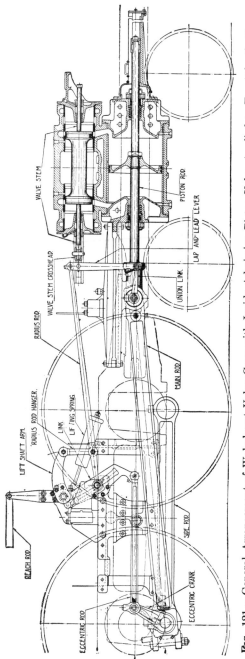

VALVE STEM

VALVE STEM CROSSHEAD

RADIUS ROD

PISTON ROD

LAP AND LEAD LEVER

UNION LINK

MAIN ROD

LIFT SHAFT ARM.

RADIUS ROD HANGER.

LINK

LIFTING SPRING

REACH ROD

SIDE ROD

ECCENTRIC CRANK

ECCENTRIC ROD

FIG. 121.—General Arrangement of Walschaert Valve Gear with Inside Admission Piston Valve Applied to E6s Atlantic Type Locomotive, Pennsylvania Railroad.

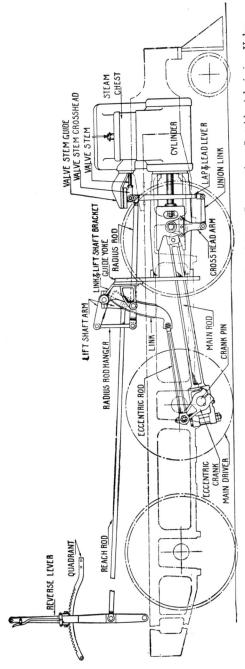

FIG. 122.—General Arrangement of Walschaert Valve Gear Applied to Mogul Type Locomotive, Outside Admission Valve.

crank is split, so that it can be drawn to a tight joint by means of the binding bolt.

Referring to Fig. 124, the binding bolt and slot are sometimes placed on the other side, or inside, of the main pin. The eccentric crank end, to which the eccentric rod is attached, is arranged with a suitable pin end, whereby adjustment for wear may be conveniently made.

The eccentric crank shown here is a steel casting having a wrought-iron case-hardened bushing pressed over the eccentric pin, so that the wearing surfaces at the connection to the eccentric rod are the usual brass

Fig. 123.—Eccentric Crank and Rod.

or composition metal, and the hardened bushing. The pin is provided with a steel collar and nuts as shown in Fig. 124.

The motion imparted to the gear by the eccentric crank, as the wheel revolves, may be seen from a study of Figs. 125 and 126. It is evident that with the eccentric crank set as in Fig. 125 no motion would be produced at the eccentric pin, since its center is on the center of the axle.

In order that motion be given to the eccentric rod, it is necessary to move the *eccentric pin center away from the center of the axle,* as shown in Fig. 126. The amount by which the center of the eccentric pin is set away from the center of the axle determines the *throw* of the eccentric crank. This throw equals twice the distance the eccentric pin center is set off from the center of the axle, as will be obvious from a study of Fig. 126.

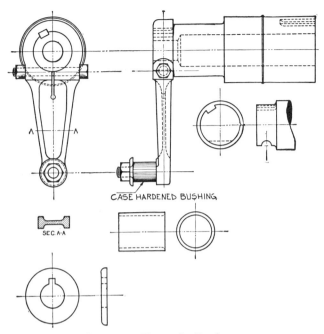

FIG. 124.—Eccentric Crank.

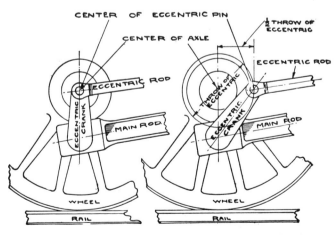

FIG. 125.—Eccentric Crank
on Center of Axle.

FIG. 126.—Eccentric Crank
away from Center of Axle.

The length of the eccentric crank is such that, with the center of the eccentric crank-pin set the proper distance away from the center of the axle to produce the required throw, the center of the eccentric crank-pin will be slightly more than one-quarter of a turn, or 90°, away from the center of the main crank-pin. The center of the eccentric crank-pin would be exactly 90° away from the center of the main crank-pin if it were not for the fact that the link foot-pin is above the center line of the axles. This point will be treated in greater detail under " Distortions " of the Walschaert valve gear.

The Eccentric Rod. The eccentric rod connects the eccentric crank pin with the link, as shown in Fig. 123. Since the connection to the eccentric crank-pin must provide for turning through a complete revolution, a suitable phosphor bronze bearing, as shown in Fig. 127, is usually

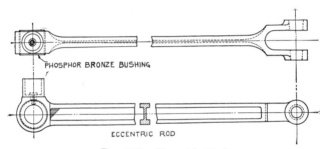

PHOSPHOR BRONZE BUSHING

ECCENTRIC ROD

FIG. 127.—Eccentric Rod.

employed. This is generally made in the solid bushing type and renewed as the parts wear. The end which is attached to the link turns through a small angle and here a case-hardened wrought-iron bushing and pin are used. The bearing is made in the link, so that no bushings are used in this end of the rod. The connecting pin holes are usually made to fit a tapered pin, as shown in Fig. 127.

It is desirable to have the eccentric rod as long as it can be made conveniently, in order that the irregularity due to the angular motion may be kept within reasonable limits.

The Link, Link Block, and Saddle. Figs. 128 and 129 show common designs of links as used on the Walschaert gear. The link is made of wrought iron or axle steel and is case-hardened. A case-hardened bushing is pressed in at the lower end for a bearing as described in connection with the eccentric rod. The bridles are bolted on, as shown in Figs. 128 and 129, to form the support for the link. Case-hardened bushings are pressed over the pins, which work in hardened bushings in the link bracket.

The link block is made to slide in the link slot, with suitable attachment to the radius rod. The link block is held in position by the radius rod and reversing mechanism. The block is usually made of wrought iron or axle steel and hardened.

The link is pivoted at points A, Fig. 129, by means of the bearings, which latter are attached rigidly to the frame of the engine. This construction provides a stationary link, there being only an oscillating motion about points A. Unlike the Stephenson gear, where the link itself is raised and lowered by the reverse lever, in this case the link block is moved over

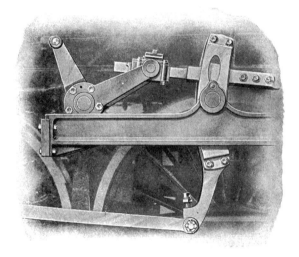

FIG. 128.—Lift Shaft, Link and Radius Rod Connection.

the stationary link. This feature of the valve motion explains why the Walschaert gear is sometimes known as a *radial gear*.

The radius of the link is equal to the length between the centers of the pin holes in the radius rod and is measured from the center of the link slot, as indicated in Figs. 129 and 130.

The bottom of the link for connection to the eccentric rod should be brought down as nearly to the center line of the axles as is convenient, provided the foot of the link is not extended so far as to decrease by too great an amount the effective travel of the link block produced by the throw of the eccentric crank.

Fig. 121 shows that the foot of the link will swing about the center of the link pivots a distance practically equal to the throw of the eccentric crank. However, the link block receives only a part of this motion, depending upon its position in the link. If the link block is in the center of the link, the block will receive no motion from the link, and if moved away from the center of the link, its travel will be increased proportionally.

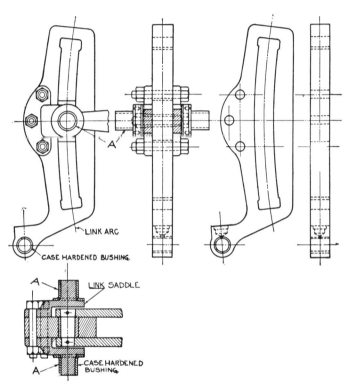

LINK ARC

CASE HARDENED BUSHING.

A   LINK SADDLE

CASE HARDENED BUSHING.

Fig. 129.—Link with Light Saddle. Walschaert Valve Gear.

Two general types of link support, to provide for the travel of the link block over the link, are shown in Figs. 128 and 129.

The Radius Rod. The motion of the link is transmitted to the lap and lead (or combination) lever by means of the radius rod, as shown in Fig. 131. A common design of radius rod is shown in Fig. 130, while Figs. 128 and 131, on pages 107 and 111, illustrate two arrangements for the attachment of the radius rod to the link and lift shaft. It is to be noted that the forked end of the radius rod, as shown in Fig. 130, is to provide for some such arrangement for the connection to the link.

The pin holes in the end of the fork are for the link block pin, giving a bearing between the pin and the hardened bushing pressed into the block. This pin, on account of the fact that the link block must pass

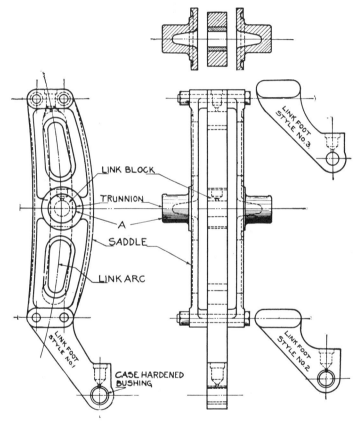

LINK BLOCK
TRUNNION
A
SADDLE
LINK ARC
LINK FOOT STYLE No.1
LINK FOOT STYLE No.3
LINK FOOT STYLE No.2
CASE HARDENED BUSHING

FIG. 129A.—Link with Heavy Saddle.   Walschaert Valve Gear.

by the link support, is designed with tapered ends and held in place by taper pins at each end, without the use of a nut.

The inner pin holes through the fork provide for the attachment of the radius rod hanger, or lifter, in which the bearing is made between the pin and a hardened bushing pressed into the hanger.

The end of the radius rod connecting with the lap and lead lever is

110   THE WALSCHAERT VALVE GEAR

provided with a wrought-iron bushing, which is case-hardened, so that
the bearing is made between this hardened bushing and the pin, which
is also hardened.

In order to reduce the angular effects as much as possible, the length
of the radius rod should be made as long as the conditions of the design

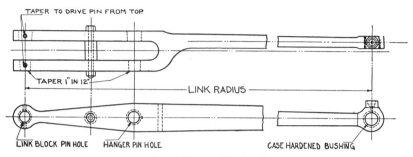

FIG. 130.—Radius Rod.

in hand will permit. This length should be at least eight times, or better
still, ten or twelve times, the length of the travel of the link block. Evi-
dently this length determines the radius of the link.

The radius of the link must always be made equal to the distance between the lap and lead lever and link block pin hole centers of the
radius rod, as indicated in Fig. 130, so that when the link is in the mid-
position and the radius rod is moved up and down by shifting the reverse
lever there will be no movement imparted to the valve.

Lap and Lead Lever. The lap and lead lever, sometimes called the
" combination " lever, is the part of the gear which combines the motion
of the link with that obtained from the main crosshead and transfers this
combined motion to the valve stem. It transforms the motion taken
from the crosshead to the amount desired for the particular design at
hand, as shown in Figs. 139 and 140.

In more recent designs of passenger locomotives where extreme lightness
of parts is desired, the crosshead arm as a means of connecting the lap and
lead lever to the crosshead is omitted. The same result is accomplished
by connecting the union link directly to the wrist pin, as in Fig. 132. This
arrangement, however, necessitates a very short lap and lead lever, as
may be seen in Fig. 132.

A recent design of a lap and lead lever is shown in Fig. 133. Here
the top end is forked to reach over the radius rod only, making the bearing

for this connection between the hardened pin and a hardened bushing pressed into the radius rod. The connection to the valve stem is made at the valve stem crosshead by means of a case-hardened wrought-iron pin fitting into the forks of the crosshead, which are provided with case-hardened bushings, so that the bearing surface is between the pin and

Fig. 131.—Valve Stem Crosshead Radius Rod, etc.

Fig. 132.—Walschaert Valve Gear Applied to Atlantic Type Locomotive.

the bushing. The pin is secured in place in the lap and lead lever by means of the taper pin, shown in Fig. 133. The lower end of the lap and lead lever is provided with a hardened bushing as indicated, which is pressed in, so that the bearing at this connection is made between the hardened bushing and the hardened pin.

Other forms of connections to the radius rod and valve stem are shown in Figs. 134 and 131. In the former the lap and lead lever is forked to

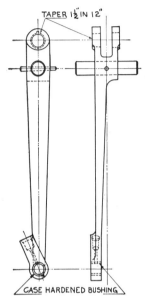

span over the valve stem crosshead and radius rod, while in the latter the top end of the lap and lead lever is straight and the connections of the radius rod and valve stem are made by forking the valve stem crosshead and the radius rod end.

The motion obtained from the crosshead is equivalent to that produced by a second eccentric placed on the axle a quarter of a turn, or 90°, away from the eccentric crank-pin center, and thus the combination gives the same effect as two eccentrics 90° apart. The motion produced by the crosshead during one stroke is reduced to such an extent by proportioning the two arms of the lap and lead lever, that when the link block is in the center of the link and no motion is derived from the link, the lap and lead lever will move the valve a distance equal to *twice* the lap of *the valve, plus twice* the *lead.* Hence the name "lap and lead lever." During this motion the lap and lead lever swings about the radius rod connection as a pivot.

FIG. 133. — Lap and Lead Lever as Applied to Gear shown in Figs. 121 and 132.

The fact that the lead is constant and does not vary as the reverse lever is hooked up will be discussed later.

The Walschaert valve gear may be used with either the common D slide valve or with the piston valve. These valves may be either *inside admission* or *outside admission.* The gear is most commonly used in connection with an inside admission piston valve. The piston valve is used in preference to the flat D slide valve; since, with the latter, in order to get the valve stem in line with the lap and lead lever, it is necessary to bring the center of the valve and steam chest on the outside of the center of the cylinder, as shown by the dotted line, Fig. 135. This widens the engine excessively. To avoid this widening, however, a complicated crosshead or a special double hanger may be introduced, whereby the motion of the lap and lead lever is taken from its outside position across or inward to the usual position of the valve stem for the D slide valve, which is inside of the line of motion of the lap and lead lever, as shown by the full lines

FIG. 134.—Valve Stem, Crosshead and Guide.

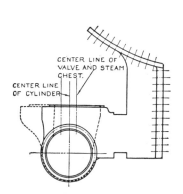

FIG. 135.—Cylinder and Slide Valve
Seat, Front View.

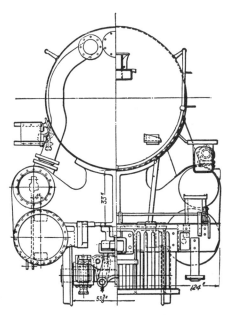

FIG. 136.—Cylinder and Piston Valve,
Front View.

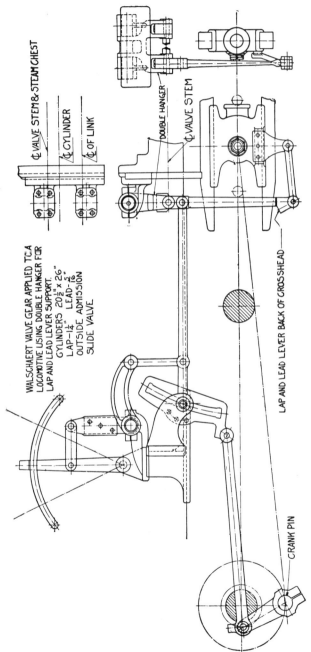

FIG. 137.—Walschaert Valve Gear with Double Hanger for Lap and Lead Lever Applied to a Philadelphia and Reading Atlantic Type Locomotive.

in Fig. 135. With the piston valve, the center of the valve may easily be brought in line with the center line of the lap and lead lever without widening the engine, and while still maintaining straight-line motion in the parts, as is apparent from a study of Fig. 136.

Fig. 137 illustrates an application of a double hanger arrangement, while Fig. 138 shows a design of valve stem crosshead to transfer the motion to the line of the valve stem.

The connections to the lap and lead lever for outside and inside admission valves are made in the manner shown in Figs. 139 and 140, respectively. In the case of the *inside* admission piston valve, the radius rod is connected to the lap and lead lever *above* the *valve stem connection*, while in the case of the *outside* admission valve the radius rod connection is made *below* that of the *valve stem.*

The reason for this arrangement is evident from a study of Figs. 139 and 140. The radius rod connection, forming a pivot about which the lap and lead lever swings as the main crosshead moves the lower end back and forth, must be below the valve stem connection when using an outside admission valve, as in Fig. 139, because this arrangement of the parts causes the slide valve to be drawn back when the crank-pin is on the front dead center and the piston on

Fig. 138.—Walschaert Valve Gear, using Special Crosshead on Valve Stem for Outside Admission Valve as applied to a Pacific Type Locomotive of the New York, New Haven and Hartford Railroad.

the extreme forward end of its stroke. Consequently, there will be lead opening at the front port, as is shown in Fig. 139.

When the Walschaert gear is used with the inside admission piston valve, the arrangement of these parts must be as in Fig. 140, because with

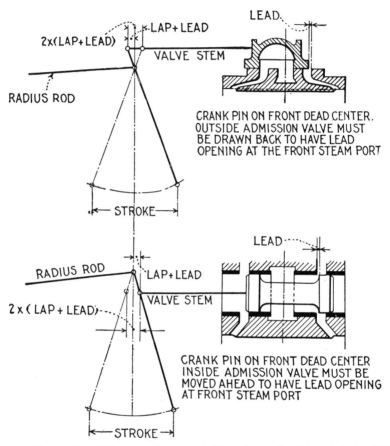

FIG. 139.—Connection of Lap and Lever and Valve Stem, Outside Admission Valve.
FIG. 140.—Connection of Lap and Lever and Valve Stem, Inside Admission Valve.

the crank-pin on the front dead center and the piston on its extreme forward position, in order to have lead at the front port, the piston valve must be moved ahead of its central position as indicated in Fig. 140.

Lap and Lead Lever Connector or Union Link. The lap and lead lever connector (sometimes called the " Union Link ") connects the bottom of the lap and lead lever with the crosshead arm, as shown in Fig. 131, or in detail in Fig. 141. The lap and lead lever connector should stand horizontal either when the piston is in the middle of its stroke, or when it is at the extreme ends of its stroke.

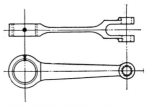

FIG. 141.—Union Link.

The crosshead arm shown in Figs. 122 and 131 is merely an extension to the crosshead to provide a means for connecting the union link to the crosshead and lap and lead lever, so that the union link will be in a horizontal position when the crosshead is in either the middle or the ends of its stroke. The length of the lap and lead lever connector must be made such that when the crosshead is in the middle of its stroke, the lap and lead lever stands in a vertical position. Fig. 131 illustrates common designs of crosshead arm and union link. As already mentioned, in some of the later designs of locomotives, the crosshead arm is omitted.

Valve Stem Crosshead and Guides. The valve stem crosshead and guides shown in Fig. 134 are the parts of the gear which carry or support the lap and lead lever and the connecting parts, and also guide or control the movement of the valve stem, keeping it central with the valve chamber.

There are two general styles of valve stem supports, one with a bar guide arrangement and the other with the guide cast in one piece with the back steam chest head. Fig. 134 illustrates the usual method of coupling the bar style of valve stem crosshead. Here the guide is formed by a bar, the front end of which is attached to the back steam chest head and the back end to the main guide yoke.

The valve stem crosshead is usually a box arrangement, sliding over the bar, with suitable arrangements for the lap and lead lever and valve stem attachments. With this style, the guide must be " lined up " with the center of the valve chamber in assembling the parts on the erecting floor. This design generally necessitates a forked lap and lead lever style of connection.

Fig. 131 shows the style of valve stem crosshead and guide in which the guide is cast in one piece with the steam chest head. This design makes the guide self-centering with the center of the valve chamber. Consequently, the guide is always central with the motion of the valve when the back steam chest head is in place. An arrangement of this kind has the advantage that it can be erected, taken down, and replaced without

any lining up. The guides, on the top of the crosshead, are so constructed
that they can be easily adjusted for wear by means of liners. This arrangement also permits the use of a straight design of lap and lead lever without

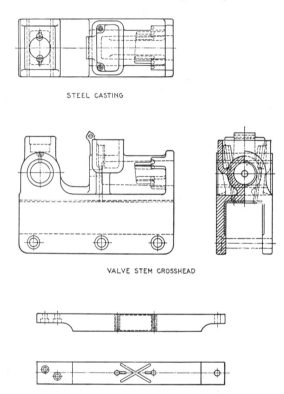

STEEL CASTING

VALVE STEM CROSSHEAD

BAR TYPE VALVE STEM CROSSHEAD GUIDE

Fig. 142A.—Detail of Valve Stem Crosshead and Guide.

the forked end, as the valve stem crosshead can be made with wings or
forks. The lever is connected to the valve stem crosshead by a pin passing
through its forks. Fig. 142 shows two common designs of valve stem
crossheads for these types of connection.

Valve Stem. Figs. 131 and 134 show the location of the valve stem.
It is the part of the gear which connects the valve motion proper with
the valve. When slide valves are used, a yoke is provided for the connection to the valve, as is shown in Fig. 55 for the Stephenson gear. Fig.
143 illustrates the usual construction of valve stem for use with a piston

valve. However, there are almost as many different styles of valve stems as there are different styles of piston valve, differing only in the detail design for connections to the valve and valve stem crosshead. In the

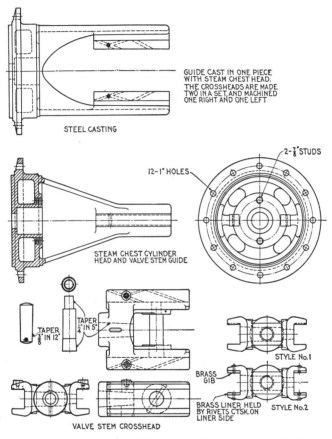

FIG. 142B.—Detail of Valve Stem Crosshead and Guide.

valve stem shown in Fig. 143, the connection to the valve stem crosshead is made by means of the taper-fitted end of the stem and a flat taper key. Sometimes this connection is made by means of threads and nuts on the rods, placed each side of the valve stem crosshead. This design may be seen by referring to Fig. 134. In such cases an adjustment for the length of the valve stem may easily be made. In some cases the valve stem is pressed or driven into the valve, usually at its center, the fit being at each end of the valve, and on the portions of the rod marked A, Fig. 143. In addition to the press or driving fit, some stems are provided with keys, as shown here. The solid collar forms a shoulder to press against and

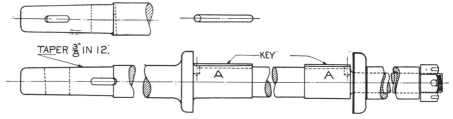

TAPER $\frac{3}{8}"$ IN 12.

FIG. 143.—Valve Stem for Piston Valve.

also helps to carry the end thrust produced when the valve is traveling in the forward direction. The end thrust produced in the other direction is supported by means of the loose collar, sleeve and nut.

OPERATING PARTS OF THE GEAR

The reverse shaft with its connection to the radius rod, the reverse shaft arms, the lifting spring, the reach rod, the reverse lever, and quadrant (when used), are the parts of the gear which make up the general mechanism for operating and controlling the valve motion.

The Reverse Shaft. The reverse or lift shaft shown in Fig. 144 is the part of the gear which connects the reach rod and radius bar in such a way that as the reverse lever is moved back and forth, the link block is raised and lowered in the link. In most locomotives, the lift shaft extends across the engine to connect the right and left motions with the one reach rod, and is supported at each end by bearings attached to the engine frame. It is provided with arms for the attachment to the radius rod on each side and one arm at about right angles to these for the reach rod connection on the right side. The balancing spring is usually attached to a short arm located midway between the bearings of the lift shaft. With some designs of locomotives, particularly the articulated type, the lift shaft is omitted and a separate reversing arm and suitable bearing are used on each side of the engine, as will be explained later.

Fig. 144 illustrates a common design of reverse shaft. The connection to the radius rod is generally made in one of two ways. Fig. 128 shows a reverse shaft and radius rod connection in which the radius rod is directly

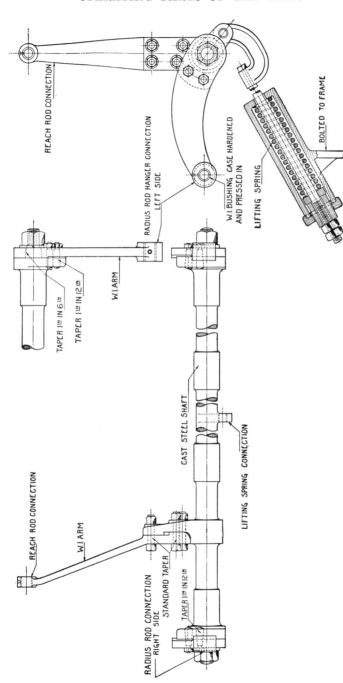

Fig. 144.—Reverse Shaft and Arms.

connected to the lift shaft arm by means of a " slip block " arrangement.
In such a case the reverse shaft arm is made in two parts, the outer part
being easily removable.   This permits of readily disconnecting the lift shaft

FIG. 144A.—Walschaert Valve Gear in Course of Erection.

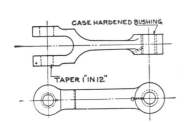

FIG. 145.—Radius Rod Lifter.

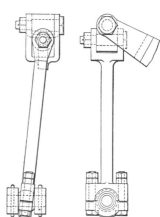

FIG. 146.—Radius Rod Lifter.
Mallet Locomotive.

and radius rod.   With this arrangement the radius rod slides back and forth
through the " slip block " with the movement of the link, and proper pre-
cautions must be taken to provide for an adjustment for wear.   With this

design of connection for the lift shaft and radius rod, the latter is made in two parts. The back part is forked to span over the link block and is bolted to the front part by through bolts as shown in Fig. 128.

Another style of reverse shaft and radius rod connection, also commonly used, is that in which the arm of the lift shaft is connected to the radius rod by means of a link called the radius rod hanger, or *lifter*.

This type of construction is shown in Fig. 131. Sometimes the link

Fig. 147.—Mallet Rounding Curve.

bracket is attached to the valve gear frame from behind the link, and in such case the reverse shaft and radius rod lifter are usually placed in front of the link, as is shown in Fig. 132.

Fig. 145 illustrates a common design of radius rod lifter. If this style of connection is used on an articulated locomotive, the radius rod lifter on the front engine must be of special design, because of the lateral or " sidewise " motion of the front engine in going around a curve. The valve gear frame and consequently the link and radius rod are then not in a permanent position relative to the boiler, the relative positions constantly changing, due to the swing of the front engine under the boiler, as the locomotive runs over a curved section of track.

Since on this type of locomotive the lift shaft arms for the front engine are usually attached to the boiler, special means must be provided to allow the radius rod hanger to adjust itself to the lateral movement of the front engine under the boiler, so that this movement may not interfere with the motion of the valves. This is accomplished by using an exceptionally long lifting link, as is shown in Fig. 146, having a double jaw in its upper end, and a universal or " ball and socket " joint at the radius rod, which allows the lower end of the lifter to follow the movement of the front engine. The necessity for employing this device will be appreciated by considering Fig. 147, which shows the front end of a Mallet locomotive rounding a curve.

In some cases in the design of articulated locomotives the rear lift shaft may be placed sufficiently below the boiler so that a shaft can be attached to operate the left side gear. However, the usual method of operating the left side gear is to locate the shaft at the rear of the firebox, connecting directly to the reverse lever pivot, as in Fig. 148. Here both front and rear lift shafts are attached to the boiler on both sides of the engine, and the connection to the reverse lever is made by suitable reach rods on both sides of the engine.

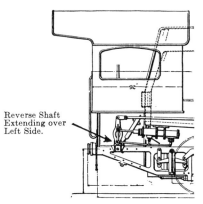

Reverse Shaft Extending over Left Side.

FIG. 148.—Mallet Reverse Shaft under Cab.

Another method of reach rod connection employed by the Baldwin Locomotive Works on Mallet locomotives is to place a long reach rod made in two sections through the center of the engine below the boiler and join the two sections together by means of a suitable joint and guide placed directly over the coupling pin in the frame. The front section of the reach rod may turn with the front engine frame, while the rear section remains central with the rear engine. The rod guide is placed in a suitable opening in the high-pressure cylinder saddle, the guides being bolted to the saddle walls. The two sections of the reach rod are connected directly to the front and back reverse shafts respectively. This design eliminates the use of the brackets and long hangers on the sides of the boilers.

Balancing or Lifting Spring. The lift shaft balancing or lifting spring is the device which is provided to take the weight of the link blocks and radius rod ends from the reverse lever, so as to permit these parts to be raised and lowered with ease. One end of the spring is attached to the short lever on the lift shaft and the other end fits into a suitable holder provided with an adjusting nut for securing the proper tension in the spring. Fig. 144 illustrates a common style of lift shaft balancing spring applied to the lift shaft.

Reach Rod. The reach rod shown in Fig. 121 is the part of the gear which connects the lift shaft with the reverse lever. Two common types of reach rod have already been explained under the Stephenson gear and are illustrated in Fig. 59. Generally, with all types of locomotives except articulated Mallets there is one reach rod located on the right side of the engine to connect directly with the reverse lever.

With the long reach rod which is required in most of the modern designs of locomotives using the Walschaert gear, it becomes necessary to support the rod against the lateral swing of the engine when in motion, and also to provide means for making a stiff, yet light construction. This is usually accomplished by providing a slot and roller support, as shown in Fig. 149.

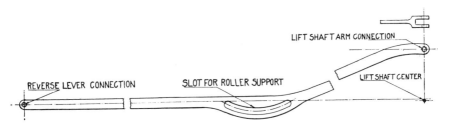

FIG. 149.—Reach Rod with Slot for Roller Support.

The shape of the curved slot is such that the rod is free to take the positions determined by the paths of each end as the reverse lever is moved from one extreme position to the other. This construction is especially desirable for passenger and fast freight locomotives.

Fig. 161 illustrates the slot and roller support for the round style of reach rod. This reach rod is provided with a second support back near the cab, in connection with the screw reverse mechanism used on this particular engine.

In Fig. 162 another flat bar style of reach rod is supported by a similar design of slot and roller used in connection with a late design of valve gear.

Screw Reverse.   The screw reverse was invented to meet the requirements of the heavy valve gears used on large passenger and fast freight locomotives; in which the common reverse lever and quadrant, as described

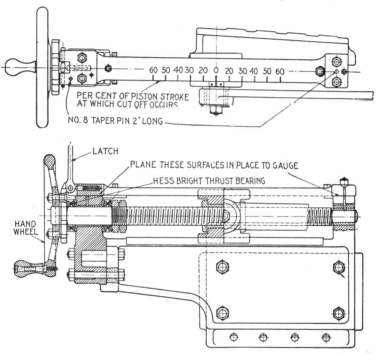

FIG. 150.—Screw Reverse.

under the Stephenson gear, and illustrated in Fig. 60, have been found inadequate to fulfill the requirements.   The common reverse lever, used on many locomotives equipped with the Walschaert gear, acts just as in the case of the Stephenson gear.

The screw reverse, shown in Fig. 150, is mounted on the boiler by means of a suitable bracket located in the cab.   It consists primarily of a large screw, Fig. 151, running through a nut operating a crosshead which works in suitable guides.   The reach rod is attached to this movable crosshead.

The screw is operated by means of a suitable hand wheel and is provided with a latch for securing it in position. Ball thrust bearings are provided

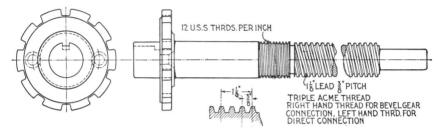

FIG. 151.—Detail of Screw.

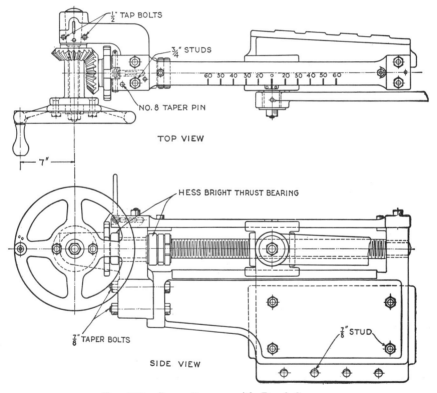

FIG. 152.—Screw Reverse with Bevel Gears.

to take the lateral thrust, as shown in this illustration. The screw usually consists of a double or triple "Acme" thread having about a one inch to one and one-quarter inch lead and is from two to two and one-half inches in diameter. The upper guide is provided with a graduated scale upon which a mark on the crosshead registers the percent of the piston stroke at which cut-off takes place. In some designs, in order to provide greater convenience in the operation of the gear, it has been found advantageous to connect the screw to the hand wheel through the medium of bevel gears, as shown in Fig. 152.

Power Reverse. On large locomotives where the valve gear parts are heavy and cause considerable difficulty in shifting the valve, the valve gear is operated by a power reversing apparatus. Mallet locomotives,

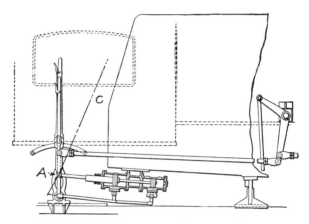

Fig. 153.—Hydro-pneumatic Reverse Gear.

from the start, required a power reverse gear because of their heavy and complex valve motions.

Recently many passenger, freight and shifting engines have become so heavy as to require power mechanisms to handle their valve gears, in order to obtain efficient service. One common type of power reverse known as the " hydro-pneumatic " reverse gear uses both compressed air and oil in separate cylinders, and is illustrated in Fig. 153. This arrangement consists of one compressed-air cylinder and one oil cylinder with a single or common piston rod connected to the main reverse lever.

On a suitable location marked A, Fig. 153, on the main reverse lever, a second lever is pivoted for operating the gear by means of the power device. At this same point on the main reverse lever the piston rod of the power reversing apparatus is also attached.

A *forward* movement of the second or operating lever (the small lever in Fig. 153), which turns on the pivot, throws its lower end *backward*, opening the valve (see position *C*, Fig. 153) of the air and oil cylinders, thus making a passage for the air pressure to enter the rear end of the air cylinder, forcing the air piston *forward* and, with it, the entire gear. The effect is the same as though the main reverse lever were moved forward in the usual manner.

This air passage may be seen by referring to the lower section of Fig. 154, which shows the operating valve and levers enlarged. The forward movement on pivot *A* just described, which is indicated by line *C*, Fig. 153, will cause the lower end of the operating lever to be drawn backward

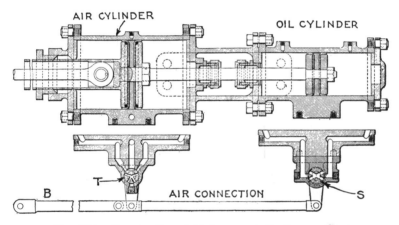

FIG. 154.—Cross-section of Hydro-pneumatic Reverse Gear

and hence to pull the rod *B* backward and turn the air valve *T* so that air pressure will pass up through the ports shown in the air cylinder back of the piston, and the device will work as described above. The rod *B* is also attached to the oil valves *S* and in like manner will turn the oil valve so that its *X*-shaped ports will open the passages from one side of the oil piston to the other, thus causing the oil to be on both sides of the oil piston at the same time. As the oil piston moves, the oil is pushed from in front of the piston through the valve to the back side of the oil piston and in this way the oil cylinder serves as a lock and regulator of the movement of the valve gear. This arrangement of " oil cushioning " allows the operating piston to follow the movement of the gear, to which it gives a

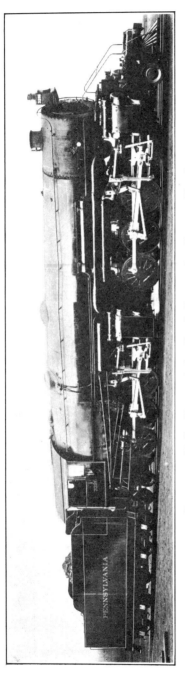

Fig. 155.—Mallet Four-cylinder Simple Locomotive (2-8-8-2 Type).

moderate and uniform motion because of the small passage for oil through the oil valve.

By stopping the movement of the operating lever, the gear moves the main reverse lever up to the corresponding relation with the operating lever, and then automatically shuts off the air supply and locks the oil cylinder.

This automatic stop is due to the fact that when the main reverse lever stands straight with the operating lever, in any position along the quadrant, the position of the lever arrangement for operating the air and oil valves is always such as to close these valves. That is, the movement of the main reverse lever, in coming to the position of the operating lever, moves the rod B so as to close the valves. Hence, when the two levers stand together the air and oil valves are closed, and the oil piston locks the gear, because the oil is shut up in the oil cylinder on both sides of the oil piston.

In unlatching the operating lever, the same movement raises the main latch. This cannot again drop until the two levers stand side by side. When in this position, the levers are latched in the quadrant, and a positive mechanical locking of the gear is secured in addition to that produced by the oil lock.

The handle part of the main reverse lever is made for the purpose of operating the engine by hand in the absence of air pressure, or in case of any derangement of the power-operating device.

For the backward movement of the operating lever, its lower end is thrown forward on pivot *A*, Fig. 153, and the lever *B* is pushed forward. This registers the ports in the air and oil valves so that air pressure enters the air cylinder on the front side of the air piston, forcing it backward, and with it the entire gear as described for the forward motion. Likewise in this case the oil is free to pass from one side of the oil piston through the oil valve ports to the other side and thus to form a lock and regulator, as in the other movement.

Fig. 155 illustrates the hydro-pneumatic power reverse gear as applied to a Mallet four-cylinder simple locomotive, built by the American Locomotive Company for the Pennsylvania Railroad Company.

Ragonnet Power Reverse Gear. Figs. 156 and 157 illustrate a well-known power reverse gear, the invention of Mr. E. L. Ragonnet. This device has passed through the experimental stage, and is regarded as a solution of the power reverse gear problem.

The gear is preferably operated by air, although an auxiliary steam connection is provided. Distribution is controlled by an ordinary D slide valve arranged for outside admission. The piston rod is connected to a crosshead, which is coupled to the reverse shaft by means of a suitable reach rod. The crosshead gibs are held in place by a cast-steel plate, having an arm projecting downwards. This crosshead arm is connected by a suitable link with the lower end of a floating lever. The upper end of this floating lever is pivotly connected to, and supported by, the valve stem, which in turn is carried by a cylindrical guide. The movement of the valve is controlled from the cab through the agency of a rocker. The upper end of this rocker is connected by a light rod with a small reverse lever, and the lower end through a link with the floating lever a short distance below the valve stem. The rocker is provided with tappets, *A*, which strike the ends of projecting set screws, 46, when the limit of travel of the valve is reached. These set screws require no adjustment after the gear is properly applied, and merely limit the throw of the reverse shaft arm in either direction.

The small reverse lever is locked in any desired position by an ordinary toothed quadrant, Fig. 157. Assuming the lever 47 in mid-position and the slide valve normally covering both ports, when the lever is moved into forward gear (to the right, referring to the illustration), the combining lever, 27, swings about its lower end as a fulcrum, and the slide valve moves to the right, admitting air to the left-hand end of the cylinder. The piston now moves to the right, and the combining lever, 27 (pivoting about its intermediate or reverse lever connection *B*), returns the valve to its central position, unless the progressive movement of the reverse lever is continued. Thus it will be seen that when the lever is shifted

Fig. 156.—Application of Ragonnet Power Reverse Gear.

to any desired location, the piston moves in the proper direction until the valve gear reaches a corresponding point, whereupon the valve is automatically returned to its central, or lapped position, and the gear brought to rest.

Since the exhaust, or inside lap of the valve, is materially greater than the outside lap (which is very small), air is held on both sides of the piston

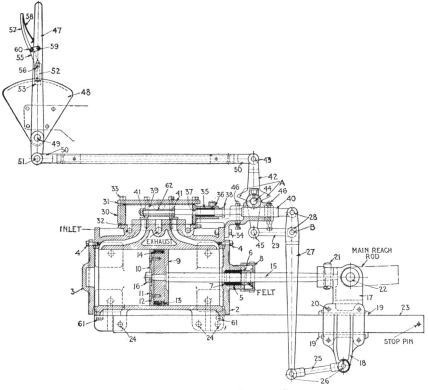

FIG. 157.—Ragonnet Reverse Gear.

1. Cylinder.
2. Cylinder Head, front.
3. Cylinder Head, back.
4. Cylinder Head, Studs and Nuts.
5. Piston Rod Packing.
6. Piston Rod Gland.
7. Piston Rod Gland Ring.
8. Piston Rod Gland Nut.
9. Piston Head.
10. Piston Follower.
11. Piston Follower, Studs and Nuts (4).
12. Piston Follower Nutlock (4).
13. Piston Packing (3).
14. Piston Packing.
15. Piston Rod.
16. Piston Rod Nut.
17. Crosshead.
18. Crosshead Lug.
19. Crosshead Gibs (2).
20. Crosshead Bolts and Nuts (4).
21. Crosshead Key.
22. Crosshead Pin and Nut.
23. Guide.
24. Guide Bolts (3).
25. Crosshead Link.
26. Crosshead Link Pins and Nuts (2).
27. Combining Lever.
28. Combining Lever Pins and Nuts (2).
29. Combining Lever Link.
30. Valve Chest.
31. Valve Chest Cap.
32. Valve Chest Cap Gaskets (2).
33. Valve Chest Columns and Nuts (8).
34. Valve Chest Bolts and Nuts (2).
35. Valve Stem Packing.
36. Valve Stem Gland.
37. Valve Stem Gland Ring.
38. Valve Stem Gland Nut.
39. Valve.
40. Valve Stem.
41. Valve Stem Nut and Collars.
42. Rocker.
43. Rocker Pin and Nut (Top).
44. Rocker Pin and Nut (Middle).
45. Rocker Pin and Nut (Bottom).
46. Safety Stop Set Screws and Nuts (2).
47. Hand Lever.
48. Hand Lever Quadrant.
49. Hand Lever Fulcrum Pin and Nut.
50. Hand Lever Rod Ends (2).
51. Hand Lever Rod Pin and Nut.
52. Hand Lever Latch.
53. Hand Lever Latch Plate.
54. Hand Lever Latch Washer.
55. Hand Lever Latch Link.
56. Hand Lever Latch Bolts (2).
57. Hand Lever Latch Handle.
58. Hand Lever Latch Handle Spring.
59. Hand Lever Latch Handle Pin.
60. Hand Lever Latch Handle Pin.
61. Drain Cock Complete (2).
62. Valve Stem Thimble.

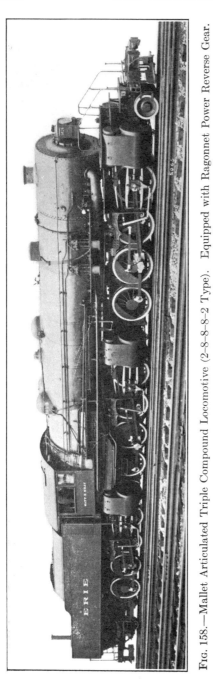

FIG. 158.—Mallet Articulated Triple Compound Locomotive (2-8-8-2 Type). Equipped with Ragonnet Power Reverse Gear.

at the same time. It will thus be seen that the mechanism is prevented from creeping or vibrating by an elastic cushion formed by compressing the air in one end of the cylinder or the other. In no case does the valve open to exhaust when holding the gear in any desired cut-off position. Owing to this arrangement, the gear is very economical in the use of air—in fact, when the piston and piston rod packing are properly maintained, the loss of air, when holding the valve gear in a fixed position, is practically nothing. The method of holding the valve gear, through the medium of an air cushion instead of by a rigid latch and quadrant, materially lessens the wear and tear of the valve gear and its connections.

The cylinder is oiled through a small lubricator, conveniently placed in the cab, and suitable means of lubrication are provided on all moving parts.

The entire mechanism is so simple in construction, and has proved so reliable in service, that, as a rule, no auxiliary hand gear of any description is applied. Its application to what is now (1917) the largest locomotive in the world is shown in Fig. 158. This engine is known as an articulated triple compound, in which there are six distinct valve gears, all operated by one Ragonnet power reverse mechanism.

American Locomotive Company's Power Reverse Gear. The American Locomotive Company has recently put into service a new design of power reverse gear, known as the " Mellin Power Reverse," the general arrangement of which is shown in diagram I of Fig. 159. This gear may be arranged to operate with compressed air or steam. In this description it will be assumed that steam is used.

As will be seen by examining diagram I of Fig. 159, the reverse gear consists of the reversing cylinder, 1, and reversing piston, 2, to which crosshead, 3, is connected by means of rod, 4. The crosshead, 3, is made to slide over guide, 5. Reach rod, 6, is connected to the reverse shaft of the valve motion. The admission and exhaust of steam are controlled by reversing valve, 7, which is operated from the reverse lever in the cab, by means of the lever system shown.

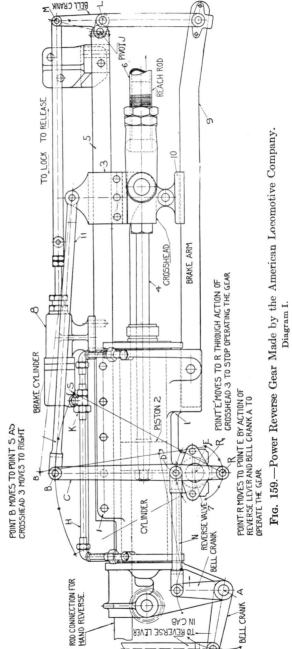

Fig. 159.—Power Reverse Gear Made by the American Locomotive Company.

Diagram I.

Brake cylinder, 8, contains a brake piston and spring which is connected by means of the brake lever system to brake arm, 9, acting on brake shoe, 10.

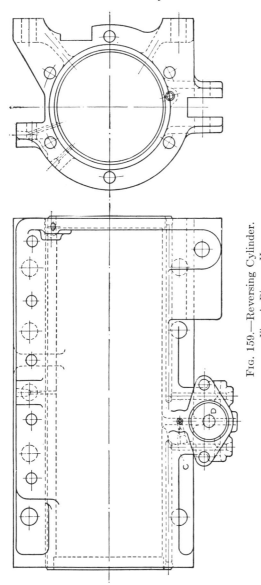

FIG. 159.—Reversing Cylinder.
View A, Diagram II.

In order to understand in detail the construction and operation of this gear, it will be well to study diagrams II to VI inclusive, which afford clearer illustrations for this purpose than can be had from a complete assembly of the parts.

Diagram II of Fig. 159 shows the reversing cylinder in detail. Referring to view A of this diagram, steam enters at C and passes through the port to the reversing valve chambers D, from which it is admitted to, and exhausted from, each end of the reversing cylinder by the operation of the reversing valve. View B (diagram II) with section BB illustrates the reversing valve chamber and port construction to a larger scale.

Diagram III illustrates the reversing valve. Section AA is a view through the port and shows its shape and size with the amount of steam and exhaust laps.

Diagram IV illustrates the reversing valve in place in the valve bushing 1, with the operating lever 2, attached to the reversing valve by means of a taper pin and key. The section AA, taken through the ports, shows

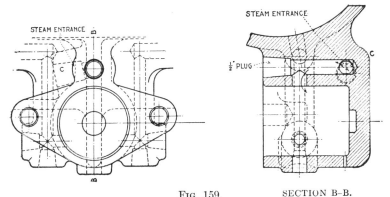

FIG. 159.
View B, Diagram II.

SECTION B–B.

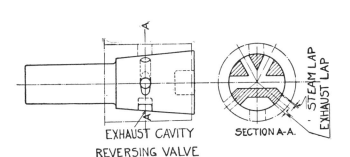

EXHAUST CAVITY
REVERSING VALVE

SECTION A-A.

FIG. 159.
Diagram III.

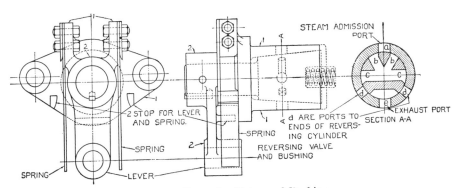

FIG. 159.—Reversing Valve and Bushing.
Diagram IV.

the reversing valve in the central position in the bushing. The reversing valve is rotated in the bushing by means of the operating lever 2, and turns through equal angles each side of its central position, so that ports *b* in the valve register with the admission port *a* in the bushing, and the other ends *C* of the valve port register with port *d* in the bushing. This establishes communication with either end of the reversing cylinder, depending on which way the reversing valve is turned. When the valve is rotated to admit steam at one end of the reversing cylinder, the other end of the reversing cylinder is opened to the exhaust by means of the exhaust cavity shown.

Diagram V shows the brake release valve. This valve is arranged with an automatic float or check valve *D* (with a seat at each end) which

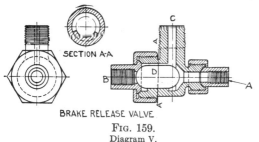

SECTION A-A

BRAKE RELEASE VALVE
FIG. 159.
Diagram V.

is moved from one seat to the other by the action of the steam as it enters the brake release valve. When steam enters at *A* it forces the valve *D* over, and seats it at end *B*, in which position the valve closes the end *B* and opens a passage from *A* through *C* to the brake cylinder. Likewise, when steam enters at *B* it forces the valve over and seats it at end *A*, in which position the valve *D* closes the end *A* and opens a passage from *B* through *C* to the brake cylinder.

Diagram VI illustrates the brake cylinder, brake piston and brake spring arrangement. The brake spring *C* acts on piston *D* and applies the brake to the main crosshead of the reversing gear (see diagram I). Steam to release the brake enters brake cylinder *E* at *A*, acts on piston *D* against the force of the brake spring and moves the brake piston in the direction opposite to that produced by the action of the spring, thus releasing the brake (see diagram I). The tension of the brake spring is adjusted by means of the nut as shown.

By referring again to diagram I, the application and function of the various parts may be learned and a complete operation of the gear followed.

When the reversing gear is *not* in motion, the action of the brake spring in brake cylinder, 8, will always apply the brake and lock the gear. The reversing gear is shown in the central position in diagram I. This corresponds with the middle notch position of the reverse lever in the cab. Suppose the reverse lever in the cab is moved to the extreme forward notch; then the horizontal arm of bell crank A moves upward and its vertical arm moves to the right as shown by the arrows. Bell crank A is connected to lever C by rod N. Since the reversing gear crosshead, 3, is locked by means of the brake device, this movement of the reverse lever and bell crank A swings lever C about point B as a fulcrum or center to the position shown at B–E. The movement thus produced at R, which is attached to the operating lever R_1R of the reversing valve (shown in diagram IV), causes lever C to move from its central position to point E and hence turn the reversing valve by means of the operating lever to position R_1E and admit steam against the left side of the reversing piston, and at the same time open the other end of the reversing cylinder to the exhaust. The steam admitted to the reversing cylinder then forces the reversing gear to the right as indicated by the arrows. Before the gear operates, however, the brake must be released. This is accomplished by the steam which has entered the main reversing cylinder, passing through pipe H to the brake release

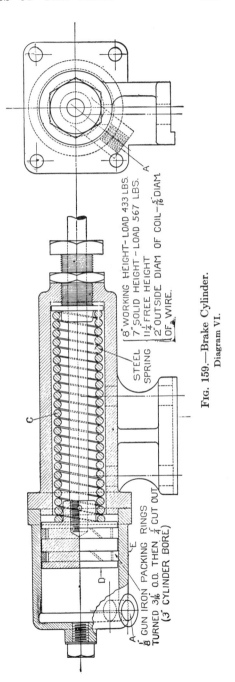

Fig. 159.—Brake Cylinder.
Diagram VI.

valve K, and thence to the brake cylinder. Release valve K closes communication with the opposite side of the main reversing piston and admits the steam to the brake cylinder to act on the brake piston, which action overcomes the tension of the brake spring and forces the piston and brake apparatus to the right. This movement causes bell crank MJL to turn about its pivot J, drop the brake arm, 9, away from the brake shoe, 10, and unlock the gear. When the brake is released the steam acting on the left of the reversing piston moves the reversing gear to the right, and with it the valve motion.

Lever C is connected to the crosshead 3 by link 11 so that as the crosshead moves to the right it will draw lever C with it. Since the reverse lever in the cab has been moved to the forward notch, point D will be moved to the right, and be located on the line BE. When the gear is in motion, point D becomes a fulcrum or center for lever C to swing about as it is moved by the crosshead 3. This movement of the crosshead will cause lever C to occupy the position shown by the line RS, when the crosshead has moved to the end of its travel.

In this position point R is again in the middle position of its swing and has moved the reversing valve back to its central position and has thus shut off the admission of steam. The brake spring will then again lock the gear, by drawing the brake piston to the left. This movement will bring the short arm of the bell crank MJL upward and with it the brake arm 9, thus applying the brake to crosshead 3.

In a like manner the movement of the reversing gear may be traced for any position or movement of the reverse lever in the cab.

The mechanism is arranged to have the lower end R of the lever C in the middle position and hence the reversing valve in its central position, whenever the lever C occupies a position corresponding with the position of the reverse lever in the cab. That is, when lever C moves to a position to correspond with the position assumed by the reverse lever in the cab, the admission of steam is shut off, and the gear ceases to operate. The brake spring will then lock the gear in this position.

Fig. 160 shows an application of the American Locomotive Company's power reverse gear to a Santa Fe (2–10–2) type locomotive.

Rushton Power Reverse. The Rushton power reverse gear was designed and patented by Mr. K. Rushton and has been applied to locomotives built by the Baldwin Locomotive Works. It is essentially a screw reverse driven by means of an air motor through a pinion and gear.

Fig. 160.—Santa Fe (2-10-2) Type Locomotive Equipped with Mellin Power Reverse Gear. Built by the American Locomotive Company.

RELATIVE CRANK=PIN AND PISTON POSITIONS FOR DIFFER= ENT VALVE EVENTS AT FULL FORWARD GEAR

The Walschaert valve gear, as previously stated, may be applied to a slide or piston valve having either inside or outside admission. It will be well, therefore, to study the relative positions of the parts when the gear is applied to both the outside admission slide valve and the inside admission piston valve. The action of the gear as a whole may best be observed by tracing the movement of the parts through a complete revolution of the drivers.

Fig. 122 represents the application of the Walschaert valve gear to a Mogul (2–6–0) type locomotive having *outside admission slide valves.*

Before tracing the movement of the gear through one complete revolution of the drivers, it may be well to establish clearly in mind the fundamental principles of design of the Walschaert gear for outside and inside admission valves. The eccentrics may either *lead* or *follow* the main crank-pin. This means that the eccentric may be a certain part of a revolution either ahead or behind the main pin when the wheels are running in the forward direction.

The position of the eccentric crank relative to the main crank-pin depends upon two things:

First: With a Valve Having Outside Admission. The valve stem is connected to the lap and lead lever at a point above the connection of the latter with the radius rod. If the link block is in the lower half of the link when in forward gear, the eccentric crank leads the main pin. If the link block is in the upper half of the link when in forward gear, the eccentric crank follows the main pin.

Second: With a Valve Having Inside Admission. The valve stem is connected to the lap and lead lever at a point below the connection of the latter with the radius rod. If the link block is in the lower half of the link when in forward gear, the eccentric crank follows the main pin. If the link block is in the upper half of the link when in forward gear, the eccentric crank leads the main pin.

Inasmuch as the position of the valve (when the piston is at the end of its stroke) is dependent on the lap and lead lever only, it is evident that the lead given by the Walschaert gear *is the same for all points of cut-off.* This is the principal feature which distinguishes this gear from the Stephenson motion as far as steam distribution is concerned. All

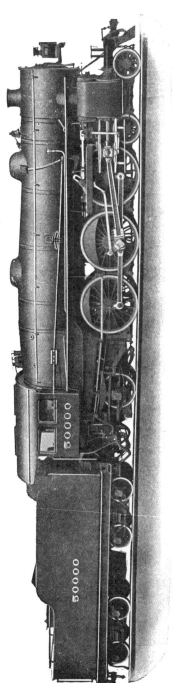

Fig. 161.—Pacific Type Locomotive Using Top of Link for the Forward Motion. Eccentric Crank Leads or Goes Ahead of Main Crank-pin.

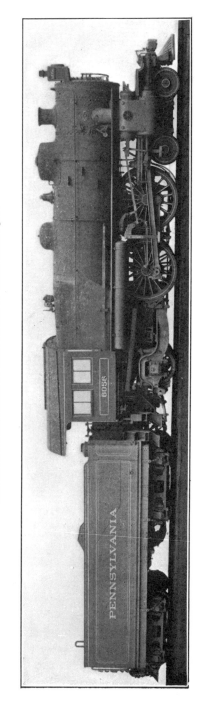

Fig. 162.—Atlantic Type Locomotive Using Bottom of Link for the Forward Motion. Eccentric Crank Follows Main Crank-pin.

parts of the Walschaert motion should be correctly laid out and constructed from a diagram, and the gear designed to give the lead most desirable for the usual running speed.

The parts having been correctly made, it is impossible to alter the lead without seriously deranging the motion. In this respect the Walschaert gear is less flexible than the Stephenson, but when the correct steam distribution is obtained, it is less liable to derangement and the engine is more easily kept " square."

Figs. 161 and 162 illustrate the two methods of arranging the Walschaert valve gear. In Fig. 161 is shown the American Locomotive Company's experimental engine No. 50,000. In this case the valves have inside admission and the forward motion is taken from the *upper half* of the link. It is to be noted that the eccentric crank *leads* the main crank pin when running forward. By referring to Fig. 162 the other design may be observed. This is an illustration of an Atlantic type (4–4–2), locomotive built by the Pennsylvania Railroad Company. This engine also has inside admission valves, but the forward motion is taken from the *lower half* of the link, hence the eccentric *follows* the main crank-pin when the engine is running in the forward direction, as may be seen in Fig. 162. The chief difference in the construction to produce these different effects is in the location and connection of the lift shaft. In the former case, Fig. 161, the lift shaft is pivoted in front of the link, and in the latter case, Fig. 162, it is set back of the link.

The position of the connection of the valve stem to the lap and lead lever, relative to the connection of the radius rod to the latter, depends *only* on whether the valves have *inside* or *outside* admission and is independent of whether the top or bottom of the link is used for the forward motion. The arrangement of the reversing mechanism, or the position of the eccentric crank, in no way affects the relative positions of these two connections to the lap and lead lever, as shown in Figs. 139 and 140.

In Fig. 122 the valve has outside admission, therefore the valve stem connection to the lap and lead lever is *above* that of the radius rod connection. The forward motion is taken from the bottom of the link; consequently, the eccentric crank *leads* the main pin when the engine is running forward. Fig. 121 shows the Walschaert gear applied to a locomotive using an inside admission piston valve. Hence the valve stem is connected *below* the radius rod connection to the lap and lead lever. The bottom of the link is used for the forward motion; consequently, the eccentric *follows* the main crank-pin in forward running.

Fig. 163 represents the position and direction of action of the parts for the different valve events with an outside admission slide valve. The motion is shown with the reverse lever in full forward gear. In this arrangement, using the bottom of the link for the forward motion, the eccentric crank must lead, or go ahead of the main crank-pin. The reason for this may be seen by a careful study of Fig. 163.

The crank-pin is on the forward dead center and with the engine running in the forward direction the crank-pin is moving backward as indicated by the arrow. The piston has just started its backward stroke. In order that steam may be admitted to the cylinder against the front side of the

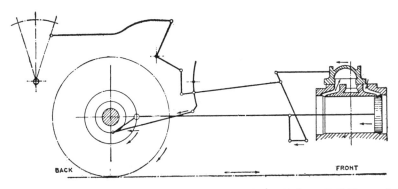

Fig. 163.—Relative Position of Parts for Outside Admission Valve. Full Forward Gear.

piston (to continue the forward running of the engine) the slide valve must be drawn back on its seat. At this instant the valve and piston are traveling in the same direction.

In order to produce this direction of motion of the valve, the eccentric crank must be in the lower quarter, or set ahead of the main crank-pin, so that it will move backward. Its effect will be to draw the bottom of the link backward and move the valve so as to open the front port for the admission of steam. If the eccentric crank-pin were set back of, or following the main crank-pin, it would be moving "forward" for this position of the parts, and its effect would be to move the bottom of the link forward, closing the front port to the admission of steam. This action would be contrary to that required to continue the forward running of the engine.

When the main crank-pin is on the front dead center, the bottom end of the lap and lead lever is in its extreme forward position; but since the valve must be drawn back from its central position an amount equal to the lap plus the lead, in order to give lead opening at the front port, it is evident that the valve stem connection must be *above* the radius rod pivot connection. If the two connections were interchanged, that is, if the valve stem connection were placed *below* the radius rod connection, the valve would be moved forward, so that there would be no valve opening at the front port, as required for this position of the gear parts.

Referring to diagram No. 1, Fig. 164, the parts are shown in full forward gear with the crank-pin on the back dead center. The piston is in its extreme backward position, so that a slight movement of the wheel in the forward direction indicated by the arrow will cause the piston to begin its forward stroke. For this position of the parts, the link is in its central position; therefore the valve would likewise be in its central position if it were not for the motion given to it by the lap and lead lever. The travel of the crosshead to the back end of its stroke has caused the lap and lead lever to swing about its pivot point connection with the radius rod. This movement has drawn the bottom end of the lap and lead lever backward, while the top end (and with it the valve), has been pushed ahead, as indicated by the arrow, giving *lead* opening at the *back port*. The valve at this instant is traveling forward.

Diagram No. 2, Fig. 164, shows the parts when the crank-pin has turned around in the forward direction, from the position shown in diagram No. 1, until the valve is cutting off the supply of live steam at the back port, during the forward stroke of the piston. The valve has admitted the supply of steam to the back of the piston through the back port, and has reversed its direction and returned to the cut-off position at the back port. The front port is still open to the exhaust. The movement from the position shown in diagram No. 1 comprises the *period* of *admission*.

Diagram No. 3 shows the position of the parts when the crank-pin has passed around to the position for the valve to open the exhaust at the back port during the forward stroke of the piston. The movement from position shown in diagram No. 2 to that shown in diagram No. 3 comprises the *period* of *expansion* occurring between the point of *cut-off* and the point of *release*.

During the time the crank-pin is moving from the position shown in diagram No. 3 until it reaches a position slightly above the front dead

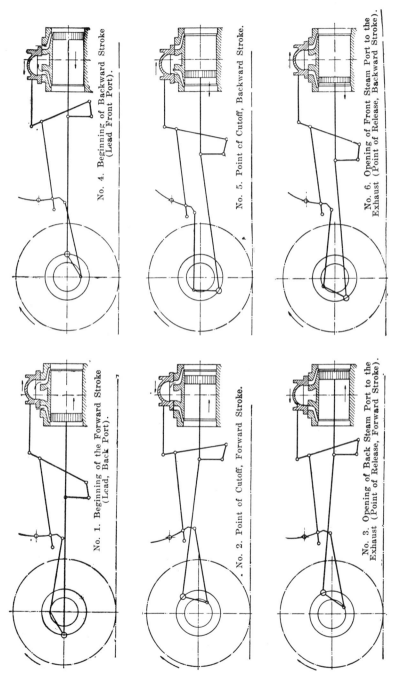

No. 4. Beginning of Backward Stroke (Lead Front Port).

No. 5. Point of Cutoff, Backward Stroke.

No. 6. Opening of Front Steam Port to the Exhaust (Point of Release, Backward Stroke).

No. 1. Beginning of the Forward Stroke (Lead, Back Port).

No. 2. Point of Cutoff, Forward Stroke.

No. 3. Opening of Back Steam Port to the Exhaust (Point of Release, Forward Stroke).

FIG. 164.—Outside Admission. Relative Crank-pin and Piston Positions for Valve Events, Full Forward Gear.

center position shown by diagram No. 4, the *period* of *compression* at the front port has occurred for the forward stroke of the piston.*

Diagram No. 4 brings the crank-pin to the front dead center, and the piston to its extreme forward position. Here the link is again in its central position and the lap and lead lever (since the crosshead has pushed its lower end forward) has drawn the valve back for the lead opening at the front port. From this position the piston begins its backward stroke and the same relative movements take place as for the back port during the forward stroke of the piston.

Diagram No. 5 shows the parts when the crank-pin has passed around from the front dead center position shown in diagram No. 4, during which time the valve has opened the front port for admission of steam in front of the piston, has reversed its direction and moved forward until cut-off has occurred, as shown by diagram No. 5. Here the back port is open to the exhaust.

Diagram No. 6 shows the parts in position for release at the front port. Here the crank-pin has turned from the position shown in diagram No. 5 in the direction indicated by the arrow, until nearly the back dead center position, or to the position where the valve causes release to occur. During the movement from the position shown in diagram No. 5 to that shown in diagram No. 6, the *period* of *expansion* takes place for the backward stroke of the piston. From this position (diagram 6) until the crank-pin reaches nearly the back dead center comprises the *period of compression* at the back port during the backward stroke of the piston. (See footnote, also Chapter V.)

Inside Admission Valves. Fig. 121, page 102, represents the gear as arranged for inside admission piston valves. Here, the bottom of the link is used for the forward motion. It is evident that the eccentric crank-pin must follow the main crank-pin, as previously stated. This change in the relative position of the eccentric crank-pin is necessary from the fact that the inside admission piston valve must be moved forward in order to open the front steam port to admit steam against the front side of the piston. By referring to Fig. 121 it is to be noted that this motion is directly opposite to that for the same conditions in the case of the outside admission slide valve shown in Fig. 122.

---

* The fact that the valve has *lead* causes the admission of steam into the cylinder to occur slightly before the piston has reached the extreme end of its stroke. The period of compression is finished at the opening of the port for admission of steam, and hence the period of compression occurs between the points of exhaust closure and admission, the latter occurring shortly before the crank pin is on dead center. (See Chapter V.)

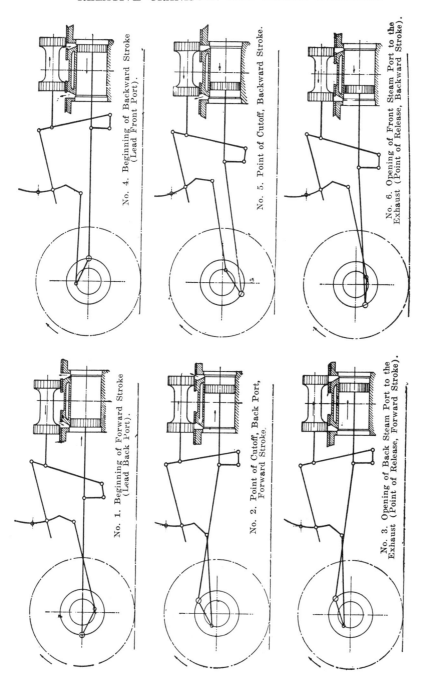

No. 4. Beginning of Backward Stroke (Lead Front Port).

No. 5. Point of Cutoff, Backward Stroke.

No. 6. Opening of Front Steam Port to the Exhaust (Point of Release, Backward Stroke).

No. 1. Beginning of Forward Stroke (Lead Back Port).

No. 2. Point of Cutoff, Back Port, Forward Stroke.

No. 3. Opening of Back Steam Port to the Exhaust (Point of Release, Forward Stroke).

FIG. 165.—Inside Admission, Relative Crank-pin Piston Positions for Valve Events, Full Forward Gear.

In Fig. 121 it is seen that for the position shown, when turning in the forward direction, the crank-pin moves backward and the eccentric crank-pin moves forward, pushing the bottom of the link forward, and opening the front port for admission of steam.

From the fact that the inside admission piston valve must be moved in a forward direction to produce lead opening at the front port, it is further seen that the valve stem connection to the lap and lead lever must be placed below the radius rod " pivot " connection.

Fig. 165 shows the relative positions of the gear parts when used in connection with the inside admission piston valve. Here the gear is shown in full foward position. It is to be noted that the relative directions of motion of the valve and piston are directly opposite to those in the case of the outside admission slide valve.

The same relations may be found by tracing the diagrams 1 to 6 inclusive, Fig. 165, as were seen in the case of the slide valve arrangement. Referring to diagram No. 1, Fig. 165, the crosshead has drawn the lower end of the lap and lead lever to its extreme backward position, as in the case of diagram 1, Fig. 164, of the slide valve; but the swinging pivot of the lap and lead lever at the radius rod connection is *above* the valve stem. Hence the valve is *drawn backward* so that the inside of the valve has opened the back port an amount sufficient to give lead opening at the back port, admitting steam back of the piston. In like manner the remaining diagrams may be traced through for one complete revolution of the wheel. Comparison between corresponding diagrams in the two figures brings out very clearly the differences in the arrangement of the Walschaert valve gear for inside and outside admission valves.

Diagram No. 2, Fig. 165, shows the parts in the position for cut-off at the back port during the forward stroke of the piston and when the motion is in full forward gear. From the position shown in diagram No. 1 to the position in diagram No. 2, the period of *admission* has occurred at the back port during the forward stroke of the piston.

Diagram No. 3 shows the position of the parts at release for the back port. Here the back outside edge of the valve is just opening the back port to the exhaust.

During the time the crank-pin is turning from the position shown by diagram No. 2 until it reaches the position shown in diagram No. 3, *expansion* occurs, for the forward stroke of the piston.

The position shown in diagram No. 4 is that of lead opening at the front port.   Here the crank has turned through one-half of a revolution and is on the front dead center, while the piston is on its extreme forward position.   The link is central again, the lap and lead lever has moved to the position opposite to that shown in diagram No. 1, Fig. 165, and has carried the valve ahead for lead opening at the front port.

During the time the crank-pin is turning from the position shown in diagram No. 3 to that shown in diagram No. 4, *compression* occurs at the front port for the forward stroke of the piston.   (See footnote, page 148, also Chapter V.)

Diagram No. 5 shows the parts after the crank-pin has turned around in its path and the piston is traveling along its backward stroke to a position where the valve is cutting off the supply of steam at the front port.   This position is, therefore, that of cut-off during the backward stroke of the piston.   From the position in diagram No. 4 to that of diagram No. 5 *admission* occurs at the front port during the backward stroke of the piston.

Diagram No. 6 illustrates the position for release at the front port. The front outside edge of the valve is just opening the front port to the exhaust.   From the position shown in diagram 5 to that of diagram 6, *expansion* occurs at the front port during the backward stroke of the piston.

From position shown by diagram No. 6 until the crank-pin reaches about the back dead center, *compression* takes place for the backward stroke of the piston.   (See footnote, page 148, also Chapter V.)

RELATIVE CRANK=PIN AND PISTON POSITIONS FOR DIFFER= ENT VALVE EVENTS AT SHORT CUT=OFF POSITION

Fig. 166 represents the same arrangement of valve motion for outside admission slide valves as that shown in Fig. 164, except that the reverse lever is " hooked up " and the engine is cutting off at about 25 percent of the piston stroke.   A comparison between the corresponding diagrams in these two figures brings out very clearly the differences in the relative positions of the crank-pin and piston for the different valve events when the motion is working in full forward gear and when running with short cut-off.   Such a comparison also shows the effect on the various events of " hooking up " the reverse lever.

Considering diagram 1, Fig. 166, the main crank-pin, eccentric crank, link and crosshead are in the same positions as they are in the corresponding diagram in Fig. 164.   The link block, however, is nearer the center of

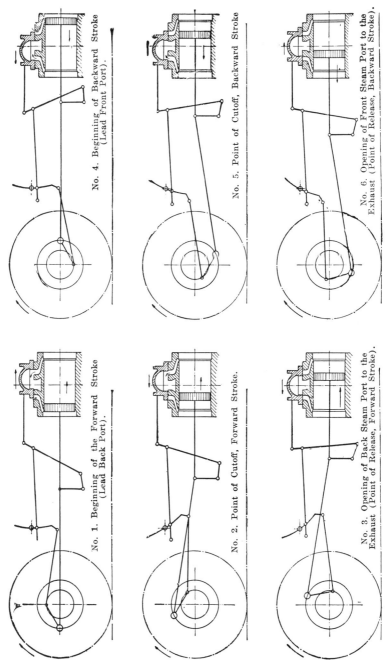

No. 1. Beginning of the Forward Stroke (Lead Back Port).

No. 2. Point of Cutoff, Forward Stroke.

No. 3. Opening of Back Steam Port to the Exhaust (Point of Release, Forward Stroke).

No. 4. Beginning of Backward Stroke (Lead Front Port).

No. 5. Point of Cutoff, Backward Stroke

No. 6. Opening of Front Steam Port to the Exhaust (Point of Release, Backward Stroke).

FIG. 166.—Outside Admission, Relative Crank Pin and Piston Position for Valve Events, at Short Cut-off.

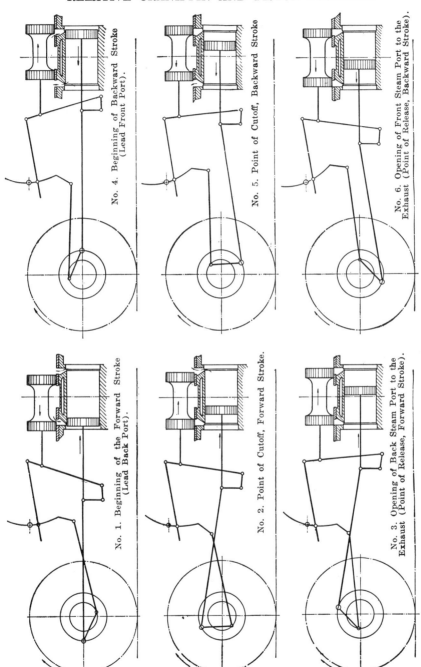

No. 4. Beginning of Backward Stroke (Lead Front Port).

No. 5. Point of Cutoff, Backward Stroke

No. 6. Opening of Front Steam Port to the Exhaust (Point of Release, Backward Stroke).

No. 1. Beginning of the Forward Stroke (Lead Back Port).

No. 2. Point of Cutoff, Forward Stroke.

No. 3. Opening of Back Steam Port to the Exhaust (Point of Release, Forward Stroke).

Fig. 167.—Inside Admission, Relative Crank Pin and Piston Position for Valve Events at Short Cut-off.

the link, which condition has had the effect of shortening the valve travel and causing the events to take place earlier in the piston stroke. This condition has *not* altered the lead. The length of the radius rod is the same as the radius of the link. Thus, as the link is in its central position, the raising of the link block does not cause any movement of the front end of the radius rod. This point, which is the pivot or fulcrum of the lap and lead lever, is in the same position as in the diagram of Fig. 164 previously considered. Consequently the lap and lead lever has moved the valve to the same position as before; and the lead is the same as when the reverse lever was in full gear.

In diagram No. 2, Fig. 166, the parts are shown for the position of cut-off at the back port for the forward stroke of the piston. It is to be noted that cut-off occurs much earlier than in the corresponding diagram of Fig. 164.

The position for release at the back port during the forward stroke of the piston is shown in diagram No. 3, Fig. 166. It is to be noted that release takes place slightly earlier than in the case for full forward gear shown in the corresponding diagram of Fig. 164. However, the period of expansion, which occurs during the time the piston travels from the position shown in diagram No. 2, Fig. 166, until it reaches the position shown in diagram No. 3, is much longer than the period of expansion for the full forward gear shown in the corresponding diagrams, Fig. 164. In like manner the conditions may be compared for the front port during the backward stroke of the piston.

In Fig. 167, diagrams 1 to 6, the piston valve with inside admission is shown with the reverse lever hooked up to have cut-off occur at about 25 percent of the piston stroke. By comparing these diagrams with the corresponding ones of Fig. 165, the relative positions of the valve and piston may be seen.

EFFECTS OF RAISING AND LOWERING THE LINK BLOCK

First: On the Travel of the Valve. The travel of the link foot pin F, Fig. 168, is practically equal to the throw of the eccentric crank, while the travel of the link block B is determined by the distance the link block is moved away from the link pivot, or point A, Fig. 168. The travel of the link foot pin remains constant while that of the link block is variable for the different positions from full gear to mid gear, for both forward and backward motions. The reason for this variable valve travel is obvious from a study of Fig. 168.   In full gear, with the link block at point B, the link block travel is indicated by the distance T, while the link foot pin travel is indicated by the distance S.   The travel of the link block T depends on the length of the radius $A\,B$, and as this radius is shortened by drawing the link block toward the center A of the link, the travel T is correspondingly shortened.   When the center of the link block falls on the center A of the link there is no travel of the link block. The same conditions hold true for the upper portion of the link.

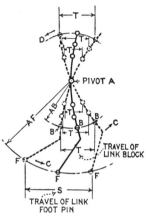

FIG. 168.—Effects on the Valve Travel of Drawing Up the Reverse Lever.

This effect on the travel of the link block is carried to the valve so that the amount of valve travel is controlled by the position of the link block in the link.   It is greatest at the farthest position away from the link center and becomes smaller as the block is made to work nearer the link center

Second: On the Direction of the Running.   When the link block is below the center of the link, and as the foot of the link is moved forward, the link block, and consequently the radius rod, move forward.   In case the link block is above the center of the link and the link foot is moving forward, the top of the link, link block and radius rod are moving backward in the direction opposite to that when the block is in the lower half of the link, consequently reversing the direction of the valve movement relative to the piston.   This reversing of the movement of the valve relative to the piston, as the link block is moved from one side of the center of the link to the other as shown by arrows C and D in Fig. 168, causes the two directions of running of the engine.

When the link block is in the lower half of the link, the motion is said to be "direct," that is, the motion of the link block is in the same direction as that of the link foot.   When the link block is in the upper half of the link, the motion is said to be "indirect," that is, the motion of the link block is opposite to that of the link foot.

When the forward motion is taken from the lower half of the link, the forward motion is said to be "direct," and the backward motion "indirect." If the forward motion is taken from the upper half of the link, the forward motion is "indirect" while the backward motion is "direct."

Third: Effects upon the Lead. Lead is the amount of port opening when the crank-pin is on dead center. Therefore, in order to observe the effect on the lead of raising and lowering the link block, the engine must be placed on one dead center as shown in Fig. 169. This position of the piston, crank-pin and eccentric crank brings the link in its central position. This condition is a fundamental requirement in the design of the gear. The position of the eccentric crank-pin and length of eccentric rod must be

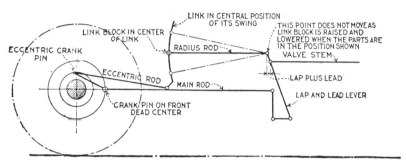

FIG. 169.—Effects upon the Lead of Drawing Up the Reverse Lever.

such that when the main crank-pin is on either dead center, the link must be in its central position. The central position of the link is when the center of the link arc falls on the center of the radius rod connection to the lap and lead lever. Since the radius of the link is made equal to the length of the radius rod and since the center of the link arc falls on the center of the radius rod connection to the lap and lead lever, then when the crank pin is on either dead center, and the link block and radius rod are raised and lowered over the link by means of the reverse lever, there is no motion imparted to the valve. Consequently, as this position of the gear is the only one for lead opening, *raising and lowering the link block has no effect upon the lead of the valves.*

DISTORTIONS OF THE WALSCHAERT VALVE GEAR

In the study of principles relating to valve motion, great difficulty has always been found in analyzing the conversion of the rotary movement of the main crank pin into the reciprocating motion required for the valve. With the Walschaert valve gear this source of trouble arises from the relative motions of the piston and crank-pin caused by the angular motion of the main rod, and also from those of the eccentric crank-pin and the link, produced by angularity of the eccentric rod.

These two sources of irregularities in the relative motion of the piston and valve are common to all types of valve motion. The chief effect of the distortions which are peculiar to the Walschaert valve gear is on the movement of the link.

In addition to these distortions the manner of link block and radius rod end suspension, with the angular movement of the radius rod, produce certain irregularities at the valve. Also the movement of the lap and lead lever *connector* has a slight influence on the port opening, and is, therefore, a source of small distortion. However, when the lap and lead lever *connector* is properly attached to the lap and lead lever, the motion produced by the former does not produce any distortion in the relative motion of the piston and valve. This is because the actuating part is the straight-line movement of the crosshead, so that the motion imparted to the valve by the lap and lead lever is coincident with the motion of the piston for all positions of the piston.

A condition which seriously affects the movement of the valve relative to the piston, with the Walschaert gear, and in fact, all valve motion constructions, is the rise and fall of the engine on its springs as it travels over irregularities in the track. The engine will also settle after a period of operation, and usually differently on each side of the engine, this being due to the weakening of the springs. Any change of this nature will cause the eccentric rod to " go long " on one side and " short " on the other. Having this to contend with, it is almost impossible to maintain absolutely perfect conditions of the gear for any considerable length of time.

However, the irregularities of the main and eccentric rods, and that of the link block suspension may be compensated for in a measure.

The angularity of the main rod is discussed in Chapter II on the Stephenson gear, under the heading of " Relation between Motion of Piston and Motion of Crank-pin." (See page 60.)

The effects of the angularity of the main rod and eccentric rod are to distort the valve from its desired position, making the valve events unequal at the front and back ports of the cylinders. To equalize these events at each port, it is necessary to counteract the irregular motion of the rods by making the link swing an equal distance each side of its central position.

The swing of the link should be preferably 40°, and in no case over 45°. That is, it should be made to swing about 20° each side of its central position.

A great deal of the success of the gear depends upon the proper lay-out to rectify these irregularities. This is done to a certain extent by back-setting the link foot pin.

The manner in which the back-set of the link foot pin compensates for the angularity of the eccentric rod is seen from a study of Fig. 170,

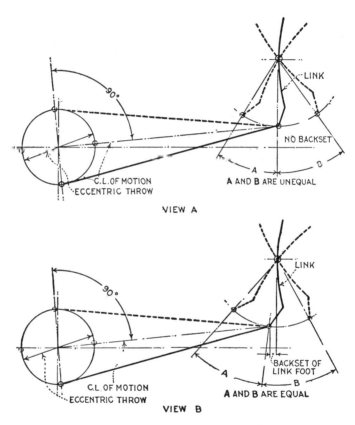

Fig. 170.—Back-set of Link Foot Pin.

views A and B. View A shows the foot of the link on a line drawn tangent to the link arc through its center, with the link in its middle or central position. The link is in its central position when the center of the link arc falls directly on the center of the radius rod connection to the lap and lead lever. This position of the link may be determined on the engine by the fact that when the link is in its central position, the link block may be moved up and down in the link throughout the entire length of its travel without producing any movement at the valve.

The link must stand in its central position when the main crank-pin is on either front or back dead center; and, furthermore, it must be made to swing equally on each side of the central position.

The condition with no back-set in the link foot pin, as shown in view *A*, Fig. 170, shows the eccentric rod and crank so proportioned that the link stands in its central position when the main crank-pin is on either dead center. However, the link, with this position of the link foot pin,

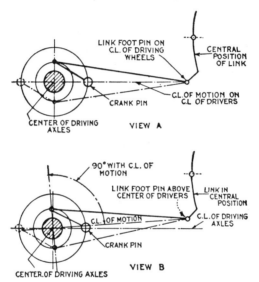

FIG. 171.—Link Foot on and Above Center Line of Axle.

does not swing equally on each side of its central position, as is evident from a study of view *A*.

View *B*, Fig. 170, shows the proper back-set of the link foot pin and the proper length of the eccentric crank and position of the eccentric crank-pin for a given condition; so that the link is made to swing equally on each side of its central position as well as being on its central position when the main crank-pin is on either dead center. In order to reduce the angular effect of the eccentric rod, the link foot pin should be brought as nearly as is practicable to the center line of the driving wheel axles, as shown in Fig. 171, view *A*. With this arrangement the eccentric crank is placed 90° away from the main crank-pin. View *B*, Fig. 171, shows the link foot pin placed slightly above the center line of axles, as is often necessary to prevent undue lengthening of the link foot, with the resulting increased eccentric throw required. With this arrangement the eccentric crank-pin must be set at 90° to the *center line* of *motion;* which latter is a line drawn through the link foot pin center and center of main axle when the link is in its *central position.* This explains the reason why the eccentric crank-

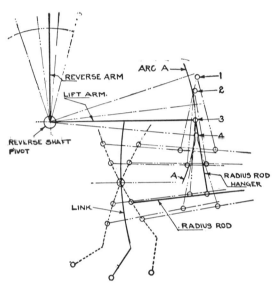

FIG. 172.—Radius Rod Hanger.

The distance points 1, 2, and 4 are away from Arc A indicates error introduced by length of Lift arm used and the location of the Lift Shaft Pivot.

Position No. 1. Full Gear Backward Motion. Position No. 2. Running Cut-off, Backward Motion. Position No. 3. Running Cut-off, Forward Motion. Position No. 4. Full Gear, Forward Motion.

pin is off the quarter positions when the main crank-pin is on either dead center.

With the link foot pin considerably above the center line of the axles, the distortional effects of the eccentric rod (as the engine moves up and down on its springs and also as the engine settles on its springs through use) will be greater than those resulting when the link foot pin is placed closer to the center line of the axles.

In order to find the proper proportions and locations of parts of the gear, it is necessary to plot them on the drawing board for each new design.

The error produced by the link block suspension on the lift arm is due to the fact that as the radius rod follows the motion imparted to it by the link, the movement of the forward end of the radius rod will be unequal on each side of the central position, unless the link block suspension members are properly designed and correctly located to compensate for the irregularities due to this motion. Two common methods of link block suspension are shown in Figs. 161 and 128. Figs 144a and 161 show the construction employing the radius rod lifter, connected to the radius rod in front of the link. (However, this same construction is sometimes used back of the link and connected to an extension of the radius rod. Fig. 128 shows the construction using a sliding block attached to the lift shaft arm and connected to the radius rod extension back of the link.)

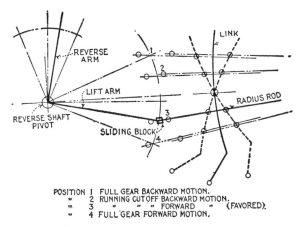

POSITION 1 FULL GEAR BACKWARD MOTION.
"   2 RUNNING CUTOFF BACKWARD MOTION.
".   3   "   "   " FORWARD   "   (FAVORED).
"   4 FULL GEAR FORWARD MOTION.

Fig. 173.—Radius Rod Sliding Block.

In the construction employing a radius rod lifter as in Fig. 172, it becomes necessary to design the location of the pivots and the length of the various members so that the link block will produce an equal motion each side of the central position of the link for all positions of the link block in the link.

This condition is extremely difficult to obtain, so that the position of the link block for the forward motion is favored. Likewise in the construction employing the sliding block, as in Fig. 173, the length of the lift shaft arm with its pivot must be so determined in reference to the link, that it will cause the link block to maintain its equal travel on each side of the central position of the link for all positions of the link block in the link. For this construction the forward motion positions of the link block are also favored.

FIG. 174.—American (4–4–0) Type Locomotive Equipped with Light Design of Walschaert Valve Gear.

FIG. 175.—Santa Fe (2–10–2) Type Locomotive Equipped with Heavy Design of Walschaert Valve Gear.

To help reduce the errors in this connection, practice has demonstrated that link block suspension should be such that (when in full gear position) the length of *one-half* of the link slot required is equal to twelve and one-half inches for inside admission gears, and eleven inches for outside admission gears. These dimensions allow for one-half of an inch clearance between the ends of the block and the link slot.

As mentioned previously, the radius rod hanger may be connected either in front of, or behind the link. In Figs. 121, 137, 144*a* and 174, the radius rod hanger is in front of the link. These figures show the general design of the Walschaert gear where lightness of parts is desired. The link is supported on a bracket attached to a cross-yoke. Here the light type of saddle shown in Fig. 129, view *A* is used. Fig. 175 shows the radius rod hanger back of the link. The link is supported on a gear frame attached to the yoke and cross-yoke, in which case the saddle shown in Fig. 129, view *B*, is employed.

LAYOUT OF WALSCHAERT GEAR

In the foregoing discussion the principles involved in the construction and adjustment of the Walschaert gear have been brought out, with a statement that it is necessary with any new design of the gear to lay out the motion on a drawing board and actually to determine the proportions and locations of the parts by plotting through the movement for different crank-pin positions. In order to demonstrate the above principles and to show a method for laying out the gear, it may be well to outline the work for a particular design.

Fig. 176 represents a Walschaert valve gear layout for a Pacific (4–6–2) type locomotive having twenty-four by twenty-eight inch cylinders and seventy-two inch diameter drivers, hand operated reverse gear and with the back end of the radius rod supported by means of a hanger from the reverse shaft arm. The piston valves have inside admission with six-inch travel, one and one-sixteenth inch lap, one-fourth inch lead and three-sixteenths inch exhaust clearance.

Lay out all basic lines, such as centers of cylinders, drivers and any limiting points, as boiler, frames, cylinder heads, guides and guide yokes, etc., to a scale one-fourth size. Having laid out the center lines, draw the crank-pin circle to scale with a diameter equal to the stroke of the piston. Then with a radius equal to the length of the main rod, cut the crosshead path at *A* and *B*, Fig. 176, locating the front and back positions of the crosshead. Then scribe the arcs EE from A and B with a radius equal to the length of the main rod to prove the crosshead travel.

Draw lines AO and BO cutting the crank-pin circle at G and H. Locate the point C exactly halfway between G and H. Draw CO extended to C_1. Points C and C_1 are the front and back dead centers. Then draw C_2OC_3 at right angles to COC_1, locating the top and bottom quarters.

Locate T at a convenient point on the valve stem, draw the vertical line FTR representing the central position of the lap and lead lever, which swings an equal distance each side of the vertical center position to produce equal lap and lead at both ends of the stroke for both steam ports. The proportions of the lap and lead lever are found by the use of the formula given on page 247. (See Fig. 176 for solution.)

Location of Link. It is desirable to locate the center of the link pivot on the same horizontal line as the point of radius rod connection to the lap and lead lever at F_1, also to have the radius of the link foot pin D tangent to the center line of the axles. These conditions are seldom possible, especially in case of the piston valves with inside admission; in which case, the radius rod connection to the lap and lead lever is *above* the valve stem connection.

The length of the link foot pin radius D must not be excessively long in order to bring the link foot on line with the axles, but it is necessary, however, in order to keep down the eccentric crank throw, to sacrifice this ideal condition in many cases and to keep the radius D within reasonable limits so that the total throw of the eccentric crank will not exceed about twenty inches, or (preferably) not more than eighteen inches.

In order to accomplish this, it is necessary to make some concessions. The point W, or the link pivot center, may be placed below the pivot F on the lap and lead lever, until the maximum inclination of the center line of the radius rod FW is one inch in twelve inches, without any serious effect on the gear as a whole. The link, however, must be set square with the line FW (as described on page 156 for finding the central position of the link), whatever this inclination may be. The radius of the link foot pin D may be located *three inches* above the center line of the axles without any serious error.

Describe the central link arc, or the arc representing the central position of the link, SWS_1, from point F (the connection point of the radius rod and lap and lead lever) with a radius K equal to the distance FW, cutting the arc of the link foot pin path (shown with radius D) at S. Draw the straight line

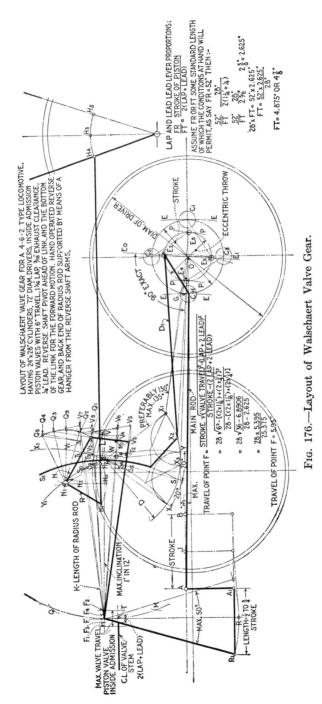

Fig. 176.—Layout of Walschaert Valve Gear.

WS. Now locate points X and Y exactly 20° each side of the straight line WS from the link pivot center. Prove that points X and Y are equidistant from S. With a radius SX from S draw the arc XY. With a radius K equal to FW from point W draw the arc MFQ, for locating the center of the link arc when the link is not in its central position. Then from X with a radius K, equal to the distance FW, cut the arc MFQ at Q and from Y cut the arc MFQ at M. Then from Q draw the link arc XWX_1, and from M draw the link arc YWY_1, locating the desired swing of the link. Now determine the amount of travel of the point F (or radius rod and lap and lead lever connection), which is derived directly from the link by the above determined swing. This is given by the use of the formula on page 248. (See Fig. 176 for solution.) Then lay off *half* of this amount of travel each side of point F (the central position of the connection of the radius rod and lap and lead lever), on the valve stem, as at points F_1 and F_2. These points locate the position to be determined by the full gear positions of the link block. Further divide the distances FF_1 and FF_2 in halves as at points F_3 and F_4. These points represent the half travel position for the half gear positions of the link block.

Locate the position of the link block on the link arc for the full forward and half travel positions. With a radius K equal to FW, from F_1 draw the arc S_0S_2, from F_2 draw arc T_1T_2, from F_3 draw S_3S_4, and from F_4 draw arc T_3T_4. The points of intersection of these arcs with the link arcs at the different positions plotted, locate the position of the link block on the link arc. Those drawn from F_1 and F_2 are for the full gear, and those from F_3 and F_4 for the half position of the link block with the forward motion below the link center (or pivot point W), and the backward motion above the link center.

The point of radius rod suspension is determined by a knowledge of the approximate sizes of the parts. In this case it is taken equal to the distance L back of the link center and equal to WV in the figure.

Since in a properly set motion the equalization of cut-off is also dependent upon the location of the reverse shaft pivot, it is customary to locate the reverse shaft pivot center to give the best steam distribution at the running cut-off, rather than in full gear. The center of the reverse shaft when a link or hanger suspension of the radius rod is used should be toward the center of the link, so that the end of the lifting arm of the reverse shaft will travel in an arc having a direction similar to that of the link arc. This condition is necessarily true with the sliding block construction of radius rod suspension.

Draw the lines $F_1S_2V_2$, $F_2T_2V_5$, $F_1S_0V_1$, $F_2T_1V_7$, $F_3S_4V_4$, etc., etc., representing the front and back positions of the suspension point V of the radius rod for the full-gear and half-gear positions of the link block in forward and backward motions as shown at points V_2, V_5, V_4, V_6, V_3, V_8, etc. In order to keep the slip of the link block down to a minimum and consequently to minimize the disturbing effect on the steam distribution, the length of the radius rod lifter M_1 must be selected with care so that it will cause the least amount of slipping of the block in the link.

After locating the suspension points V_1, V_2, V_3, V_4, etc., select a convenient length for the radius bar hanger or lifter. Beginning with points V_1 and V_7, the ideal location for the lift arm of the reverse shaft is found by striking arcs with a radius M_1 (equal to the length of the radius rod hanger or lifter selected), from V_1 and V_7, locating the suspension point Q_4 for full backward motion; from V_3 and V_8 the point Q_3 for the half backward motion position; from V_4 and V_6 the point Q_2 for half forward motion, and from V_2 and V_5 the point Q_1 for the full forward motion. The points Q_1, Q_2, Q_3, Q_4, represent the ideal location of the path of the suspension end of the reverse shaft arm from which is suspended the radius rod. This condition would require a different length of arm for each position. The length of the reverse shaft arm required to pass sufficiently close to all these ideal points would have to be extremely long. This arrangement would not be possible, and it is, therefore, necessary to compromise as to the length of the reverse shaft arm, using a length not greater than that of the link slot, if the boiler clearance will permit.

Since the ideal length of reverse shaft arm cannot be obtained and since it is desirable to have the best condition at, or near, the running cut-off position of the link block, select the points Q_2 and Q_3, which are the ideal locations of the suspension points for half forward and half backward gears, respectively.

Then with the radius N (selected to give a length of reverse shaft arms which will pass as nearly as possible through the ideal point with the limits mentioned above), from points Q_2 and Q_3 strike the arcs intersecting each other at point N_1. This is the location for the reverse shaft pivot center to give the best possible condition at half gear in the forward and backward motions. By taking the points Q_1 and Q_4, and striking the arcs with the same radius N, the point N_2 is located. This is the best possible location for the reverse shaft center at *full* gear in both motions.

From the point N_1 strike the path of the reverse shaft arms, with the radius N, passing through the points Q_2 and Q_3. The difference of the distances from Q_4 to Q_5 and from Q_1 to Q_7 represents the error caused by using the short reverse shaft arm. As mentioned before, it is well to try several times to find the best length for radius N, or the length of the reverse shaft arm, to locate the pivot center of the reverse shaft so that it will bring the path of the end of the lift shaft arm as near as possible to the ideal positions of the suspension points.

Reverse Lever and Connections. From the reverse shaft pivot center N_1 with a radius R, which is selected to meet the particular requirement of reverse lever throw and its limitation in the cab, scribe the path of the reach rod arm of the reverse shaft. When the radius rod is on the exact center, or the link block stands in its central position on the link arc, drop a vertical line N_1H_0 from the reverse shaft center N_1. With the reverse lever in the central or vertical position, the distance H_0H_3 between reach rod arm and reverse lever is the length of the reach rod, which should be adjusted to meet this condition when the engine is hot. Points H_1 and H_2 should be swung an equal distance each side of H_0, giving the corresponding points H_4 and H_5 for the location of the reverse lever in the maximum positions.

The reverse lever should be so located in the cab that it may be placed in the extreme forward and backward positions without interfering with the piping or other obstructions, by about six inches, especially if power reverse gears are used.

Eccentric Crank Position and Throw. The location of the eccentric crank and the proper throw are of importance equal to that of the location of the reverse shaft. Again, by referring to Fig. 176, having determined the position of the path of the link foot pin XSY (in the arc determined by the radius D swung from the center of the link pivot), select a point X_1 so that by drawing the lines WX_1 from the link center and X_1O from the main axle center, the angle thus formed at X_1 is equal to about 130°, and in no case exceeds 135°. Now with a radius SX from X_1 as a center, locate X_2. Then with X_2 as a center locate X_3. X_2 should fall midway between X_1 and X_3. Prove location of X_2 by striking arcs from X_2 through X_1 and X_3 on the arc determined by radius D. Then draw line E_0E_1 exactly 90° with X_2O, through O the center of the main axle.

Next determine the eccentric throw as follows: With a length D_1 equal to the length of the eccentric rod from X_1 and X_3 scribe arcs PP, making the eccentric crank circle tangent to both arcs. After drawing the eccentric crank throw circle E_2, E_3, E_4, E_5, prove the accuracy of this throw as follows: Points E_4 and E_5, from the method used in their determination will cause the link to occupy its proper extreme position 20° each side of the central position. It is also necessary (when the link stands in the central position, at X_2 on the link foot pin arc), that the eccentric crank pin should fall on the line E_0E_1 which is drawn at 90° to the position of the center line of the eccentric rod when the link is in the central position. Therefore from X_2 with a radius D_1 (equal to the length of the eccentric rod), cut the eccentric crank circle above and below the center of the axle. This arc should intersect the line E_0E_1 on the eccentric crank circle at E_2 and E_3.

By inspection it is seen that when the main crank-pin is on the front or back dead centers the eccentric crank-pin must be at E_2 or E_3. This brings the link on its central position, causing it to have no effect on the valve travel at this point. At the same time the lap and lead lever is in full control of the valve, and is in either the full forward or full backward position. Causing the valve to move an amount equal to lap plus the lead on either side of its central position.

When the main crank-pin is on the top or bottom quarters C_2 or C_3, the link is at the front or the back position X_3 or X_1 and the lap and lead lever is near the vertical position. This is because the angularity of the main rod prevents the crosshead from assuming the middle of its stroke indicated at point J. At this time the link has full control of the valve and the lap and lead lever has no effect on the valve travel. For this reason it is desirable that the lap and lead lever *connector* (union link) A_1R_1 should be horizontal at the end of the crosshead stroke. However, the other condition of having the union link horizontal when the piston is in the middle of its stroke is commonly used.

Now that the center lines and limiting points of the gear have been determined upon it remains to build up the parts to meet the particular conditions at hand. In order to get proper clearance of parts it may be necessary to trace the gear through one complete revolution of the crank pin as in Fig. 177. Such a diagram affords, also, an opportunity to study the relative position of the parts while in different positions.

The size of the various parts is dependent upon many conditions. In recent designs of locomotive valve gears extreme lightness of parts has been the aim. In this connection with the gear of the class $E6$s locomotive of the Pennsylvania Railroad Company, shown in Fig. 132, as well as that of the 4-4-0 type locomotive built by the Baldwin Locomotive

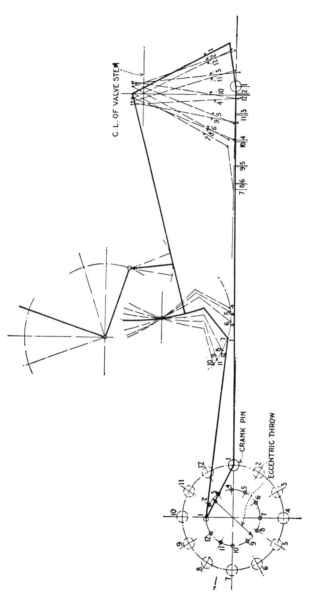

Fig. 177.—Walschaert Valve Gear Traced through One Revolution.

Works for the Philadelphia and Reading Railway Company, to the latter company's design, shown in Fig. 174, it may be well to note that the revolving and reciprocating parts, and especially the valve gear parts, seem extremely light. In these designs every detail toward weight reduction has been carefully considered. The weight of the piston valve, the valve stem and the valve stem crosshead, which are the main inertia parts, has been greatly reduced from that of the ordinary practice. The lap and lead lever, the link, and in fact, the entire valve gear construction, may seem light; but as some of the principal stresses in these parts are caused by the inertia forces due to their own weight, it has been found that this reduction in weight has been one of the best safeguards against breakages.

CHAPTER IV

BAKER LOCOMOTIVE VALVE GEAR

The Baker locomotive valve gear, manufactured by the Pilliod Company, is shown in Fig. 178 as applied to a switch locomotive. It is now in use on a large number of locomotives in the United States, Mexico and Canada. This gear is a form of outside radial gear similar in many respects to the Walschaert valve motion, with the exception of the reversing mechanism, which is developed from that of the Marshall gear, Fig. 179. In the Marshall and the Baker gears the radius bars and reverse yoke take the place of the link used in the Stephenson and Walschaert motions.

The Baker locomotive valve gear derives its motion from two points: namely, the eccentric crank and crosshead, much as in the case of the Walschaert gear. The Baker gear is a development of the Baker valve motion, which has been in use on traction engines for the past few years.

In general principle the Baker gear is the same as when originally designed, but a few changes have been made from time to time to make it better adapted to the modern locomotive. Referring to Fig. 180, the names of the parts of the Baker locomotive gear are, crosshead arm A, union link BC, lap and lead lever CED (one piece), bell crank DFG, gear connecting rod GHI (one piece), radius bar HJ, reverse yoke LJK, gear reach rod LP, eccentric crank MN, eccentric rod MI, valve rod EO.

The original Baker gear was patented by Mr. A. D. Baker in March, 1903, and applied to traction engines as shown in Figs. 181 and 182. The, development of the reversing mechanism of this gear, from the Marshall gear shown in Fig. 179, may be appreciated from the following discussion. Referring to Fig. 183, showing the Marshall gear, the eccentric F is shown at an angle of 90° with the crank-pin E. The eccentric rod is constrained in its motion by the link A, pivoted at the center B to the reversing member C. The valve rod is connected directly with the eccentric rod, at an intermediate point G. The proportions of the eccentric rod are fixed so as to reduce the throw of the eccentric to a suitable travel of the point G for the required lap and lead. This required travel is an amount equal to twice the lap, plus twice the lead, of the valve. With the eccentric and crank-

Fig. 178.—Baker Gear Applied to a Six-wheel Switcher (0-6-0 Type).

pin 90° apart, when the crank-pin is on the dead center E, the center of the eccentric will be at the top quarter position F and the lower end of the link A (to which the eccentric rod is attached) will coincide with the pivot point D. With the crank on the opposite dead center as shown at E', the center of the eccentric will be on the lower quarter position shown at F'. In this position of the eccentric the lower end of the link A will again coincide with the pivot point D.

When the eccentric center is on any position of its throw between the points F and F', the front end of the eccentric rod will be at some distance from its mid position on the arc a–b. Therefore the travel of the valve

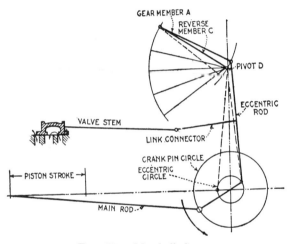

FIG. 179.—Marshall Gear.

with the gear set as shown in Fig. 183 will be equal to twice the sum of the lap and the lead.

In changing the travel of the valve to obtain long or short cut-off, or in reversing the engine, the reversing member C is moved around its pivot D by means of a reach rod and reverse lever. After moving the reversing arm C to the position shown in Fig. 184, then, as the engine moves in the direction indicated by the arrow, the lower end of the link A is drawn to the left as in Fig. 185. As the crank-pin continues to revolve, the lower end of the link A returns to the center D. When the crank-pin reaches the other dead center and the steam port is open an amount equal to the lead, then again (as the crank-pin continues to turn), the link A will move to the right of the reversing member C and open the other steam port, see Fig. 186.

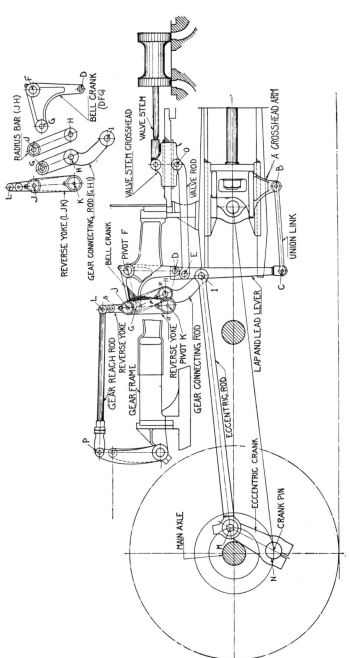

RADIUS BAR (J H)

BELL CRANK (DFG)

REVERSE YOKE (L J K)

GEAR CONNECTING ROD (G H I)

VALVE STEM CROSSHEAD

VALVE STEM

VALVE ROD

BELL CRANK

PIVOT F

A CROSSHEAD ARM

B

UNION LINK

GEAR REACH ROD

REVERSE YOKE

G

GEAR FRAME

REVERSE YOKE
PIVOT K

GEAR CONNECTING ROD

LAP AND LEAD LEVER

C

ECCENTRIC ROD

ECCENTRIC CRANK

CRANK PIN

MAIN AXLE

Fig. 180.—Names of Parts, Baker Locomotive Valve Gear.

To reverse the motion of the engine it is necessary to reverse the motion of the valve by moving the reversing member C to the position shown in Fig. 187.

In order to understand more clearly the manner in which the reversing member C and the radius bar A furnish the means for reversing the engine, and serve the same purpose as the link and block of the Walschaert and Stephenson gears, it will be well to study views A, B and C, Fig. 188. View

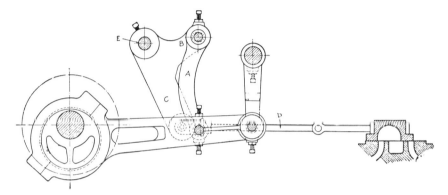

FIG. 181.—Baker Traction Engine Gear.

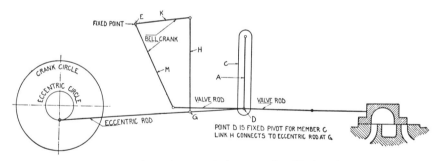

FIG. 182.—Line Diagram, Baker Traction Engine Gear.

A shows the reversing member C in the extreme forward position; the lower end of the radius bar A moves in the arc of the circle ab, whose center is at B (the point of attachment of the upper end of the radius bar A). The lower end of the radius bar, and likewise the floating end of the eccentric rod, will have an up-and-down motion equal to the distance X, view A. As the eccentric rod is drawn to the left its floating end is raised along the arc ab and as it is moved to the right this end is lowered along the arc ab. Now as the reversing member is drawn toward its central position, the

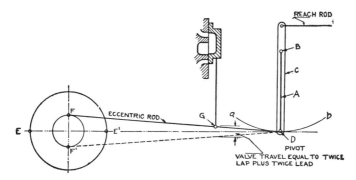

Fig. 183.—Line Diagram, Marshall Gear.

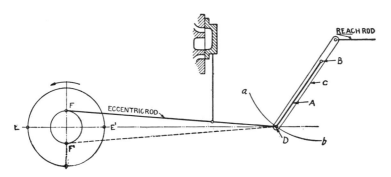

FIG. 184.—Line Diagram, Marshall Gear, Full Forward Motion.

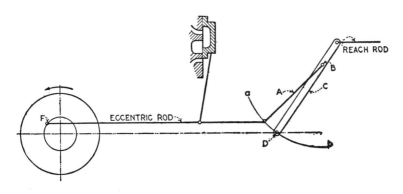

FIG. 185.—Line Diagram of Marshall Gear, Full Forward Motion.

arc *ab* will be brought nearer to a horizontal position, and a reduction will take place in the amount of the vertical motion *X* imparted to the floating end of the eccentric rod.

When the reversing member is in its central position, the extreme positions of the lower end of the radius bar are at the same height; so that the vertical movement *X* is nothing, as shown in view *B*, Fig. 188. As the reversing member is moved from the central position to the *full backward travel*

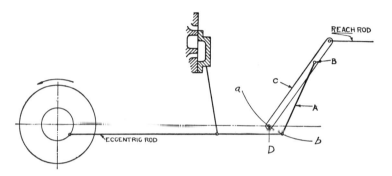

FIG. 186.—Line Diagram of Marshall Gear, Full Forward Motion.

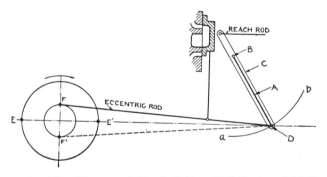

FIG. 187.—Line Diagram of Marshall Gear. Full Backward Motion.

position, as in view *C*, the arc *ab* is inclined in the opposite direction from that in view *A*. Therefore, as the eccentric rod is drawn to the left, its floating end is *lowered* along the arc *ab;* and when the eccentric rod is moved to the right, its floating end is *raised* along the arc *ab*. It is evident that this motion is exactly opposite in effect to that produced when the parts are in the position as shown in view *A*. This reversal in the movement of the floating end of the eccentric rod produces the means of reversing the engine, just as raising and lowering the link block answers the same purpose in the case of the Walschaert gear.

It is clear from a study of Fig. 189, with the reversing member in the positions indicated by the letters *X* and *Y*, that the points of extreme travel of the valve are unequally spaced on either side of the central position of the valve. This produces an unequal cut-off, one that cannot be squared at both ends of the cylinder during the forward and backward strokes of the piston. In fact, an equalization of the periods of admission is a recognized impossibility with the Marshall gear because of variations introduced by the angularity of the different parts. In order to overcome the variations in valve travel due to the angularity of the parts Mr. A. D. Baker introduced between the eccentric rod and the valve, a bell crank, as shown in Figs. 181 and 182. With this arrangement, the travel of the valve is sufficiently altered to give practically an equal steam distribution for both the forward and backward strokes of the piston.

In this design, which constitutes the traction engine gear, the connection *H*, Fig. 182, from the eccentric rod, instead of going directly to the valve, connects to the horizontal arm *K* of the bell crank. Its motion is delivered to the valve rod by the vertical arm *M* of the bell crank. By changing the length

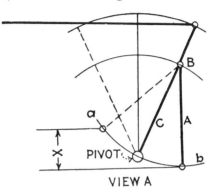

VIEW A

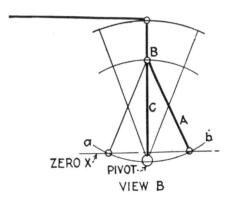

VIEW B

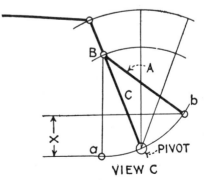

VIEW C

Fig. 188.—Reversing Principle of Marshall Gear.

of the connecting link *H*, as well as the lengths of the bell crank arms *K* and *M*, with the angle between them, and also the pivot point *E* of the bell crank, it is possible to obtain an equalization of the points of cut-off for the two strokes of the piston.

The next step in the development of the Baker gear as applied to the locomotive is in the design known as the Baker-Pilliod locomotive valve gear, Fig. 190, in which the gear is driven by an eccentric crank attached to the main crank-pin as in the Walschaert and the present Baker gears. Fig. 190 shows the Baker-Pilliod gear arranged for inside admission valves. Since this gear was not in use for any considerable length of time, but was superseded almost immediately by the present Baker locomotive valve gear, it is cited here only as a step in the development of the latter.

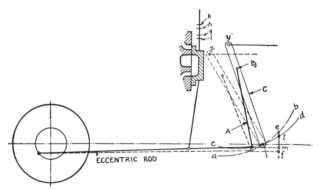

Fig. 189.—Effects on Marshall Gear of Drawing Up Reverse Lever.

A line diagram of the Baker locomotive valve gear as used at present is shown in Fig. 191. The manner in which the principles of the Baker traction engine valve gear are adapted to locomotive conditions may be learned from the following discussion. The eccentric rod of the traction valve gear is cut off at *G*, Fig. 182. The gear connecting rod *H* is made with a slight turn in it and connects to one arm of the bell crank. The other arm of the bell crank is connected to the valve rod in a manner as shown in Fig. 192. The dotted lines in this figure represent the eccentric rod as it extends to the reversing mechanism in the case of the traction engine gear. By stopping the eccentric rod at point *G*, Fig. 182, the motion of point *G* (as produced in the traction engine gear, equal to twice the lap plus twice the lead) is destroyed.

It has, therefore, been necessary to introduce a second motion to the

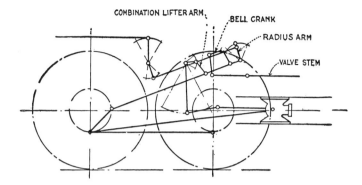

FIG. 190.—Baker-Pilliod Gear.

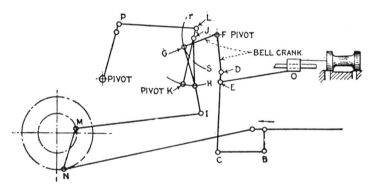

FIG. 191.—Line Diagram of Baker Gear (Inside Admission).

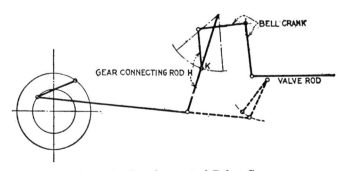

FIG. 192.—Development of Baker Gear.

valve rod by means of a suitable connection to the crosshead. This provides for the lap and lead movement at the valve. The mechanism is similar to that of the lap and lead lever arrangement in the Walschaert gear, and is shown in Fig. 180. The valve rod receives the motion of the lower end of the bell crank combined with that produced by the lap and lead lever connection with the crosshead. The reversing mechanism of the Baker locomotive valve gear, instead of being attached to the floating end of the eccentric rod as in the case of the Baker traction engine gear, is placed on the frame with the bell crank in the manner illustrated in Fig. 191. The radius bar JH is attached to the reverse yoke as in the case of the Baker traction gear.

In this manner the Baker locomotive valve gear has been designed so that it not only does away with the eccentrics as used on the Stephenson gear, but also with the curved link; so that there is no sliding friction whatever in the gear. The eccentric crank, crosshead arm, union link, and lap and lead lever, are characteristic of the Walschaert gear, while the remaining parts are suggestive of the Marshall gear.

The eccentric crank MN, Fig. 191 (also Fig. 180), is placed 90° behind the main crank-pin; consequently, the motion from it alone would call for a valve without lap and lead, and would admit steam to the cylinder for the entire length of the stroke. The motion from the crosshead gives to the valve the additional travel necessary to make up for lap and lead, so that in this respect the Baker and Walschaert gears are identical, each being a " constant lead " gear. However, the valve positions at corresponding points of the crank-pin travel are different in the two gears; which fact permits different claims to be made for the two gears.

The motion of the eccentric is transmitted to the foot of the gear connecting rod GHI by means of the eccentric rod MI. The point J on the reversing bar is fixed for any definite position of the reverse lever. Therefore, the point H at the lower end of the radius bar JH, attached to and supporting the gear connecting rod, is free to swing about the point J as a center and will follow the arc ab as the gear is moved. The point G (the upper point of the gear connecting rod), being attached to the bell crank arm, is therefore constrained in its motion, and will swing on the arc rs with the point F as a center. As the foot of the gear connecting rod is moved backward and forward by means of the eccentric crank, the gear connecting rod and radius bar (swinging about their centers H and J) will cause the end G of the bell crank to be moved up and down along the arc rs.

The lower end of the bell crank, being connected to the lap and lead lever at point D, and swinging about point F as a center, will cause the upper end of the lap and lead lever to swing back and forth and give the required motion to the valve.

Fig. 191 shows a line diagram of the Baker gear as arranged for an inside admission piston valve, while Fig. 193 is a line diagram showing the arrangement for outside admission valves. Figs. 194 and 195 show the gear parts as used for inside and outside admission valves respectively. Both styles are used on the Mallet locomotive shown in Fig. 17, in which the front engine is arranged for outside admission and the rear engine for inside admission. The alterations of the parts as shown in Figs. 194 and 195 are the only ones required to change from inside to outside admission valves. In these parts, the proportions of each member are standardized and do

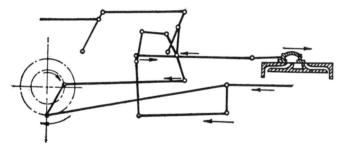

FIG. 193.—Line Diagram of Baker Gear (Outside Admission).

not require redesigning for different classes or sizes of locomotives. In the design of the reversing mechanism, the arrangement of the pivot points with respect to each other, and the proportions of the various members together with a definite angle between the two arms of the bell crank are so determined that as the eccentric crank moves through its path the bell crank is made to swing an equal distance each side of its central position for all positions of the reverse lever. The gear connecting rod is in its central position when the crank pin is on the dead center.

Upon these facts depends the process of equalization of cut-off for various positions of the reverse lever: hence, having once determined such a relation of the parts for both inside and outside admission valves, it becomes unnecessary to change the design for another size or type of engine to which it is desired to attach the gear. However, the proportions of the lap and lead lever with its connecting members must be designed to suit the amount of lap and lead desired for each particular case. Likewise the lengths of the eccentric rod and eccentric crank with the required amount of throw of the latter must be determined for each case as it arises. The central position of the reverse yoke is determined so that it will stand at right angles with a line drawn through the center of the main axle and the center of the pin connecting the eccentric rod to the gear connecting rod. This is necessary in order that the movements of the eccentric rod may be equal on each side of the mid-position of the reverse yoke. When the piston stands in the middle of its stroke, the lap and lead lever must stand vertical, and must be so located that a line drawn through the center of the union link pin and that of the bell crank will pass through the center of

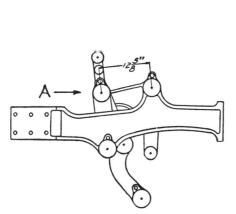
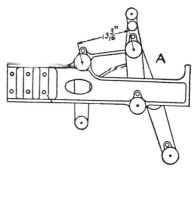

FIG. 194.—Bell Crank,   FIG. 195.—Bell Crank,
Inside Admission Arrangement.   Outside Admission Arrangement.

the bell crank pivot, as is shown in Fig. 180. From this fact, in outside admission arrangement, the bell crank, being back of the reverse yoke, requires a longer union link, for connecting the lower end of the lap and lead lever with the crosshead, than is necessary with the bell crank arrangement for inside admission valves. This may be seen by referring to Fig. 17, showing both styles. Fig. 196 shows the Baker gear applied to a Pacific type locomotive with inside admission valves, where the short union link is used. With either of these arrangements, the eccentric *always follows* the crank-pin. It stands the same for both inside and outside admission valves. The lap and lead lever connections for inside and outside admission valves are the same as in the case of the Walschaert gear. With the inside admission valves, the valve rod is connected to the lap and lead lever between the bell crank and union link connections; while in the case of outside admission valves, the valve rod connection to the lap and lead lever is above the bell crank connection. The relation between the length of the arms of the lap and lead lever (with both inside and outside admission valves) on the Baker gear is the same as in the case of the Walschaert gear. (See page 116.) In order to change from inside to outside admission valves, it is necessary to reverse the motion of the valve relative to the piston. The manner in which this is accomplished has already been mentioned and is shown in Figs. 194 and 195. In the case of the inside admission valve the bell crank pivot is placed *ahead* of the reversing yoke. With the outside admission valves the bell crank pivot is *back* of the reversing yoke. This change in the position of the bell crank pivot with the corresponding connection to the lap and lead lever, as already explained, produces the necessary change in the motion of the valve relative to the piston, to accommodate an

Fig. 196.—Application of Baker Locomotive Valve Gear to a Pacific Type Locomotive.

outside or inside admission valve as desired. This will be made apparent
by tracing through the movement of the parts as shown by the arrows
in Figs. 197 to 202 inclusive.

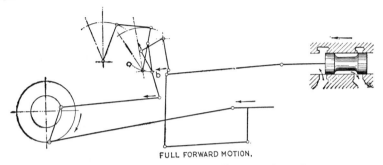

FULL FORWARD MOTION.

Fig. 197.—Inside Admission Full Forward Motion.

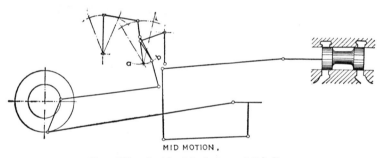

MID MOTION.

Fig. 198.—Inside Admission.   Mid Gear.

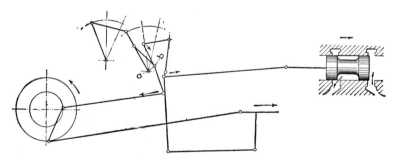

FULL BACKING MOTION.

Fig. 199.—Inside Admission Full Backward Motion.

To shorten the cut-off, the reversing yoke is drawn nearer to its central
position. The reason for this is also evident from a study of Figs. 197 to

202 inclusive.   The first three of these illustrations show the arrangement
for inside admission valves in full forward, mid and full backward gear,
respectively, while the last three show similar positions for outside admission
valves.   Fig. 203 shows the Baker gear traced through one complete
revolution of the drivers.

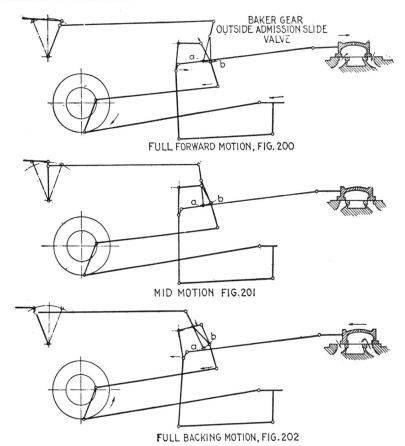

BAKER GEAR
OUTSIDE ADMISSION SLIDE
VALVE

FULL FORWARD MOTION, FIG. 200

MID MOTION FIG. 201

FULL BACKING MOTION, FIG. 202

FIG. 200-202.—Outside Admission Full Forward, Mid, and Full Backing Positions.
Motion and Back Gear.

In many designs of locomotive using the Baker valve gear, it has been
found advantageous to use the screw reverse or the power reverse, just as
in the case of the Walschaert gear.   In this connection it may be well to
note Figs. 204 and 205 in addition to those already shown.   Fig. 204 illustrates a Mountain (4–8–2) type locomotive using a Baker gear equipped

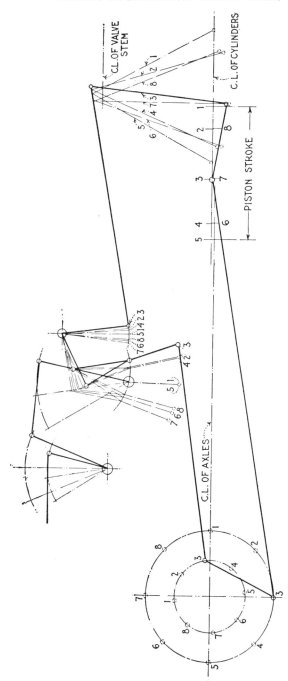

FIG. 203.—Diagram of Baker Locomotive Valve Gear, Showing Different Crank-pin Positions in Full Forward Gear, Lap and Lead Lever Placed in Front of the Crosshead in Accordance with Latest Design.

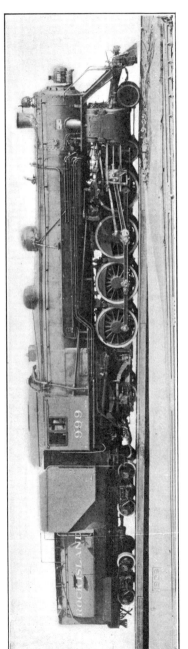

Fig. 204.—Mountain Type Locomotive with Baker Gear and Screw Reverse.

Fig. 205.—Pacific Type Locomotive with Baker Gear and Ragonnet Power Reverse.

Fig. 205A.—Baker Gear with Lap and Lead Lever Placed Ahead of Crosshead.

with the screw reverse, while Fig. 205 shows the application of the Baker gear to a Pacific type locomotive built by the American Locomotive Company, using the Ragonnet power reverse.

In some of the later designs of locomotives using the Baker Gear the lap and lead lever is placed ahead and is supported from the valve stem crosshead the same as is done with the Walschaert gear. Fig. 205A shows the latest design of Baker gear employing a short lap and lead lever supported from the valve stem crosshead. In this design the crosshead arm is omitted.

SOUTHERN LOCOMOTIVE VALVE GEAR

The Southern locomotive valve gear, sold by the Southern Locomotive Steam Engine Valve Gear Company, is a radical departure from all previous outside gears as applied to the locomotive. It was invented by Mr. William S. Brown, a locomotive engineer on the Southern Railway. From a study of Fig. 206, which shows a side view of this gear and gives the names of the parts, it is seen that the usual crosshead connection is not used. The entire gear is suggestive of the Marshall type, as explained under the development of the Baker gear. (See page 174.) The chief difference is the fact that instead of using the reversing yoke, Fig. 180, a stationary guide is provided, the arc of which has a radius equal to the length of the radius bar. The sliding block attached to the radius bar or hanger, and also to the reach rod, has the same effect on the

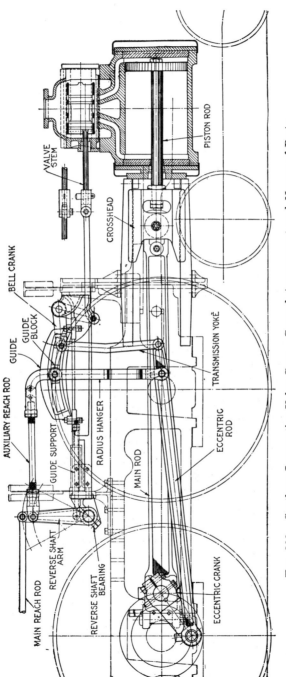

FIG. 206.—Southern Locomotive Valve Gear. General Arrangement and Names of Parts.

gear as the reversing yoke has on the radius bar in the case of the Marshall gear and also of the Baker gear. The transmission yoke attaches to a bell crank similar, in a measure, to that of the Baker gear, while the vertical arm of the bell crank is attached to the valve stem.

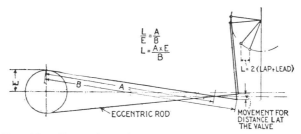

FIG. 207.—Eccentric Rod Giving Lap and Lead to Valve.

The Southern locomotive valve gear is a radial gear of the constant lead type. The amount of lead is determined by the ratio of the two arms of the eccentric rod, the same as described for the Marshall gear, and as shown in Fig. 207

FIG. 208.—Southern Locomotive Valve Gear.

This gear may be applied to any class of locomotive having either inside or outside admission valves. Fig. 206 shows the gear arranged for outside admission valves. It is to be noted that the eccentric crank *leads* the main crank-pin by exactly 90° when the engine is running forward.

To arrange the gear for inside admission valves the eccentric crank-pin must *follow* the main crank-pin by 90° when the engine is running forward.

This arrangement may be seen by referring to Fig. 208, which shows a photograph of a Pacific locomotive with the Southern gear applied with inside admission piston valves. This gear is so designed that all movements are as direct as possible. Inasmuch as it is made up of but few parts there is a correspondingly small number of pins and bearings to maintain. This is one of the chief claims made for it. There is no sliding friction except that which accompanies reversing the engine or changing the cut-off, in which cases the guide block is made to slide in the guide. However, the link is rigidly held in a horizontal position. This does away with wear at this point, as the block moves in the link only when the cut-off is being adjusted by the reverse lever. This feature eliminates trouble arising from slipping of the block in the link while the engine is running, and allows the cut-off to be easily adjusted while the engine is running at a high rate of speed without danger of having the gear "get away" from the operator. This latter feature, it is claimed,

Fig. 209.—Mikado Type Locomotive Equipped with Southern Locomotive Valve Gear.

will be appreciated by the enginemen and will induce them to work the engines at as short a cut-off as possible, with a resulting saving in fuel. Fig. 209 shows the application of the Southern gear to a Mikado (2–8–2) type locomotive.

THE JOY VALVE GEAR

The Joy valve gear is of the radial type, but employs no eccentrics. Arm 1, Fig. 210, is pivoted to the guide yoke at fixed point D and connected to arm 2 at C. The other end of arm 2 is fastened to the main rod at A. Arm 3 connects with arm 2 at B, and is pivoted on a link-block at F, extending beyond to G. The valve rod is actuated by means of arm 4, one end of which is attached to the valve stem and the other to arm 3. The link

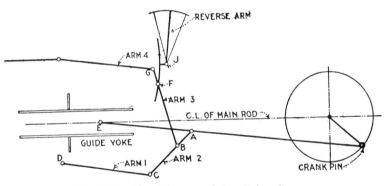

Fig. 210.—Line Diagram of Joy Valve Gear.

block is in the center of the link when the engine is on dead center. It is evident, therefore, that the valve opening on dead center (or in other words, the lead), is dependent upon the ratio between the lengths of arm 3. The Joy gear therefore gives constant lead.

The link is pivoted at J and controlled by the reversing arm. The link-block, carrying the arm 3, moves up and down in the link. As this link is tipped in either direction it controls the direction of motion of the valve and consequently the admission of steam to either end of the cylinder. Fig. 210 shows the arrangement of the Joy gear as used for outside admission valves. Fig. 211 illustrates the application of the Joy gear to a Philadelphia and Reading three-cylinder engine in which the inside cylinder is equipped with the Joy gear and inside admission valves. Fig. 212 is a line drawing of this three-cylinder Atlantic type locomotive. The main rod for

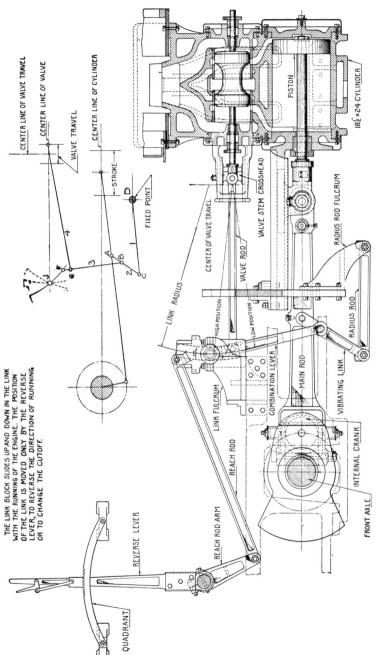

THE LINK BLOCK SLIDES UP AND DOWN IN THE LINK WITH THE RUNNING OF THE ENGINE. THE POSITION OF THE LINK IS MOVED ONLY BY THE REVERSE LEVER, TO REVERSE THE DIRECTION OF RUNNING OR TO CHANGE THE CUTOFF.

FIG. 211.—Joy Valve Gear Applied to an Atlantic Type, Three-cylinder Locomotive.

the inside cylinder connects to the front driving axle. The two outside cylinders have Walschaert valve gears to operate their valves. The eccentric

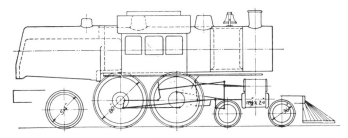

FIG. 212.—Three-cylinder, Simple Engine, Using Joy Valve Gear on Inside Cylinder and Walschaert Valve Gear on Outside Cylinders.

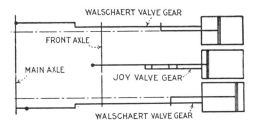

FIG. 213.—Arrangement of Cylinders and Valve Gears, Three-cylinder Engine.

motion for the Walschaert gears is taken from the main driving axles. Fig. 213 is a diagram illustrating the arrangement of cylinders and valve gears.

THE YOUNG LOCOMOTIVE VALVE, VALVE GEAR AND REVERSE GEAR

Fig. 214 is a cut illustrating the Young valve, valve gear and reverse gear applied to a locomotive.

This mechanism was invented by Mr. O. W. Young, and the entire equipment is designed to accomplish the following purposes:

Improved distribution of steam; to actuate the valve by a direct connection with the crosshead; and to eliminate the principal sources of error inherent to gears that derive their motion wholly or in part from the rotation of the crank-pin.

The valve gear may be controlled by any reversing mechanism, and the reverse gear may be used to control any valve gear.

The motion is derived entirely from the reciprocating movement of the

FIG. 214.—Young Valve Gear and Reverse Gear.

pistons.   Each piston causes valve movement equal to lap plus lead on its *own* side and valve travel on the *opposite* side.

Fig. 215 illustrates the Young piston valve and Fig. 216 the Young reversing gear.   Comparative tests made on two Pacific type locomotives of the same class, one equipped with Young valves and valve gears, and the other with ordinary piston valves and the Walschaert valve gear, is

FIG. 215.—The Young Valve.

reported to have shown a creditable performance for the Young valves and valve gear.   Of special interest is the performance of the engine equipped with the Young valves and valve gear at starting and at high speeds.   It is claimed that with this valve and gear a " smarter " engine is obtained at starting, more power is available, and greater speeds are obtainable than with similar engines equipped with the Walschaert gear. This result is

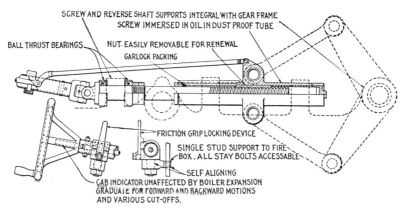

Fig. 216.—The Young Reverse Gear.

claimed to be due to the extra long travel given to the valve by the valve gear and the exceptionally open construction of the valve itself.

THE GOOCH STATIONARY LINK

The Gooch link motion is another form of valve gear in which the link is stationary. The link is curved in the reverse way from the Stephenson

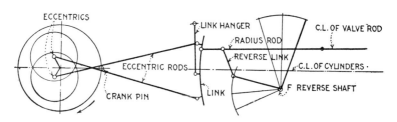

Fig. 217.—Gooch Valve Gear.

link. The length of the link arc is equal to the length of the radius rod, Fig. 217. This rod is lifted by means of the reverse shaft F. The Gooch valve gear is of the constant lead type.

THE ALLEN VALVE GEAR

The invention of the Allen motion, Fig. 218, was a natural sequence to that of the shifting and stationary links. By it a compromise has been

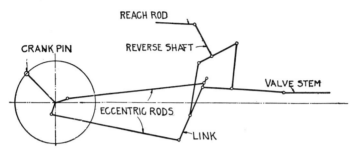

FIG. 218.—The Allen Valve Gear.

effected between the leading features of both the Stephenson and Gooch valve motions, resulting in a more direct action and better balance of the parts, with a reduced slip of the link block.

CHAPTER V

EFFECTS OF ALTERING THE VALVE AND ITS EVENTS

In order to understand the action of the valve more completely it will be well to study some of the changes brought about when the amount of lap is altered, or the lead, travel, point of cut-off, etc., are changed. For convenience, the common D slide valve will be referred to, and the study arranged in the form of concrete problems, to be solved by means of diagrams. The method will be equally applicable to piston valves with inside admission or slide valves with outside admission.

The diagram for representing the valve events is shown in Fig. 219, page 201. Here the straight line AB represents the top of the valve seat. The diameter of the circle $MNRS$, with point C as its center, is equal to the travel of the valve. The distance CD on AB represents the steam lap and DE the width of the steam port. The circle $HFJK$ represents the path of the crank-pin, the diameter of which is therefore equal to the stroke of the piston.

The method of constructing this diagram will be clear from the following example:

For instance, suppose it is desired to construct the diagram for a valve having the following data:

Steam lap = 1 inch.
Lead = 0.
Width of steam port = $1\frac{1}{4}$ inches.
Valve travel = 5 inches.
Piston stroke = 24 inches.

Draw the straight horizontal line AB, Fig. 219, and locate point C for the center of the circles at any convenient position on the line AB. Point C is the position of the steam edge of the valve when the valve is central on its seat or in its mid-position. From point C as a center, draw the valve travel circle full size, using a radius equal to one-half of the valve travel, or in this case two and one-half inches. Now lay off the steam lap from point C to either side (usually the right), a distance of one inch, represented by the distance CD in Fig. 219. Then from point D, just determined by the lap, lay off the steam port width of one and one-quarter inches, giving point E to the right. The distance DE represents the width of the steam port. To describe the crank-pin circle assume any convenient scale as three inches or one and one-half inches to the foot and, with point C as a center and a radius equal to one-half of the piston stroke (or twelve inches in this case), describe a circle, the circumference of which represents the path of the crank-pin.

In this diagram the crank-pin is represented as being on the dead center, and in the present example, there being no lead, the steam (or outer) edge

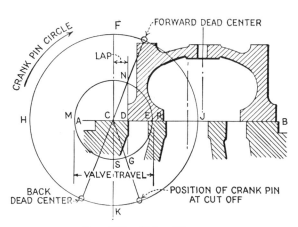

Fig. 219.—Valve Diagram.

of the valve is in line with the steam (or outer) edge of the port: from which facts the valve may be laid off on its seat as shown in Fig. 219. To determine the dead center position, or the one which the crank-pin occupies when the valve is in the position shown in Fig. 219, project the outer or steam edge of the valve upward until it cuts the *valve travel* circle $MNRS$ at the point N. Then draw a diameter of the crank-pin circle $HFJK$ through the point N, the ends of which give the respective front and back dead centers as shown in Fig. 219. By means of this diagram, the position of the crank-pin at cut-off is also determined. This is done by projecting the steam or outer edge of the steam port downward until it cuts the *valve travel* circle $MNRS$ at G. Then draw a radius of the crank-pin circle $HFJK$ through point G, the outer end of which represents the crank-pin position at cut-off, as indicated in Fig. 219.

To construct this diagram when the valve has *lead*, as in Fig. 220, locate point *C*, drawing the valve travel and crank-pin circles; also, lay off the steam or outer edge of the steam port from point *C* to the right at a distance equal to the steam lap of the valve as before. To determine the position of the steam or outer edge of the valve, lay off the steam edge of the valve from point *C* to the right at a distance equal to the *lap plus the lead*. This gives a port opening equal to the lead.

To locate the position occupied by the crank-pin for this position of the valve, project the steam or outer edge of the valve upward until it cuts the valve travel circle and draw a crank-pin circle diameter through this point, the ends of which represent the two dead centers as before.

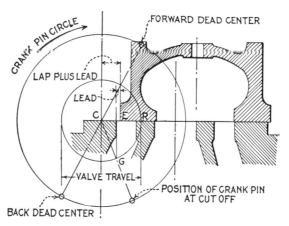

FIG. 220.—Valve Diagram Showing Lead.

The position of the crank-pin at cut-off in Fig. 220 is determined by projecting the steam or outer edge of the steam port downward until it cuts the valve travel circle. Through the point where this line cuts the valve travel circle draw a radius in the crank-pin circle, the outer end of which represents the position of the crank-pin at cut-off.

To locate the position of the piston for the relative crank-pin positions, construct the diagram shown in Fig. 221, similar to that of Fig. 219, with the addition of the upper portion representing the piston stroke. The piston stroke is laid off by prolonging the diameter of the crank-pin circle through the dead centers, a distance equal to the length of the main rod and to the *same* scale as that of the crank-pin circle. On this line the piston stroke is laid off in inches as shown in Fig. 221.

To determine the position of the piston for any position of the crank-pin, as, for instance, the position of the piston at cut-off, describe an arc with the position of the crank-pin at cut-off as a center and with a radius equal to the length of the main rod (to scale). The point where the arc cuts the line representing the piston stroke is the position of the piston at cut-off. In a similar manner the positions of the piston may be found for the other valve events if the position of the crank-pin is known. The position of the crank-pin at release and exhaust closure may be found as shown in Fig. 222. This diagram corresponds with those shown in Figs. 219 and 220. The point K represents the position of the steam edge of the valve when the exhaust edge of the valve is in line with the exhaust edge of the steam port, or the position for release or exhaust closure, depending upon the direction in which the valve is moving. When the valve has

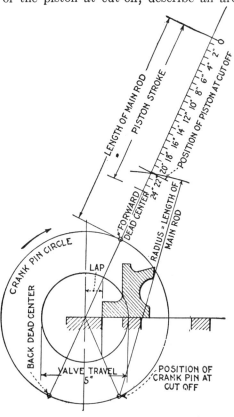

FIG. 221.—Diagram for Location Position of Piston.

exhaust lap, point K is located to the *left* of point C, at a distance equal to the amount of the exhaust lap. When the valve has *clearance*, point K must be on the opposite side of point C, or to the *right*, at a distance equal to the amount of the *clearance*. If the valve has neither exhaust lap nor clearance, but is " line on line," point K will fall on point C.

A vertical line drawn through the point K cuts the valve travel circle at points E and D. The extremity of the radius drawn through point E in the crank-pin circle determines the position of the crank-pin at *release*, while the radius drawn through point D determines the position of the crank-pin at *exhaust closure*.

Now that the methods of finding the piston positions for the different valve events are known, it will be well to combine these separate diagrams into a single diagram by which a given example may be followed through in its entirety.

In this example the following data will be used:

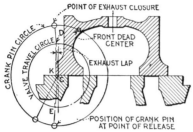

Fig. 222.—Valve Diagram Showing Exhaust Closure.

Steam lap = 1 inch.

Lead = $\frac{1}{4}$ inch.

Width of steam port = $1\frac{1}{4}$ inches.

Exhaust lap = $\frac{1}{8}$ inch.

Valve travel = 5 inches.

Piston stroke = 24 inches.

Length of main rod = 84 inches.

Center line of cylinder 2 inches above center line of axles

Find by means of this valve diagram at what percent of the piston stroke the different valve events take place, and, also draw a diagram showing the crank-pin positions (similar to that in Figs. 70 and 71).

Fig. 223 is constructed from the above data just as were Figs. 219 and 220. For convenience, the valve travel circle, lap, lead, and steam port are to one scale (six inches = one foot); while the crank-pin circle, main rod, and piston stroke are to another (three-quarter inch = one foot). Points D and E are the dead centers and point F is the position of the crank-pin at cut-off. The piston position at cut-off is determined by describing an arc from F as a center and with a radius equal to the length of the main rod to scale. The point F_1 where this arc cuts the piston stroke line D_1E_1 (which is laid off, in this case, two inches above the center line of the axle) represents the position of the piston at cut-off, as was described in connection with Fig. 221.

The position of the crank-pin at admission is represented by point A, which is found by drawing a diameter of the valve travel circle through point Z, located vertically above the steam edge of the steam port. Point A_1 is the piston position at admission; that is, the piston has traveled on its return stroke from E_1 to A_1, or slightly less than the entire stroke E_1D_1, showing that admission occurs before the piston is at its extreme forward position. To determine the percent of the piston stroke at which admission occurs, measure the distance along the return stroke (or from E_1 to A_1), and divide this distance by the total piston stroke, which in this case is twenty-four inches.   Hence for this case admission occurs at 99 percent of the return stroke.   To determine the percent of the piston stroke at which cut-off occurs, measure the distance that the piston travels from the beginning of the forward stroke, or from point D_1 to the point of cut-off, F_1, and divide this distance by the total piston stroke.   Thus, as shown in Table I for five-inch valve travel, cut-off occurs at 81 percent of the forward stroke, meaning that the piston has traveled through 81 percent of its stroke when cut-off occurs, or from D_1 to F_1 in Fig. 223.

To determine next the percent of stroke at which release and exhaust closure occur: combine with this diagram that for finding the crank-pin and piston positions at release and exhaust closure, as shown in Fig. 222. The point K in Fig. 223 is the position of the steam edge of the valve when the valve is in the position of release or exhaust closure.   Point G is the position of the crank-pin at release, and point G_1 that of the piston.

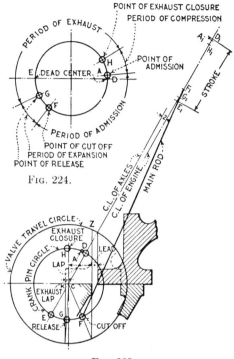

Fig. 224.

Fig. 223.

Fig. 223.—Valve Events, 5-inch Travel.

Fig. 224.—Crank-pin Positions for Valve Events, 5-inch Valve Travel.

TABLE I

5″ Valve Travel

Event.	Inches of Piston Stroke.	Percent of Piston Stroke.
Cut-off........	$19\frac{1}{2}$	81
Release........	$22\frac{5}{8}$	94
Exhaust closure..	$21\frac{5}{8}$	90
Admission......	$23\frac{3}{4}$	99

Point H is the position of the crank-pin at compression or exhaust closure and point H_1 that of the piston.   Points G_1 and H_1 are located as were F_1 and A_1.   To determine the percent of the piston stroke at which release occurs, measure the distance along the forward stroke from its beginning, or point D_1, to the point of release, or G_1, and divide by the total piston stroke.   Thus release occurs at 94 percent of the forward stroke.   The percent of stroke at the beginning of compression (exhaust closure) is found by measuring the distance along the return stroke, or from E_1 to the position of exhaust closure, H_1, and dividing by the total piston stroke.   Thus, as in Table 1, compression occurs at 90 percent of the return stroke.

Fig. 224 is a diagram showing the crank-pin positions for the different valve events, like that shown in Figs. 70 and 71.   This diagram may be added to Fig. 223, but for the sake of clearness the crank-pin positions at the different valve events are here shown on a separate figure, determined by stepping off the crank-pin positions from Fig. 223.

Thus Fig. 224 illustrates the positions of the crank-pin and its periods of admission, expansion, exhaust and compression for the data of Fig. 223.

Effect of Shortening the Valve Travel by Drawing up the Reverse Lever. To note the effects a short valve travel has upon the different valve events it will be well to study Figs. 225 and 226, which have been constructed from the same data as Figs. 223 and 224, with the exception that the valve travel is *shortened* from five inches to three inches.

Fig. 225, which is constructed like Fig. 223, shows the crank-pin positions for the different valve events along with the corresponding percents of piston stroke.   By observing the accompanying Table 2, it may be noted: first, that cut-off takes place *earlier* in the forward stroke (45 percent) than it does with five-inch valve travel shown in the Table I.   Second, that the percent of piston stroke at which release occurs is slightly less, (82 percent) indicating an earlier release of the steam.   Third, that the point of exhaust closure is also hastened, taking place at 70 percent of the return stroke of the piston.   Lastly, that admission occurs at nearly the same point, or at 98 percent of the return stroke.

Fig. 226 compares the lengths of the periods between the valve events with five-inch travel (Fig. 224), with the corresponding periods for three-inch travel, for one complete revolution of the crank-pin.   Here it is seen, first, that admission occurs at nearly the same point; second, that cut-off occurs earlier in the stroke than in Fig. 223; third, that the point of release is slightly hastened; last, that the point of exhaust closure is earlier in the piston stroke. These alterations in the valve events produced by shortened valve travel cause the following changes in the distribution of the steam throughout the stroke of the piston: first, the period of admission is shortened, due to the early cut-off. This also lengthens the period of expansion, because of the fact that the point of cut-off has been hastened by a

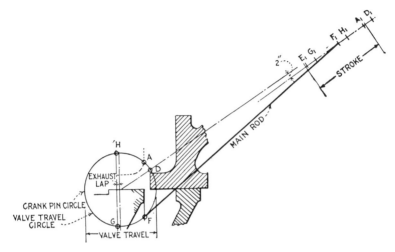

Fig. 225.—Diagram Showing Effects of Shortening the Valve Travel.
(Crank-pin and valve travel circles, drawn to different scales, happen to be the same size.)

TABLE II

3″ Valve Travel

Event.	Inches of Piston Stroke.	Percent of Piston Stroke.
Cut-off.........	$10\frac{3}{4}$	45
Release.........	$19\frac{3}{4}$	82
Exhaust closure..	$16\frac{3}{4}$	70
Admission......	$23\frac{1}{2}$	98

greater amount than has the point of release. Second, the period of exhaust is shortened, due to the fact that the point of exhaust closure is hastened by a greater amount than is the point of release. Third, the earlier point of exhaust closure produces a longer period of compression.

These facts may also be observed by a study of Tables I and II, which illustrate the alterations in the valve events produced by changing the valve travel. For instance, the point of cut-off for the five-inch valve travel is at nineteen and one-half inches of the piston stroke, and that of release is at twenty-two and five-eighth inches; giving a period of expansion of three and one-eighth inches of piston stroke.

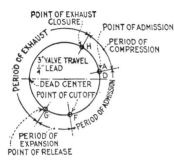

POINT OF EXHAUST CLOSURE; POINT OF ADMISSION PERIOD OF COMPRESSION 3"VALVE TRAVEL ⅟₄" LEAD DEAD CENTER POINT OF CUTOFF H A D PERIOD OF EXHAUST PERIOD OF ADMISSION G F PERIOD OF EXPANSION POINT OF RELEASE

FIG. 226.—Crank-pin Position, 3-inch Travel.

The point of cut-off for the three-inch travel occurs earlier, or at ten and three-quarter inches of piston stroke, while the point of release is only slightly hastened, occurring at nineteen and three-fourth inches of piston stroke; which affords a longer period of expansion or one of nine inches of piston stroke as compared with three and one-fourth inches for the five-inch valve travel.

In like manner the other valve events may be compared.

TABLE III

LEAD $\frac{1}{16}''$, LAP $1''$

Event.	Five-inch Valve Travel.	Three-inch Valve Travel.
	%	%
Cut-off.........	84	55
Release.........	96	89
Exhaust closure..	93	78
Admission......	99+	99−

Effects of Altering the Lead. For the sake of comparison, use the same data as heretofore given on page 204, with the exception of the lead, which will decrease to one-sixteenth inch; and compare the valve events with those when the valve has one-quarter inch lead as shown in the previous diagrams.

These effects may be observed by referring to Table I, page 205, for the one-quarter-inch lead and Table III, for the one-sixteenth-inch lead, with both five-inch and three-inch valve travels. Comparing the events for one-sixteenth inch-lead with those for increased lead, it is found that for the decreased lead all of the events are made to take place *later* in the piston stroke. Hence, an *increase* of lead *hastens*, while a *decrease* of lead *retards all of the valve events.*

Effects of Altering the Steam Lap. For this purpose use the data as before and compare the original *one-inch steam lap* with an increase of lap to one of one and one-quarter inches. By referring to Figs. 227 and 228, and Table IV, it will be noticed that for the one and one-quarter inch lap all the valve events occur earlier in the piston stroke than do those for one-inch lap; for both the five-inch and three-inch valve travels. Particularly, referring to the five-inch travel; in the case of one-inch lap, cut-off occurs at 81 percent of the piston stroke and release at 94 percent, giving a period of expansion of 13 percent of the entire piston stroke or a distance for expansion of three and one-fourth inches: while in the case of one and one-quarter-inch lap, cut-off occurs much earlier, or at 72 percent of the piston stroke; while release is nearly the same as for one-inch lap, occurring at 92 percent, giving a period of expansion of 20 percent of the entire

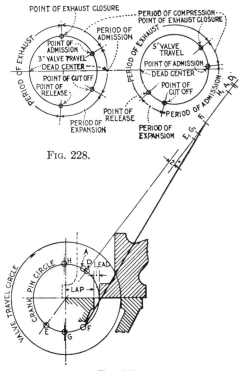

Fig. 228.

Fig. 227.

Fig. 227.—Valve Events with Lap $1\frac{1}{4}$ Inches.
Fig. 228.—Crank-pin Positions, 3- and 5-inch Travel.

piston stroke or a distance of four and three-fourth inches: so that the increase in lap, while hastening all the valve events, also materially increases the period of expansion. The lengths of the other periods may be compared in like manner.

Referring to the three-inch travel, it may be noted that all events are likewise hastened. The facts to be noticed in particular for the three-inch travel are: first, that the point of admission is materially hastened for one and one-quarter-inch lap, causing, on account of the early cut-off, the major portion of the period of admission to occur while the crank-pin is passing dead center. Second, that the period of compression is excess-

TABLE IV

LEAD $\frac{1}{4}''$

Valve Travel.	Five-inch.		Three-inch.	
Lap (inches)...................	1	$1\frac{1}{4}$	1	$1\frac{1}{4}$
Cut-off (percent)...............	81	72	45	8
Release........................	94	92	82	56
Expansion percent piston stroke.......	13	20	37	48
Expansion inches of piston stroke......	$3\frac{1}{4}$	$4\frac{3}{4}$	9	$11\frac{1}{2}$

ively lengthened, causing the engine to have an exceedingly high back pressure, which tends to prevent the engine from working properly at this valve travel.

The effects of altering the slide valve and its events may be summarized by referring to Table V, which is a combination of Tables I to IV.

TABLE V

COMBINATION OF TABLES I TO IV

Table.	Valve Travel, Inches.	Lead, Inches.	Lap, Inches.	Cut-off, Percent.	Release, Percent.	Exhaust Closure, Percent.	Admiss'n, Percent.	Inches of Piston Travel for Period of:	
								Admission.	Expansion.
1	5	$\frac{1}{4}$	1	81	94	90	99	$19\frac{1}{2}$	$3\frac{1}{8}$
2	3	$\frac{1}{4}$	1	45	82	70	98	$10\frac{3}{4}$	9
3	5	$\frac{1}{16}$	1	84	96	93	99	$20\frac{1}{4}$	$2\frac{3}{4}$
3	3	$\frac{1}{16}$	1	55	89	78	99	$13\frac{1}{8}$	$8\frac{1}{4}$
4	5	$\frac{1}{4}$	$1\frac{1}{4}$	72	92	86	99	$17\frac{1}{4}$	$4\frac{3}{4}$
4	3	$\frac{1}{4}$	$1\frac{1}{4}$	8	56	41	92	2	$11\frac{1}{2}$

Increased valve travel lengthens the period of admission, but shortens the periods of expansion and compression.

Increased lead hastens all valve events.

Decreased lead retards all valve events.

Increased steam lap, with the same lead, while hastening all valve events, hastens cut-off and point of exhaust closure more than it does release and point of admission, resulting in longer periods of expansion and compression.

CHAPTER VI

LOCOMOTIVE VALVE SETTING

THE operations involved in locomotive valve setting have been regarded by most shop men as more or less of a mystery, yet there is nothing mysterious about them. Any man of ordinary intelligence who will give a reasonable amount of careful study to these operations, can master the principles of valve motion; although, to understand them thoroughly, will require more diligent study than some may at first suppose.

The object of locomotive valve setting is to adjust the valve gear parts so that each valve will be in such relation to its piston that, when steam is admitted to the steam chest, it will also be permitted to enter one end of at least one cylinder, and thereby set the engine in motion. The movement of the valves must be such as to cause the driving wheels to turn continuously in one direction until the position of the valve is reversed; and when the valve is reversed, the wheels must revolve continuously in the opposite direction. In addition to this, the valves are adjusted so as to admit the steam to and release it from the cylinder at the proper times so as to use the steam to the best advantage and without waste.

Before proceeding to set the valve it is necessary to locate marks known as " port marks " on the valve stem or valve stem crosshead, which will indicate the positions of the valve for admission and cut-off of steam, and also to locate the positions for the four dead center positions of the driving wheels.

Finding the Port Marks. The port marks are marks on the valve stems which indicate the points of admission and cut-off for both front and back ports.

In the case of the Stephenson gear and slide valve, before making the port marks see that the valve stem will connect with the rocker arm without cramping it or twisting the ends of the valve yoke, and that the valve is " square " on its seat, so as to have its steam edges exactly parallel with the edges of the steam ports, causing admission and cut off to occur at exactly the same time for the entire length of the port.

Also see that there is *no lost motion* between the valve and the valve stem. With the D slide valve the steam chest cover or lid is removed and forward edge of the valve placed so that a piece of thin tin may be slipped between it and the edge of the front steam port. Then with the valve tram placed in a small prick-punch mark on the cylinder, make a line F on the valve stem, as shown in Fig. 229. Then move the valve forward

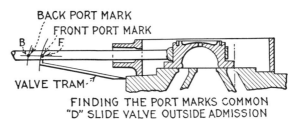

FINDING THE PORT MARKS COMMON
"D" SLIDE VALVE OUTSIDE ADMISSION

FIG. 229.—Slide Valve and Port Marks.

so that the back steam port begins to open and again place the valve so as to slip the piece of tin between it and the outer edge of the back port and make a line B on the valve stem with the valve tram from the same punch mark in the cylinder. Then a horizontal line in the middle of the valve stem may be drawn and its intersections marked with the lines F and B

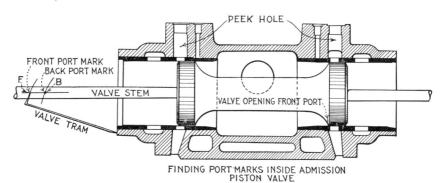

FINDING PORT MARKS INSIDE ADMISSION
PISTON VALVE

FIG. 230. Piston Valve and Port Marks.

by small centers; the center F is the front port mark, and the center B is the back port mark. The point midway between the centers F and B represents the central position of the valve.* In the case of the piston valve with inside admission, small peek holes are made in the cylinder,

* This is true only when the front and back steam laps are equal, which is generally the case in locomotive practice.

which provide means for placing the valve in the desired positions for making the port marks and other observations. Otherwise, the process for determining the port marks with the piston valve is the same as that with the D slide valve. The operation of finding the port marks with the piston valve is shown in Fig. 230. It is to be noted, however, that for the outside admission D slide valves, the front port mark F is to the front and the back port mark B is to the rear, while in the case of the inside admission piston valves the positions of the front and back port marks are reversed, the front port mark F being to the rear, while the back port mark B is to the front.

Finding Dead Centers. There are some shops in which the pinch bar is still used to move the engine when setting valves. However, there are more modern devices especially designed to raise and revolve the driving wheels while setting valves, which save considerable time and labor. A common device for this purpose is one where the main driving wheels are set upon four rollers, two under each wheel. With the side rods removed, leaving the main rods in place, these rollers are made to turn, by means of an air motor or ratchet lever, in either direction, thereby revolving the driving wheels and moving the valve gear parts and piston as desired.

The term " dead center " implies " no turning effort derived from the piston," and is that point at which the center of the crank-pin crosses the line drawn through the center of the crosshead pin and center of the main driving axle; or in other words, the engine is on dead center when the center line of the main rod, or this line extended, crosses the center line of the main driving axle as shown in Fig. 61, page 52. The two dead centers are known as the " front dead center " and " back dead center," as indicated in this illustration.

For convenience the *left front dead center* will be found first. Turn the wheel forward until the crosshead is about one inch from the extreme travel mark as shown in Fig. 231. Then use the crosshead tram, and from the point A on the front guide block describe the arc B on the crosshead; and before moving the wheel, describe the arc D on the tire of the wheel, with the wheel tram, from any point C on a rigid part of the engine, such as the frame.

Now turn the wheel forward, as indicated by the arrow, and as the crosshead recedes from the front travel mark, use the crosshead tram again and catch the arc B on the crosshead, Fig. 232, and then stop turning (taking care of lost motion as described in Rule 2, page 242). Use the wheel tram again, and from point C on the frame (the same point as was used before) describe the arc E on the tire, as shown in Fig. 232. Now from the inside or the outside of the tire with a pair of hermaphrodite calipers describe the arc ST. Next, take a small prick punch and mark two centers at the points where the lines D and E cross the arc ST and from these two points find, with a pair of dividers, the exact center between them on the arc ST, which center is indicated in the illustration by the letter R. This point is the dead center mark, and the engine is on the front dead center on the left side when the wheel is turned to bring this point on the

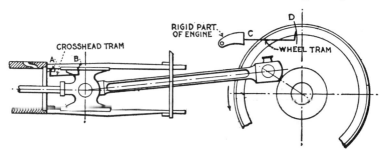

Fig. 231.—Finding Dead Centers.

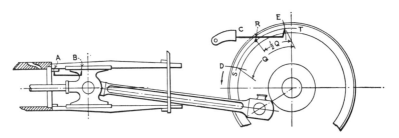

Fig. 232.—Finding Dead Centers.

In Fig. 232 the Crosshead is in the same position as in Fig. 231. The crank-pin is ahead of the dead center, while in Fig. 231 it is back of the dead center by an equal amount. The engine will be on dead center when point R is brought under the wheel tram.

tram. Describe a small circle around it to keep from getting it confused with other punch marks. Place the wheel on the dead center found by bringing point R under the tram, and make a mark on the guide at the front edge of the crosshead, which will be the forward " Travel Mark " of the piston on the left side. This mark indicates the position of the piston at the extreme forward travel. Now that one dead center is found, the same method is employed to secure the remaining three, except that when finding the two back dead centers the crosshead tram should be used from the back guide block or back end of the guide.

STEPHENSON GEAR

First Operation: Trying the Full Gear Leads. The engine may be placed on the dead center to which it may happen to stand the nearest, but in this discussion, for the sake of convenience, the operation will be started on the left front dead center by turning the wheel *backward* until the wheel tram registers with the left front dead center mark. Since the wheel is turned backward as the crank pin approaches its dead center, the valve gear must be placed in the full backward motion by placing the reverse lever in the back notch of the quadrant. Then, with the valve tram, scribe a mark on the valve stem, beginning at the parallel line on the valve stem; and let it extend considerably below the line. This gives the lead at the *left front port* for the full backward motion. (See Rule 3, page 243.)

Next, place the reverse lever in the front notch in the quadrant, and turn *backward* until the valve stem moves, which indicates that all of the lost motion in the valve gear has been taken up; then turn forward and again catch the dead center with the wheel tram. Mark the valve stem again with the valve tram, this time *above* the parallel line. (See Rule 3, page 243.)

These marks give the lead at the left front port or left front dead center for both forward and backward motions in full gear.

Since the right crank-pin generally leads on engines (excepting on those built by the Pennsylvania Railroad Company, where the left side leads), next place the engine on the right *back·dead center* in the usual manner (see Rule 2, page 242), remembering to take up the lost motion as before.

Now when the wheel is turned forward and while the reverse lever is in the extreme front notch, scribe a line on the valve stem with the valve tram above the horizontal line (see Rule 3, page 243), marking the *right back port lead* for the full *forward motion*. Then place the reverse lever in the extreme back notch and turn the engine forward until the valve stem moves slightly; then turn backward and catch the same dead center, and scribe a line with the valve tram on the valve stem below the horizontal line, marking the *right back port lead* for the full *backward* motion (see Rule 3, page 243).

Examining Tram Marks for Lead. For convenience assume the tram marks which were made on the valve stem to correspond with the marks and dimensions shown in Fig. 233. By examining the two forward motion tram marks on the right side (those above the horizontal line on the right valve stem), it is found that the right valve has one-quarter-inch lead at the front port, and that at the back port the valve overlaps the port one-sixteenth inch, giving negative lead. (See Rule 5, page 244.) Since these marks were both made while the engine was in the full forward motion it follows that the length of the forward eccentric blade must be altered in order to equalize these tram marks at both ports (Rule 6, page 244). It is found necessary to shorten the blade

$$\frac{\frac{1}{16}+\frac{1}{4}}{2}=\frac{5}{32}\ \text{inch.}$$

Mark on right cylinder F ecc. blade shortened $\frac{5}{32}$ inch. Make *no* changes, however, until all of the tram marks have been examined and all the changes necessary to be made on the eccentric blades, etc., are noted.

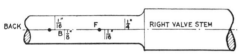

Fig. 233.—Tram Marks, for Lead, Right Valve Stem.

Before going further, it may be well to determine what effect the above changes, if made, will make in the tram marks. When an eccentric blade is shortened, the rocker arm will force the valve stem forward. By subtracting $\frac{5}{32}$ inch from the $\frac{1}{4}$ inch lead it is found that there is still $\frac{3}{32}$ inch lead at the front port opening. Then if the $\frac{1}{16}$ inch negative lead at the back port is subtracted from the $\frac{5}{32}$ inch of change, there will be $\frac{3}{32}$ inch remaining which will be the lead at the back port. Therefore, the valve will have $\frac{3}{32}$ inch lead in the full forward motion at both ports on the right side after the forward eccentric blade has been shortened $\frac{5}{32}$ inch.

After these alterations are made the lead is equalized on the right side at the front and back ports for the forward motion and found to be $\frac{3}{32}$ inch. If it were desired to change this lead in any manner to suit any particular condition of running of the locomotive, it would be done by turning the right forward eccentric on the axle (see Rule 8, page 245). It is to be remembered that the eccentric controlling the motion for which the lead is to be changed must be moved independently of the other. For example, if it were desired to change the $\frac{3}{32}$ inch lead to $\frac{1}{32}$ inch lead for both ports for the forward motion, it would be necessary to move the *forward eccentric* on the axle to reduce the lead to $\frac{1}{32}$ inch (see Rule 8). It is to be remembered, however, that when the eccentrics are cast in one piece the lead is fixed and cannot be changed for either motion without seriously affecting the lead for the opposite motion.

Next examine both back motion tram marks on the right side (those *below* the horizontal line on the right valve stem, Fig. 233). Here there is $\frac{1}{16}$ inch lead in front and $\frac{1}{8}$ inch negative lead behind; by observing Rule 6, page 244, carefully, it is found that the back eccentric blade must be shortened $\frac{3}{32}$ inch $\left(\frac{\frac{1}{8}+\frac{1}{16}}{2}=\frac{3}{32}\text{ inch}\right)$ which will leave $\frac{1}{32}$ inch negative lead at both ends. If it is desired to have $\frac{1}{32}$ inch lead at both ends, it is evident that the backing eccentric must be turned so as to give the valve $\frac{1}{16}$ inch *more lead* in order to overcome the negative lead and have the required amount of positive lead. Note: *B* ecc. $\frac{1}{16}$ inch lead on.

Now go to the left side and proceed in the same manner. After noting the alterations to be made in the eccentric blades to equalize the lead at front and back ports, and the necessary turning of the eccentrics to give the desired lead for both forward and backward motions on each side of the engine, the changes noted may be made, after which the cut-off may be tried.

Second Operation: Trying the Cut-off. If the Stephenson link motion were a perfect valve gear it would be unnecessary to try the cut-off, for if the valves were " square " in the corner notch (full gear), they would necessarily be " square " in every notch. But in previous study of the Stephenson gear it has been shown that it does not impart a perfect movement to the valve, owing to the errors introduced by the angularity of the main rod, eccentric blades, and the off-set of the link pin holes from the link arc; hence equalizing the lead at full gear only equalizes the events for that one position and travel of the valves, or for the corner notch position of the reverse lever. However, by off-setting the link bridle stud (or saddle pin) back of the link arc the proper amount, these errors of the link motion are approximately corrected; so that the valves will be almost " square " at the " running cut-off travel " when " squared " in full gear. But since the locomotive performs most of its work at early points of cut-off, it is more important to have steam perfectly equalized in the running cut-off position than in the full-gear position. In other words, it is more important to have an engine " square " when " hooked up " in the " working notch " than it is to be " square " in the " corner notch " and " lame " or " out " when " hooked up."

The " running " or " working " cut-off is usually taken at from twenty-five percent to thirty percent of the piston stroke. This would be (for the usual design of locomotive) at about six to eight inches of the piston stroke for passenger engines and seven to ten inches for freight engines.

In this discussion it will be assumed that the engine is for passenger service, and has a twenty-four-inch piston stroke; also that it is desired to try the cut-off at twenty-five percent of the piston stroke.

Turn the wheel *forward* until the right main crank-pin has passed the front dead center. As the crosshead recedes from the travel mark, measure the distance between the front end of the crosshead and the *forward travel mark*. When this distance measures twenty-five percent of the stroke (or six inches in the case cited), stop turning. Then place the reverse lever in the front notch and draw it back slowly until the valve tram is true with the right front port mark. Then latch the reverse lever there, or in the nearest notch of the quadrant, (See Rule 0, page 246.)

This is the position of the reverse lever for twenty-five percent cut-off. Now turn the wheel *backward* until the right valve stem begins to move, which indicates that all of the lost motion has been taken up. Then turn the wheel *forward* until the front end of the crosshead again measures twenty-five percent of the stroke (or six inches) from the forward travel mark and stop turning. With the valve tram make a line on the valve stem above the horizontal line (see Rule 3, page 243). This mark indicates the position of the front steam edge of the right valve when the crosshead is at twenty-five percent of its backward stroke. (See Fig. 234, page 219.)

Now go to the left side of the engine, leaving the reverse lever in the same notch, and turn the wheel forward until the left main crank-pin has passed the front dead center, continue to turn until the front end of the left crosshead stands six inches from the forward travel mark, and then stop turning. With the valve tram make a line on the left valve stem above the horizontal line (see Rule 3). This mark shows the position of the valve at the left front port when the left crosshead is at twenty-five percent of its backward stroke. (See Fig. 235, page 219.)

Now return to the right side and continue to turn the wheel forward until the right crank-pin has passed the right *back* dead center, and when the back end of the right crosshead stands six inches from its backward travel mark, stop turning. With the valve tram, scribe a second line on the right valve stem above the horizontal line. This second line indicates the position of the valve at the back port on the right side for a six-inch piston travel.

Return again to the left side and continue to turn the wheel forward until the left crank-pin has passed the left *back* dead center. When the left crosshead recedes from the backward travel mark a distance of six inches, stop turning. Make a second mark with the valve tram on the left valve stem above the horizontal line. This second line indicates the position at the back port on the left side when the piston is at twenty-five percent of its forward stroke.

The marks just determined are the positions of the valves corresponding with the positions of the pistons at twenty-five percent of their strokes and when the valve gear is set for twenty-five percent cut-off; that is, with the reverse lever in the running cut-off notch for the *forward motion only*. A similar process should be followed to determine the positions of the valves for the *backward motion*, by placing the reverse lever in the running cut-off notch for the *backward motion*, and then turning the wheel *backward*.

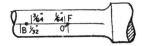

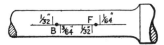

Fig. 234.—Tram Marks for Cut-off, Right Valve Stem.

Fig. 235.—Tram Marks for Cut-off, Left Valve Stem.

When trying the backward motion, the tram marks on the valve stem are made *below* the horizontal line. (See Rule 3.)

After the tram marks are made on both sides for both forward and backward motions, the readjustment of the valve gear parts necessary to equalize the cut-off all around for both forward and backward motions at twenty-five percent of the piston stroke may be made by first equalizing the cut-off at the front and back ports on each side separately; and second, by making the cut-off on both sides of the engine occur at the same distance of piston travel.

Changes to Make the Cut-off Equal. By trying the cut-off it may be discovered that although the lead was equalized in full gear, the steam distribution is not perfectly equalized in the running cut-off position of the valve gear, or when the reverse lever is in the running cut-off notch. This evil is mainly due to the errors of the shifting link motion; but it should be remembered that lost motion or imperfect construction of any of the parts of the valve gear will seriously affect the cut-off.

It will be assumed that the tram marks made when trying the cut-off correspond with those shown in Figs. 234 and 235, for the right and left sides respectively. Proceed to examine these marks to find what changes are needed to equalize the cut-off. Referring to Fig. 234, for the *right valve stem*, it is noted that for the *forward motion* (marks *above* the horizontal line) the valve covers the port $\frac{1}{64}$ of an inch at the front port and $\frac{3}{64}$ of an inch at the back port.

This fact indicates that cut-off occurs before the piston reaches the twenty-five percent position of its stroke, and also that the cut-off is " heavy " in front. To equalize the cut-off at the front and back ports on the right side, the right forward eccentric blade must be *shortened* $\frac{1}{64}$ inch, $\left(\frac{\frac{3}{64} - \frac{1}{64}}{2} = \frac{1}{64} \text{ inch} \right)$. See Rules 6, 7, and 8. Note thus: *R. F.* $\frac{1}{64}$ *inch short.*

Now examining the backward motion tram marks (*below* the horizontal line) for the right side (Fig. 234), it is found that the valve is just cutting off at the front port and that there is $\frac{1}{32}$ of an inch port opening at the back port. Hence, the cut-off is " heavy " behind and the right *backward* eccentric blade must be *lengthened* $\frac{1}{64}$ inch. $\left(\frac{0 + \frac{1}{32}}{2} = \frac{1}{64} \text{ inch.} \right)$ (See Rules 6, 7, and 8.) Note thus: *R. B.* $\frac{1}{64}$ *inch long.*

Now, by referring to Fig. 235, it is found that the forward motion there is $\frac{1}{64}$-inch port opening in front, and $\frac{1}{32}$-inch port opening behind, which shows that the cut-off is " heavy " behind. Hence the left *forward* eccentric blade must be lengthened $\frac{1}{128}$ inch. $\left(\frac{\frac{1}{32} - \frac{1}{64}}{2} = \frac{1}{128} \text{ inch.} \right)$ (See Rule 6, page 244.) Note thus: *L. F.* $\frac{1}{128}$ *inch long.*

In the case of the backward motion for the left side, the valve covers the front port $\frac{1}{32}$ of an inch, and the back port $\frac{3}{64}$ of an inch, hence the cut-off is " heavy " in front, and the left *backing* eccentric blade must be *shortened* $\frac{1}{128}$ inch. $\left(\frac{\frac{3}{64} - \frac{1}{32}}{2} = \frac{1}{128} \text{ inch.} \right)$ (See Rule 6, page 244.) Note thus: *L. B.* $\frac{1}{128}$ *inch short.*

Now if none of the defects suggested in Rule 10 is observed, the eccentric blades should be altered, and the equalization of steam in full gear must be sacrified in order to equalize the cut-off of steam in the running cut-off position of the gear. However, when the alterations necessary to equalize the cut-off are very slight (as in the case of the backward motion on the left side), it is needless to change the length of the eccentric blades, as they are already as nearly correct as could reasonably be expected in practice.

When these alterations are made, the cut-off of steam at the front and back ports on each side respectively will be equalized at about twenty-five percent of the piston stroke; but it is still to be determined whether *both sides* cut off at the same distance of piston travel. It would not be good practice to have the right side cut off at five inches, and the left side at, say seven inches of the piston stroke, even though the points of cut-off at the front and back ports on each side are equal.

Equalizing the cut-off at front and back ports causes the steam to be cut off at equal distances of piston travel, but not necessarily at the twenty-five percent position. In order to have the cut-off at the same position of the piston stroke on each side, after the adjustments are made to equalize the cut-off at the front and back ports, it is necesasry to determine what position each piston occupies when cut-off occurs.

To do this the forward motion will be considered first. It is to be noted that by shortening the right forward eccentric blade $\frac{1}{64}$ inch as required by the calculation on page 220, the valve stem will be moved forward $\frac{1}{64}$ inch (provided the rocker has equal lengths of arms, as is sometimes the case). This alteration causes the cut-off to be equalized at a point indicated on the valve stem by the valve tram, $\frac{1}{32}$ inch back of the front port mark and $\frac{1}{32}$ inch ahead of the back port mark. ($\frac{1}{64}$ inch $+\frac{1}{64}$ inch movement ahead $=\frac{1}{32}$ inch; $\frac{3}{64}$ inch $-\frac{1}{64}$ inch movement ahead $=\frac{1}{32}$ inch.) (See Rule 7, page 245.) But the valve tram should fall on the *port marks* to have cut-off when the piston is at twenty-five percent of its stroke, hence cut-off occurs slightly *before* the piston has reached the twenty-five percent position, as indicated by the $\frac{1}{32}$-inch space between the tram marks and the port marks. Then the right valve has traveled $\frac{1}{32}$ inch past cut-off when the piston is at twenty-five percent of its stroke. Cut-off occurs at about $5\frac{1}{2}$ inches of the piston stroke instead of 6 inches, which is at 22.91 percent instead of twenty-five percent, which was desired. ($\frac{1}{32}$ inch at the valve $=\frac{1}{2}$ inch at the piston, approximately.)

Now determine the *left* forward cut-off position of the piston by examining the left forward tram marks, Fig. 235, page 219. Here it is seen that if this alteration were made, the left forward eccentric blade would be lengthened and the left valve stem moved *back* the distance of $\frac{1}{128}$ inch (the rocker having equal arms), causing the cut-off of steam to occur *later* in the piston stroke than the twenty-five percent position. This is indicated by the fact that the valve has a port opening of $\frac{3}{128}$ inch ($\frac{1}{64}$ inch $+\frac{1}{128}$ inch $=\frac{3}{128}$ inch: $\frac{1}{32}$ inch $-\frac{1}{128}$ inch $=\frac{3}{128}$ inch) or the space between the tram marks (after alterations are made) and the port marks. Hence the piston will be *ahead* of its twenty-five percent position, or cut-off will occur on the left side at about $6\frac{3}{8}$ inches stroke ($\frac{1}{32}$ inch at the valve equal to $\frac{1}{2}$ inch at the piston, and $\frac{3}{128}$ inch at the valve equal to

$\frac{3}{8}$ inch at the piston; 6 inches $+ \frac{3}{8}$ inch $= 6\frac{3}{8}$ inches), which is 26.56 percent of the piston stroke instead of twenty-five percent as was desired. Thus the right side is cutting off at $5\frac{1}{2}$ inches and the left side at $6\frac{3}{8}$ inches of the piston stroke, causing the left side to be $\frac{7}{8}$ inch *heavy*. These are generally considered to be only fair positions in ordinary practice and should if possible be changed so that both sides cut off more nearly at the same percent of piston stroke. In order to make proper corrections the lift-shaft boxes on either side may be raised or lowered as may be required, and perhaps better the condition somewhat. This alteration is to be made only as a last resort and when one side is considerably heavier than the other, and not until after no defects can be found in the construction of the parts in question as suggested by Rule 10.

The backward motion may be examined to determine how the cut-off is on each side, in the same manner as was employed for the forward motion, but if any alterations are needed to equalize the cut-off on both sides for the backward motion, which will affect the equalization of steam at the cut-off position for the forward motion, they should not be made, as it is more important to have the forward motion perfect than the backward on all engines other than shifting engines, which should have the valves cut-off perfectly in front and back for both forward and backward motions.

By trying the cut-off it was found that the alterations required to equalize the steam at this travel were slight, and since it is considered better practice to have the steam equalized at the running cut-off than at full gear, it seems unnecessary first to equalize the lead at full gear and then destroy this equalization of lead to secure a perfect equalization of cut-off at the running position of the gear. This fact has given rise to the almost universal practice of fixing the lead in the design of the locomotive by casting the eccentrics in one piece; and fixing the position of the link bridle stud in the design of the link. With the eccentrics cast in one piece, it is impossible to change the lead. Hence, if the steam is equalized at the running cut-off position of the gear, this is considered to be sufficient adjustment for all practical purposes, because of the fact that the engine does most of its work at short cut-offs, and is not run for great lengths of time at extremely long cut-offs, where the equalization of steam will be slightly " out " and in extreme cases considerably so. When the design of the gear is such that the lead cannot be altered, simply omit the operation of equalizing the lead at full gear, and equalize the cut-off of steam at the desired percent of piston stroke in the manner described under " Trying the Cut-Off."

WALSCHAERT GEAR

Inside Admission Piston Valve.* The port marks and dead centers may be found as in the case of the Stephenson gear. After the port marks and dead centers are found, the procedure is as follows:

First: Checking the Lap and Lead Lever. Check all detail parts with their respective drawings. Disconnect the eccentric rod and clamp the link in its central position (or in that position which enables the link block to be raised or lowered in the link without giving motion to the valve). It is also good practice to hook up the gear so that the link block is in the exact center of the link. When in this position the valve would receive no motion from the link. In the operations which follow, all of the lost motion must be taken up in a manner similar to that described in the case of the Stephenson gear (see Rule 2, page 242).

Place the right main crank-pin on the front dead center, and tram to the valve stem. The distance between this tram mark and the front port mark is the lead opening or port closure as the case may be, for the front port. Next revolve the wheel to the back dead center, and again tram to the valve stem. The distance between this second tram mark and the back port mark is the condition for the back port. Measure the distance between the points trammed on the valve stem, which should be equal to *twice the lap of the valve plus twice the desired lead.* This will be found to come true providing the lap and lead lever is designed so that

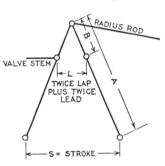

FIG. 236.—Proportions of Lap and Lead Lever.

the lengths A and B in Fig. 236 are proportional to (twice the lap plus twice the lead) and the piston stroke, that is, $\dfrac{A}{B}=\dfrac{S}{L}$, Fig. 236.

Where A is the total length of the lever between the union link and radius rod connections, B is the distance on the lever between the valve stem and radius rod connections; S is the stroke of the piston, and L is equal to *twice the lap plus twice the lead.*

Any variation from specified figures means that an error exists in the lap and lead lever, which can only be corrected by redesigning this lever, giving a different length to A or B.

* Forward motion in bottom of link.

For example: assume the following data:

Piston stroke = 28 inches,
Valve travel = 6 inches,
Eccentric throw = $22\frac{3}{4}$ inches,
Steam lap = $\frac{7}{8}$ inch,

and that it is desired to set the valves for $\frac{3}{16}$ of an inch lead all around. In this case the distance between the front and back tram marks on the valve stem should be twice the lap plus twice the lead, or 2 ($\frac{7}{8}$ inch + $\frac{3}{16}$ inch) or $2\frac{1}{8}$ inches.

Now assume that the tram marks made on the valve stem correspond with those shown in Fig. 237. Since the lap is $\frac{7}{8}$ of an inch, the distance between the front and back port marks is $1\frac{3}{4}$ inches (two times the lap). Referring to Fig. 237, it is noted that the distance between the two tram marks made is $2\frac{7}{64}$ inches,

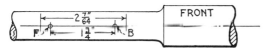

FIG. 237.—Tram Marks for Checking Lap and Lead Lever.

which is $\frac{1}{64}$ *of an inch short* of the proper distance, $2\frac{1}{8}$ inches. This shows that the lap and lead lever is "out" (see Rule 11, page 242), and may be adjusted as follows: Assume the length B on the lap and lead lever (or the distance between the radius rod and valve stem connections) to be $3\frac{9}{16}$ inches. By the use of the formula $\dfrac{A}{B} = \dfrac{S}{L}$,

$$A = \frac{B \times S}{L} = \frac{3\frac{9}{16} \text{ inches} \times 28 \text{ inches}}{2\frac{1}{8} \text{ inches}} = 47 \text{ inches}. \quad \text{See Rule 11, page 247.}$$

$$[L = 2(\tfrac{7}{8} \text{ inch} + \tfrac{3}{16} \text{ inch}) = 2\tfrac{1}{8} \text{ inches.}]$$

Then 47 inches is the length A, between the union link and radius rod connections, or the total length of the lap and lead lever. Hence the length of the lap and lead lever between the *union link and valve stem connections* (distance A–B) should be *shortened* to $43\frac{7}{16}$ inches, so as to make the total length of the lever (that is, the distance between the union link and radius rod connections—distance A, Fig. 236) equal to 47 inches. Similar operations should be carried out on the left side to determine the accuracy of the left lap and lead lever.

Second: Trying the Lead. Now that the length of both lap and lead levers has been adjusted and the proper amount of lead obtained, the lead at the front and back ports for both forward and backward motions on both sides of the engine may be equalized.

Reconnect the eccentric rod and unclamp the link. Place the gear in the *forward motion* with the link block at a point in the link that will give the specified maximum valve travel, or six inches in this case, when the wheels are revolved in the forward direction. This position of the link block is obtained by experiment, or may be calculated from Rule 12, page 247, and a knowledge of the dimensions of the link and eccentric throw. Next, place the main crank-pin which stands nearest to a dead center position on this dead center; say for instance the *right main crank-pin* on its *front dead center*. Again scribe a line on the valve stem above the horizontal line (see Rule 3, page 243). The distance between this tram mark (see Fig. 238) and the port mark *F* shows the condition at the front port on the right side for the *forward* motion.

Now draw the reverse lever backward and latch it in position so that

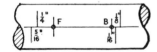

FIG. 238.—Right Valve Stem Tram Marks, Trying Lead.

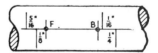

FIG. 239.—Left Valve Stem Tram Marks, Trying Lead.

the link block will be at the proper point for the specified valve travel, of six inches, in the *backward motion;* again take up all lost motion by turning the wheels forward until the valve stem moves; and then turn backward to the dead center position and with the valve tram make a second line on the right valve stem below the horizontal line (see Rule 3, page 247). This second mark indicates the condition at the front port on the right side for the *backward* motion.

Now place the reverse lever in full *forward* gear and go to the left side of the engine and continue to turn the wheels in a forward direction until the *left crank-pin* is on its *back* dead center, taking up all lost motion. With the valve tram scribe a line on the left valve stem above the horizontal line. This line indicates the condition at the back port for the *forward* motion on the left side. Then place the reverse lever in full *backward* gear and after taking up the lost motion make a second line with the valve tram on the left valve stem below the horizontal line. This second mark indicates the condition at the back port on the left side for the *backward* motion. (See Fig. 239.)

In like manner make similar marks for both forward and backward motions for the *right back* and *left front* dead centers, being careful to take up all lost motion.

Third: Alterations to Equalize the Lead. Now that the tram marks on both right and left valve stems in the forward and backward motions have been made, the lead may be equalized: first, by making the tram marks the same for the *forward* and *backward* motions at each port; and second, by equalizing the lead at $\frac{3}{16}$ inch at the *front* and *back ports* on *both sides* of the engine. For example, assume that the tram marks just made on the valve stems correspond with those shown in Figs. 238 and 239 for the right and left valve stems respectively. Begin by examining the marks on the right valve stem. Here it is noted that for the forward motion there is $\frac{1}{4}$ inch lead at the front port and $\frac{1}{8}$ inch lead at the back port and that for the backward motion there is $\frac{5}{16}$ inch lead in front and $\frac{1}{16}$ inch lead at the back port. Since both forward and backward motions are " heavy " at the same port (or in front) it is evident that the eccentric rod must be lengthened by such an amount as to move the valve forward a distance of $\frac{1}{32}$ of an inch.

$$(\tfrac{5}{16} \text{ inch} - \tfrac{1}{4} \text{ inch}) \div 2 = \tfrac{1}{32} \text{ inch.}$$

$$\frac{1}{32} \times \frac{22.75}{6} = \frac{1}{8} \text{ inch, approximately.}$$

Therefore lengthen the eccentric rod $\frac{1}{8}$ inch. See Rule 13.

The positions of the gear parts before the alterations are made, are indicated by the full lines, Fig. 240. After lengthening the eccentric rod, the parts will assume the positions indicated by the dotted lines. From this diagram it is evident that, after this alteration to the eccentric rod is made, the valve will be moved *ahead* when the gear is in the *forward motion* by a distance of $\frac{1}{32}$ of an inch; and when in the *backward* motion the valve will be moved *back* by $\frac{1}{32}$ of an inch; and the errors for both forward and backward motions will be the same at the right front port. The lead for the forward and backward motions at the remaining three ports should be equalized in a similar manner. After the necessary alterations are made on the right side, the lead at each port for both forward and backward motions will be equalized as shown in Fig. 241.

Now it is necessary to make the lead equal for both front and back ports, by altering the length of the valve stem or else the length of the radius rod. (See Rule 14, page 248.) In this case the radius rod or else the valve stem must be *shortened* by $\frac{3}{32}$ of an inch. ($\frac{9}{32}$ inch $-\frac{3}{16}$ inch desired lead $=\frac{3}{32}$ inch; $\frac{3}{16}$ inch desired lead $-\frac{3}{32}$ inch $=\frac{3}{32}$ inch: see Rule 14.)

This alteration will draw the valve back $\frac{3}{32}$ inch and equalize the lead

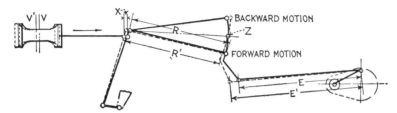

Fig. 240.—Effect of Altering Eccentric Rod.

Full lines indicate position of parts with incorrect length of eccentric rod. Dotted lines indicate correct position of parts after alteration on eccentric rod has been made.

at $\frac{3}{16}$ inch for the *forward* and *backward motions* at the *front* and *back* ports on the right side.

Now examine the tram marks on the left valve stem (Fig. 239) and make similar alterations to equalize the lead on this side. It is noticed by examining Fig. 239 that there is $\frac{5}{16}$-inch lead opening at the front port for the forward motion, and only $\frac{1}{8}$ inch lead for the backward motion. At the back port, the lead for the forward motion is $\frac{1}{16}$ inch and that for the backward motion is $\frac{1}{4}$ inch. To equalize these port openings for both motions the valve must be moved $\frac{1}{2}(\frac{5}{16}$ inch $-\frac{1}{8}$ inch$)=\frac{3}{32}$ inch,

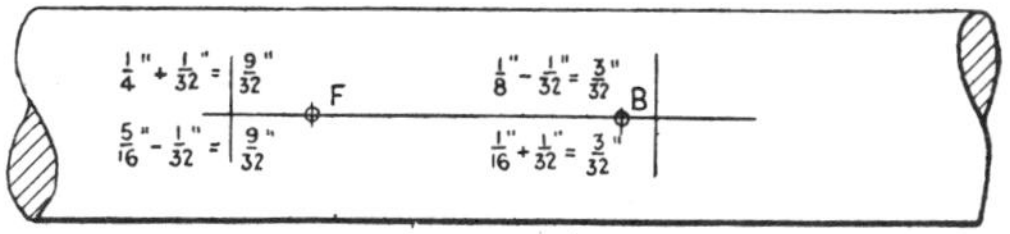

Fig. 241.—Tram Marks, Right Valve Stem, Lead Equalized.

or $\frac{1}{2}(\frac{1}{4}$ inch $-\frac{1}{16}$ inch$)=\frac{3}{32}$ inch. (See Rule 13, page 248.) The movement of the valve must be such as to decrease the lead at the front port for the forward motion, and increase it for the backward motion. This requires that the valve be moved back $\frac{3}{32}$ of an inch which changes the port openings for the forward motion to $\frac{5}{16}$ inch $-\frac{3}{32}$ inch $=\frac{7}{32}$ inch at the front port and to $\frac{1}{16}$ inch $+\frac{3}{32}$ inch $=\frac{5}{32}$ inch at the back port. For the *backward motion* the port opening at the *front port* will be $\frac{1}{8}$ inch $+\frac{3}{32}$ inch $=\frac{7}{32}$ inch and at the back port it will be $\frac{1}{4}$ inch $-\frac{3}{32}$ inch $=\frac{5}{32}$ inch. In this case, the eccentric rod must be *shortened* ($22\frac{3}{4}$ inches $\times\frac{3}{32}$ inch$)\div 6$ inches, or $\frac{11}{32}$ of an inch. (See Rule 13, page 248, also page 224.)

After these alterations are made, the tram marks on the left valve stem will be equalized for the forward and backward *motions* at each port and will be as indicated in Fig. 242.

It now remains to equalize the lead at both front and back ports on the left side. This is done by adjusting the length of the valve stem or of the radius rod. (See Rule 14, page 248.) In this case the valve must be drawn back by an amount equal to $(\frac{7}{32}$ inch $-\frac{5}{32}$ inch$)\div 2 = \frac{1}{32}$ of an inch; also $(\frac{7}{32}$ inch $-\frac{3}{16}$ inch desired lead $= \frac{1}{32}$ inch; $\frac{3}{16}$ inch desired lead $-\frac{5}{32}$ inch $= \frac{1}{32}$ inch. After this alteration has been made the leads on the left side will be equalized at the desired amount of $\frac{3}{16}$ of an inch.

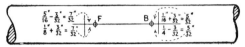

FIG. 242.—Tram Marks, Left Valve Stem, Lead Equalized.

Now the engine has been gone over and the necessary alterations made to the valve gear parts for an equalization of the lead at full gear for both forward and backward motions, but it is always good practice to check over the gear after the alterations are made and the parts are reassembled. This may be done conveniently in the following manner: Place the right crank-pin on a dead center, throw the reverse lever from one extreme position to the other, and note if the right valve stem moves. Then place the left crank-pin on a dead center and note whether the left valve stem moves when the link block is raised and lowered in the link.

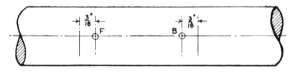

FIG. 243.—Tram Marks, Right Valve Stem after Altering Radius Rod.

If the parts are properly adjusted there should be *no movement* of the valve during these operations. (See Rule 15, page 248.)

Fig. 243 illustrates the locations of the tram marks on the right valve stem after the alterations on the radius rod for equalizing the lead have been made. The same condition will exist at the left valve stem.

The Walschaert gear has inherent peculiarities that frequently cause slight irregularities in the travel of the valve. If, in full gear, this irregularity does not amount to more than one-quarter inch out of " square " relative to the piston between the front and back positions of the valve, it may be ignored and the squaring of the travel may be considered as nearly perfect as the design will allow.

In special cases it may be desirable to square the valve travel when the gear is hooked up to give the cut-off at which the engine is most frequently used. Thus, on a passenger locomotive, the most satisfactory results may be secured when the travel is squared at one-third or one-half stroke cut-off. In such a case a slight irregularity at full stroke will probably be unavoidable, but will not prove detrimental. In any event, the particular circumstances under which the engine is to work must determine at what point of cut-off the valve travel shall be squared.

In marking the forward and backward gear positions on the reverse quadrant of a " cold engine " an allowance toward the front of the quadrant must be made on each end, to correct for expansion when the engine is under steam. The amount of such allowance is a matter of judgment, but one-quarter to three-eighths of an inch can be considered sufficient for ordinary standard gauge engines

Setting of Outside Admission Slide Valves.* With the ports exposed, place the valve with its steam edge just cutting off the ports (at each end

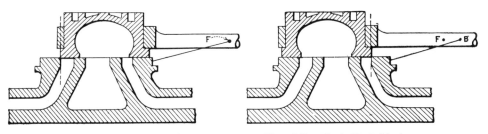

Fig. 244.—Front Port Mark.   Fig. 245.—Back Port Mark.

successively) and prick punch the valve stem at points F and B, the front and back port marks obtained by tramming from any convenient place on the valve seat or shelf (see Figs. 244 and 245 and Rule 3, page 243). The distance between F and B will be equal to twice the lap of the valve. When the valve is in position for lead opeing (main crank on either dead center) the port should be open by an amount equal to the desired lead (see Fig. 246).

If the tram is used with the valve at lead opening, then the distance

* Taken, in part, from Record No. 70 of the Baldwin Locomotive Works.

between the points so found and the port mark F on the valve stem will be equal to the lead (see dimensions V on Fig. 246).

With this statement in mind, proceed as follows:

Hook up the gear so that the link block is exactly central with the link. Place the main crank on the front dead center, and tram to the valve stem.

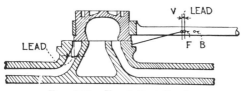

Fig. 246.—Front Port Lead.

Revolve the wheel to the back dead center, and again tram to the valve stem. Measure the distance between the points so obtained, and compare it with the specification. The distance should be equal to twice the sum of the lap and lead. Variation from the specified figures means that an error exists in the lap and lead lever, the upper and lower arms of which are made respectively proportional in length to twice the lap and lead and to the stroke of the piston. (See Fig. 247.)

Assuming that the distance L, as trammed on the valve stem, is found correct, the procedure is now as follows:

Place the gear in the forward motion, with the link block at a point in the link that will give the specified maximum valve travel when the wheels are revolved in a forward direction (this position of the link block is obtained by experiment).

Place the main crank on the front dead center and with the valve tram scribe a mark on the valve stem, measuring the distance between the point so obtained and the front port mark F. This distance should be exactly equal to the specified lead.

Revolve the wheel in a forward direction until the main crank-pin is on the back dead center, and similarly scribe a mark on the valve stem, measuring the distance between the

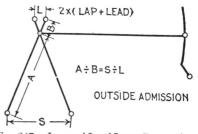

Fig. 247.—Lap and Lead Lever Proportions.

point so obtained and the back port mark B. This distance should also be exactly equal to the specified lead.

Place the gear in the backward motion and examine for lead at the front and back ports, exactly as described in the case of the forward motion, except that the wheel must be revolved in a backward direction.

If all the points so found are exactly to specification, the valve setting is square. A check should now be made by placing the piston on the front dead center, and moving the link block through its entire travel in the link. This should in no way disturb the position of the valve.

With the gear set for full travel forward and full travel backward, the maximum valve travel should be examined with the piston at half stroke. The travel so measured will not be exactly square at the front and back ports, as this location of the gear parts represent half stroke as measured from the piston travel, and does not take into consideration the angularity of the main rod.

Alterations. If, on trial, the valve gear is found to be out of square on the lead points, the following examples will serve to explain the corrections that should be made.

For instance, suppose the specification calls for the following:

Maximum valve travel, $5\frac{1}{2}$ inches,
Eccentric crank throw, 11 inches,
Constant lead, $\frac{1}{4}$ inch,
Outside lap of valve, 1 inch,
Link block below link center in forward gear.

It is very important that the following check exactly with the drawings:

Length of lap and lead lever between central fulcrum and upper and lower arm centers (see Fig. 247, dimensions B and A): |

Eccentric crank throw and length of crank arm. In the case under consideration the port marks on the valve stem (Figs. 244 and 245) will be two inches from center to center (this is twice the valve lap).

A change in the length of the eccentric rod results in a change in the position of the valve, approximately in proportion to the eccentric throw and valve travel. In the present case, this is as eleven to five and one-half or as *two to one*. In other words, for this particular example, a change of one-quarter inch in the length of the eccentric rod will move the valve approximately one-eighth inch when the link block is in full gear and the main crank-pin is on the dead center.

The influence of eccentric rod changes on the direction (ahead or back) of the movement of the valve is explained by referring to Fig. 248. An examination of this illustration will show that if the eccentric rod E is lengthened to E', then the radius rod R will be moved ahead to the position R', and the valve stem will be moved a distance X in the direction of the arrow, thus displacing the valve from position V to position V'.

The following rules may thus be formulated: If the link block is *below* the link center when running ahead, then:

In forward motion. If the eccentric rod is lengthened, the valve is moved ahead.

If the eccentric rod is shortened, the valve is moved back.

In backward motion. If the eccentric rod is lengthened, the valve is moved back.

If the eccentric rod is shortened, the valve is moved ahead.

If the link block is *above* the center when running forward, then, in each case, the valve will be moved in the direction opposite to that stated above.

Corrections made to the radius rod will have approximately full influence on the movement of the valve; that is, any variation in the radius rod will produce approximately the same variation in the movement of the valve.

The link fulcrum Z (see Fig. 248) is a fixed point; therefore, the direc-

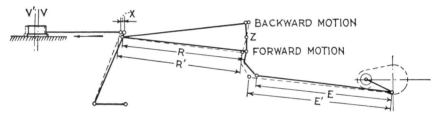

Fig. 248.—Position of Gear Parts before and after Altering Eccentric Rod.

tion of movement due to changes in the radius rod will vary directly with such changes, and the following rules may be formulated.

In either forward motion or backward motion. To move the valve ahead, lengthen the radius rod the amount desired.

To move the valve back, shorten the radius rod the amount desired.

This is true whether the link block is above or below the link center in forward gear.

With these facts in mind, two examples will be considered.

Let it be assumed that, on tramming to the right valve stem with the right main crank on the dead centers, the following irregularities in the lead are noticed for the right side of the engine under consideration. The small circles on the diagrams represent the port marks F and B (see Fig. 245) on the right valve stem, while the crosses represent the irregularities in the lead when trammed to the valve stem (see Fig. 249).

The first procedure will be to divide the error between the forward and backward motions, as follows:

Right Side:

Error in forward motion—

Front, $\frac{3}{8}$ inch $-\frac{1}{4}$ inch lead $=\frac{1}{8}$ inch error.

Back, $\frac{1}{4}$ inch lead $-\frac{1}{8}$ inch $=\frac{1}{8}$ inch error.

To square the lead, the valve must be moved $\frac{1}{8}$ inch ahead.

Error in backward motion—

Front, $\frac{7}{16}$ inch $-\frac{1}{4}$ inch lead $=\frac{3}{16}$ inch error.

Back, $\frac{1}{4}$ inch lead $-\frac{1}{16}$ inch $=\frac{3}{16}$ inch error.

To square the lead, the valve must be moved $\frac{3}{16}$ inch ahead.

As the errors in the two motions (forward and backward) occur in the same direction, it follows that the greater one partially neutralizes the

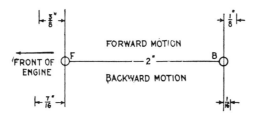

FIG. 249.—Tram Marks, Right Valve Stem before Altering Eccentric Rod.

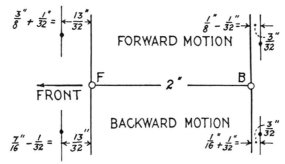

FIG. 250.—Tram Marks, Right Valve Stem after Altering Eccentric Rod.

effect of the lesser, and that the combined or average error will be the difference between the two: that is, $\frac{3}{16}$ inch $-\frac{1}{8}$ inch $=\frac{1}{16}$ inch, average error.

To divide an average error of $\frac{1}{16}$ inch equally about a central point, it will be necessary to move the right valve one-half this amount, or $\frac{1}{32}$ inch (in this case $\frac{1}{32}$ inch back in forward motion).

According to the statement on page 231 and to Rule 13, the right eccentric rod must be shortened $\frac{1}{16}$ inch (in the proportion of two to one) to move the valve $\frac{1}{32}$ inch. When this has been done the right valve stem points will tram as shown in Fig. 250.

The errors in forward and backward motions have thus been equalized, and it remains only to square the lead at the front and back ports for both motions, on the right side. The right valve as now standing is $\frac{5}{32}$ of an inch too far back to equalize the lead, namely:

$$\frac{13}{32} \text{ inch} - \frac{1}{4} \text{ inch lead} = \frac{5}{32} \text{ inch error front.}$$
$$\frac{1}{4} \text{ inch lead} - \frac{3}{32} \text{ inch} = \frac{5}{32} \text{ inch error back.}$$

As the influence of the radius rod is direct (see Rules 14 and 18) it follows that by lengthening this rod the amount required ($\frac{5}{32}$ of an inch) the right valve will be squared, and can be trammed to the dimensions shown by Fig. 251. These dimensions are the ones required by the specification.

The right valve has thus been squared and the errors corrected by the changes noted below:

Right eccentric rod shortened $\frac{5}{16}$ inch.

Right radius rod lengthened $\frac{5}{32}$ inch.

A final trial of the right valve travel, cut-off, etc., can now be made in the previously described manner.

Left Side: Let it be assumed that on tramming for lead on the left side, results are obtained as represented by Fig. 252.

Divide the error between the forward and backward motions as follows:

Error in forward motion—

Front, $\frac{7}{16}$ inch $- \frac{1}{4}$ inch lead $= \frac{3}{16}$ inch error. To square the lead, the valve must be moved $\frac{3}{16}$ inch ahead.
Back, $\frac{1}{4}$ inch lead $- \frac{1}{16}$ inch $= \frac{3}{16}$ inch error.

Error in backward motion—

Front, $\frac{1}{4}$ inch lead $- \frac{3}{16}$ inch $= \frac{1}{16}$ inch error. To square the lead, the valve must be moved $\frac{1}{16}$ inch back.
Back, $\frac{5}{16}$ inch $- \frac{1}{4}$ inch lead $= \frac{1}{16}$ inch error.

As the errors in the two motions (forward and backward) occur in opposite directions, it follows that they augment each other, and that the combined or average error will be the sum of the two: that is, $\frac{3}{16}$ inch $+ \frac{1}{16}$ inch $= \frac{1}{4}$ inch, average error. (See Rule 6.)

To divide this error equally about a central point, it will be necessary to move the left valve one-half the amount, or $\frac{1}{8}$ inch (in this case $\frac{1}{8}$ inch ahead in forward motion).

According to Rule 13 and the statement on page 231, the eccentric rod

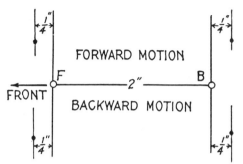

FIG. 251.—Tram Marks, Right Valve Stem, after Alterations are Made.

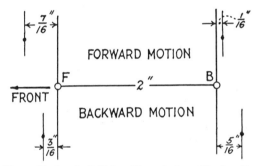

FIG. 252.—Tram Marks, Left Valve Stem, before Altering Eccentric Rod.

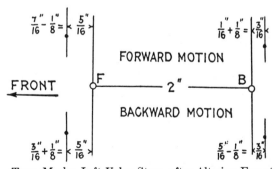

FIG. 253.—Tram Marks, Left Valve Stem, after Altering Eccentric Rod.

must be lengthened $\frac{1}{4}$ inch (in the proportion of two to one) to move the valve $\frac{1}{8}$ inch. When this has been done, the left valve stem will tram as shown in Fig. 253.

The errors in forward and backward motion have thus been equalized, and it remains only to square the lead front and back for both motions on the left side. The left valve as now standing is $\frac{1}{16}$ inch too far back to equalize the lead:

$$\frac{5}{16} \text{ inch} - \frac{1}{4} \text{ inch lead} = \frac{1}{16} \text{ inch error front.}$$

$$\frac{1}{4} \text{ inch lead} - \frac{3}{16} \text{ inch} = \frac{1}{16} \text{ inch error back.}$$

To move the valve ahead $\frac{1}{16}$ inch the radius rod must be lengthened $\frac{1}{16}$ inch (see Rule 14) and the lead will then be squared. When trammed for lead, the results will be as shown by Fig. 251. These dimensions are the ones required by the specification.

The lead on the left side has been squared and the errors corrected by the changes noted below:

Left eccentric rod lengthened $\frac{1}{4}$ inch.

Left radius rod lengthened $\frac{1}{16}$ inch.

Trial of the left valve travel, cut-off, etc., may now be made in the manner previously described.

From the above it is evident that the *errors* in the *forward* and *backward motion* are *equalized* by changing the *length of the eccentric rod;* and the *lead* is then squared by changing the *length of the radius rod.* Theoretically the radius rod should not be changed; but the amount of change necessary is so slight, that it makes practically no difference in the movement of the valve.

MALLET VALVE GEARS

Mallet compound locomotives using the Walschaert valve gear are usually equipped with power reverse gears. In setting such valves the gears of the rear engine should be set first. Put the reverse gear on the center, and adjust the reach rods to the front engine until all the link blocks are on the link centers. Remove the eccentric rods and swing each link without moving the valve stems. Set the front engine, and if properly designed both engines will then have the correct cut-off to give the proper amount of work. In some cases where Mallet compound locomotives were not pulling their rated tonnage and slipping badly in the rear engine, it was found that the back engine did not receive full valve travel because the reverse gear movement was restricted. The front reach rods had been lengthened to give the front or low-pressure cylinders full valve travel, with the result that the back or high-pressure valves cut off short while the low-pressure cylinders took steam for the full cut-off period. As a result, the receiver pressure fell to about one-half its normal amount, thus relieving the high-pressure cylinders of about one-half of their normal back pressure, overloading the high-pressure pistons and causing the slipping referred to.

For general practice in full gear the high-pressure valves should cut off at about ninety percent of the piston stroke, and the low-pressure valves should cut off at about eighty-four percent; to allow for the shrinkage of the volume of the steam leaving the high-pressure cylinders and the loss of heat in passing through the receiver.

BAKER VALVE GEAR

After the port marks are made with the standard valve tram, and the four dead centers have been located in the usual manner, as given on pages 212 and 213 respectively, it is well to see that the gear is connected properly as shown on the standard blueprint. Then check the throw of the reverse yoke, also the clearance at all points, having the eccentric crank clamped temporarily to the main crank-pin, but as near as possible to the specified throw.

To Determine the Eccentric Crank Position. For convenience in this discussion the engine is shown on the right front dead center, although it is customary to begin by placing the engine on the dead center nearest to the position in which the engine may happen to be standing. Since the gear connecting rod must stand in its central position when the main crank-pin is on either dead center, it is necessary to adjust the position of the eccentric crank to bring this condition about. The length of the eccentric crank is fixed, and it is only necessary to change its throw by moving it in or out as required. In determining the proper position of the eccentric crank, it is necessary to have the gear connecting rod stand in the same position in its travel when the engine is on either dead center. This position may be determined in the following manner:

Place the engine on the right front dead center, as shown in Fig. 254, and tram from the center of the pin connecting the eccentric rod and gear connecting rod to any stationary point, such as the guide yoke or guides, as shown by the tram points A and B of Fig. 254. (In most cases the wheel tram can be used for this work.) After scribing a line across the side of the main guide with the A end of the tram, revolve the wheel to the back dead center and scribe the guide again; if these two lines are together the gear connecting rod is in the central position for both dead center positions of the main crank-pin, and therefore the eccentric crank setting is correct. If these two lines are not together the eccentric crank must be moved in or out from the center of the axle, until these lines come together. Then secure the eccentric crank permanently to the pin. The eccentric crank should be moved an amount and in a direction which will move the

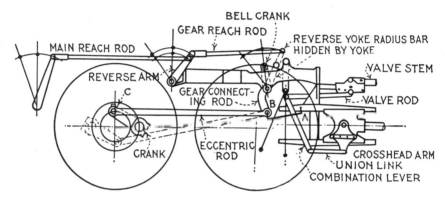

FIG. 254.—Determining Position of Eccentric Crank.

A end of the tram half the distance between the two scribed lines on the guide. The position of the reverse lever is not important while finding the eccentric crank position.

With sufficient experience, the location of the eccentric cranks can be determined while obtaining the dead centers, or the two sides of the engine may be worked together as described in connection with the setting of the Stephenson gear. This method is especially advantageous when it is required to move the engine by " pinching."

To Check the Valve Travel. Put the reverse lever in the full forward motion position; then by means of the valve tram, as the valve is moved through its travel by the turning of the wheel, scribe light marks on the valve stem at the two extreme travel positions of the valve (being careful to take care of the effect produced by lost motion in the parts; see Rule 2, page 242), and then measure the amount the valve has moved from one extreme position to the other. If there is a difference between the right and left sides of the engine, *lengthen the gear reach rod on the side of the engine where the travel is short.* After obtaining the same travel on each side of the engine in this manner, the reverse lever should be placed in its central position and the main reach rod adjusted until the dimension shown on Fig. 255 is obtained for mid gear position. Then the quadrant length should be tested for the desired travel in both full forward and full backing motions.

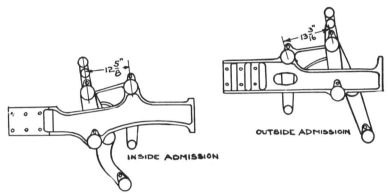

INSIDE ADMISSION

OUTSIDE ADMISSION

FIG. 255.—Dimensions for Correct Adjustment of Main Reach Rod.

Equalizing the Lead by Adjusting the Length of the Eccentric Rod. In the following discussion the inside admission gear will be referred to; and from the fact that the adjustment is exactly the opposite for the outside admission gear, it will only be necessary to describe the method of adjusting the gear for the one arrangement.

The Baker gear has a ratio of 4 to 1, that is, if the eccentric rod is altered one inch in length, the valve will be moved one-quarter of this amount or one-quarter of an inch when in *full gear* and the engine is on *dead center.* Since the inside admission gear is *direct* in the forward motion and *indirect* in the back motion, if the eccentric rod is lengthened one-quarter of an inch, the valve will be moved forward one-sixteenth of an inch, with the lever in the extreme forward motion and the engine on dead center.

If the reverse lever is in the extreme back notch, the valve will move back one-sixteenth of an inch when the eccentric rod is lengthened one-quarter of an inch, when the engine is on dead center. Shortening the eccentric rod will have the opposite effect. With the outside admission gear, the forward motion is indirect and the backing motion is direct, so that lengthening the eccentric rod will draw the valve back by one-quarter of the amount the eccentric rod is lengthened when in full gear with the engine on dead center. If the reverse lever is in the full backing position the valve will be moved forward by one-quarter the amount which the eccentric rod is lengthened, when the engine is on dead center. Shortening the eccentric rod will have the opposite effect on the valve.

Considering the arrangement of the gear for *inside admission* valves, and referring to Fig. 256, which illustrates the tram marks made while setting a valve, point F is the front port mark and point B the back port mark. The scribed lines above the horizontal line on the stem represent the forward motion marks while those below the horizontal line represent the backward motion marks.

The forward motion lead marks are made while the reverse lever is in the extreme forward notch. When making the backward motion lead marks, the reverse lever must be placed in the extreme backward motion notch.

The lead marks for the forward motion shown at A and L, Fig. 256, indicate one-quarter of an inch lead at the front port and one-eighth of

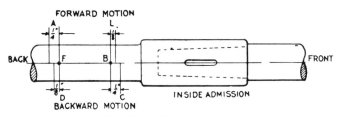

FIG. 256.—Tram Marks Showing Lead.

an inch lead at the back port. In order to equalize the lead at the front and back ports it is necessary to shorten the amount of lead at the front and lengthen it at the back port, by moving the valve back one-sixteenth of an inch. Thus, $\frac{1}{4}$ inch$-\frac{1}{16}$ inch$=\frac{3}{16}$ inch, and $\frac{1}{8}$ inch$+\frac{1}{16}$ inch$=\frac{3}{16}$ inch. Since these marks are for the forward motion, and from the fact that for inside admission gear the forward motion is direct, it is necessary to shorten the eccentric rod. Hence shorten the eccentric rod four times (ratio 4 to 1) one-sixteenth of an inch or one-quarter of an inch.

Now referring to the backward motion tram marks shown at D and C, Fig. 256, the lead at the front port is one-eighth of an inch, and the lead at the back port is one-quarter of an inch. In order to equalize the lead in the backward motion, it is necessary to move the valve *ahead* one-sixteenth of an inch. Since for inside admission gears, the motion is indirect in the backward motion, the eccentric rod must be shortened. Therefore shorten the eccentric rod four times one-sixteenth or one-quarter of an inch. To equalize the lead for the forward and the backward motions, it is necessary to shorten the eccentric rod one-quarter of an inch. This one alteration to the eccentric rod is all that is required to equalize the lead in both forward and backward motions. The above example shows the condition when the eccentric rod is one-quarter inch too long. After the eccentric rod has been shortened one-quarter of an inch the valve tram marks indicating the

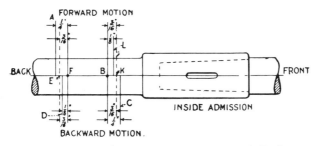

FIG. 257.—Effects of Shortening Eccentric Rod.

lead will register as shown in Fig. 257. The lead at the front and back ports for both forward and backward motions will be equal to three-sixteenths of an inch.

By referring to Figs. 256 and 257 it is seen that by shortening the eccentric rod one-quarter of an inch, the valve has been shifted back in the forward motion until lead line A is at point E, and lead line L is at point K. In

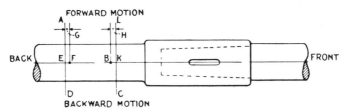

FIG. 258.—Tram Marks after Altering Eccentric Rod.

the backward motion the valve will be shifted ahead until the lead line D will be at point E and lead line C will be at point K, which will give the condition shown in Fig. 258.

After obtaining leads as shown in Fig. 258, the length of the valve rod should be adjusted, making G and H equal. When the mechanic has had some experience in valve setting, the valve rod and eccentric rod alterations can be made after one revolution of the wheels.

Referring back to the paragraph on eccentric crank setting, page 237, the position of the eccentric crank may be checked from the stem (see Fig. 256) on which the distance between A and L on the horizontal line is equal to that between C and D. This will always be the case when the eccentric

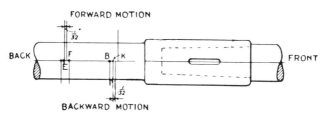

Fig. 259.—Effects of Lengthening Eccentric Rod.

crank is set correctly, whether the eccentric rod is long or short. That is, the valve movements for lead in the forward and backward motion should be equal. Again, if the eccentric rod is one-eighth of an inch too short, and the eccentric crank setting is correct, the full gear lead lines will appear where shown in Fig. 259.

After lengthening the eccentric rod one-eighth of an inch, the valve tram marks will be as shown in Fig. 258.

The foregoing applies to *inside admission gear only*, and alterations in the eccentric rod length should be *opposite* for *outside admission valves*. (See Rules 16, 17, 18.)

RULES FOR VALVE SETTING

RULE 1.   In setting the valves on an engine for which the dead centers and port marks have been previously located, it is of the utmost importance to see that the valve tram, wheel tram, and crosshead tram used are those made for the particular engine at hand and that they are of the correct standard size.   Clean out thoroughly all center-punch marks and polish the valve stem.

RULE 2.   *Lost motion when finding dead centers.*   When finding a dead center, the lost motion of the parts involved must be taken care of.   For instance, when finding the front dead center mark on the main wheel, it is clear that the main rod will *push* the crosshead as the crank-pin approaches the dead center, and will *pull* the crosshead after the pin has passed the dead center.   At the back dead center the action will be just the opposite in effect. Therefore, if there is any lost motion in the main rod, the dead center mark on the wheel will not be correct. To overcome this error, after having marked a line on the crosshead when approaching the dead center position, turn past the dead center an inch or two, then turn back again and catch the line on the cross-head with the crosshead tram. In this manner the strain against the cross-head will be in the same direction on each side of the dead center position. This rule should be strictly observed on all engines with much lost motion, otherwise the dead center marks on the wheel will not be correct, and unless the dead centers are correctly located it will be impossible to set the valves perfectly.

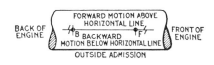

Fig. 260.—Rules for Scribing Tram Marks on Valve Stem.

RULE 3. *How to scribe tram marks.* A horizontal line should be drawn through the port marks on the valve stem and the forward motion tram marks

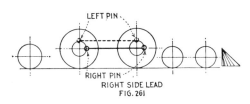

RIGHT SIDE LEAD
FIG. 261

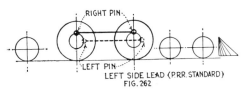

LEFT SIDE LEAD (P.R.R. STANDARD)
FIG. 262

Fig. 261.—Right Side Lead.

Fig. 262.—Left Side Lead.

at each end are scribed *above* the horizontal line, and those of the backward motion *below* the horizontal line, as indicated in Fig. 260.

RULE 4. *Meaning of right or of left side lead.* When the right and left crank-pins are arranged so that when the right crank-pin is placed on its front dead center the left crank-pin will be on the top quarter, the arrangement is known as *right side lead.* That is, as the engine moves in the forward direction, the right crank-pin will go ahead, or will lead; and will be always a quarter of a turn ahead of the left pin. If the arrangement is such that the left crank-pin will go ahead of the right pin by a quarter of a turn when running in the forward direction, the engine is said to be one of " left side lead." The Pennsylvania Railroad Company builds its engines with left side lead.

The relative positions of the right and left crank-pins for right side lead are shown in Fig. 261, while the conditions for left side lead may be seen in Fig. 262.

RULE 5. *To determine port opening and port closure from the position of the tram and port marks.*

If a tram mark comes between the port marks, it indicates so much *port closure* (sometimes called blind); if outside, so much *port opening*, for both inside and outside admission valves. But occasionally, when the valve gear parts are out very badly, a tram mark may come outside of the opposite port mark and appear as port opening. Always notice which dead center the crank-pin is on and which port mark is being tried.

RULE 6. *To determine whether to lengthen or to shorten an eccentric blade (Stephenson gear).* To equalize the lead at both front and back ports for either motion alter the length of the eccentric blades. For equalizing the lead at both ports for the *forward* motion alter the length of the *forward* eccentric blade. For the *backward* motion alter the length of the *backing* eccentric blade.

When a tram mark at one end comes outside the port mark, and at the other end comes inside the port mark, *add* the distances (in fractional parts of an inch) and divide their sum by two. This result will be the amount to move the valve. The direction in which the valve should be moved depends upon whether the valve is one of outside or inside admission. However, it must be moved so that when the amount in inches or fractions thereof is subtracted from the one tram mark and added to the other tram mark, the two tram marks will be the same distance from their respective port marks and also be on the same side, that is, both outside or both inside the port marks.

Now with the *standard* or indirect gear of the Stephenson motion (see page 43) the eccentric blade is *lengthened* to move the valve *back* and *shortened* to move the valve *ahead*, and the amount by which the eccentric blade should be altered is the same as that by which it was found necessary to move the valves. When *unequal arms* are used in the rocker, the amount the blades should be shortened will be such as to move the valve the proper amount. (See page 80, under " Rocker Arms.")

The above method is somewhat puzzling to the best of mechanics, and in order more clearly to explain this subject Fig. 263 is employed and a general rule stated which avoids any numerical calculations and thus simplifies the operation.

The two forward motion tram marks are shown above the horizontal line and are indicated by the letters F_1 and F_2; and the backward motion marks are below the line and are indicated by the letters B_1 and B_2. The point marked o indicates the exact center between the front and back port marks F and B (not the tram marks). Now examine the two forward motion tram marks. With a small pair of dividers find the exact center between the tram marks F_1 and F_2; the center thus found is indicated in Fig. 263 by the letter f and is in front of the center of the port marks, or point o. Then the valve must be moved *ahead* by *shortening* the *forward* eccentric blade an amount equal to the exact distance between points o and f, that is, bring the center of the tram mark (point f) exactly on the center of the port mark (point o).

If the rocker arms are of different lengths, alter the blade enough to cause the valve to move the distance indicated between points o and f. Now examine the two backward motion tram marks. Again locate the

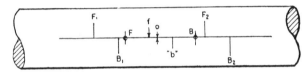

FIG. 263.—Rules for Lengthening or Shortening Eccentric Blades.

exact center between the tram marks B_1 and B_2. This center is indicated in Fig. 263 by the letter b and is *back* of the center o. Hence the valve must be moved *back*. To move the valve back the eccentric blade must be lengthened. Therefore, the backward eccentric blade should be lengthened so as to move the valve the exact distance between the centers b and o.

Always bring these two centers together. If the center between the tram marks is in FRONT *of the center of the port marks,* SHORTEN *the blade; if* BEHIND *it,* LENGTHEN *the blade.*

On a *direct* motion engine the changes should be made exactly the reverse.

RULE 7. *To equalize the running cut-off* (*indirect Stephenson gear outside admission valve*). When the difference in the cut-off in both strokes on the same side of the engine is slight, and no other defects can be located, a perfect equalization of steam for full gear position should be sacrificed in order to equalize the steam in the running cut-off. If the cut-off shows *heavy in front,* that is, carries steam farther in front than behind, *shorten* the eccentric blade, if *heavy behind, lengthen* the blade.

RULE 8. *Altering the amount of full gear lead* (*Stephenson gear*). To alter the amount of lead in either motion the *eccentrics* must be *turned* on the *axle*. To change the amount of lead for the *forward* motion the *forward eccentric* is shifted. To change the amount of the lead for the *backward* motion the *backing eccentric* is shifted. Any change in the position of the eccentrics will affect the amount of lead at *both front and back ports* by the same degree.

On all standard engines (indirect Stephenson motion), to increase the lead for outside admission valves move the rib (or belly) of the eccentric *toward* the crank-pin. To decrease the lead, move the rib *away* from the crank-pin. On all engines with direct motion move the eccentric just the reverse. (See Fig. 112.)

RULE 9. *Reverse lever position for obtaining short cut-offs.* In order to hasten the cut-off relative to the piston stroke, the travel of the valve must be shortened by " drawing up " the reverse lever toward its control position. The position for any particular cut-off may be obtained by placing the piston at the position in its stroke at which the cut-off of steam is desired, and then by " drawing up " the reverse lever until the steam edge of the valve is on line with the steam edge of the port (the valve tram on the port mark), and the nearest notch to this position of the lever will be the position at which to locate the lever for this particular cut-off.

RULE 10. *Suggestions for locating errors in the cut-off.* When the cut-off of steam is earlier on one side of the engine than on the other, it may be well before making any alteration to examine the valve gear parts and see if there are any defects in their construction or erection, such as: the position of the link bridle (or saddle) stud; the length of the link hangers; the length of the transmission bar hangers; whether the lift shaft or rocker arm boxes are sprung. This defect may be remedied by " lining up " or " down " the lift shaft or rocker boxes. The latter correction may be used when there is no transmission bar providing the reach rod is of the proper length.

When the cut-offs on both sides of the engine are practically the same, but are found to be unequal at the front and back ports on one side, the defect is best remedied by adjusting the lengths of the eccentric blades. This is done at the expense of the equalization of steam in full gear.

No fixed rules can be given for locating all defects which may be found when setting locomotive valves, but the experienced mechanic can usually, without a great deal of difficulty, locate any serious trouble by a thorough examination of the parts in question.

RULE 11. *Design of the lap and lead lever.* The lap and lead lever is designed to move the valve a distance equal to twice the lap of the valve plus twice the desired lead.

For inside admission valves, the radius rod connection to the lever is made at the top and that of the valve stem between the radius rod and union link connections (Fig. 140, page 116). For outside admission valves, the valve stem connection is at the top, as in Fig. 139, page 116.

The pin hole centers at the top of the lever are usually made as close together as the design of the radius rod and valve stem will permit. This is done so that the total length of the lever will not become excessive. The proportion of the two arms of the lap and lead lever in relation to the

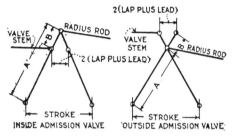

FIG. 264.—Proportions of Lap and Lead Lever.

stroke of the engine and to the lap of the valve plus the lead may be expressed as follows:

Referring to Fig. 264, for both inside and outside admission valves, the lengths *A* and *B* must be such that when the points at which the radius rod is connected to the lever, is held rigid by placing the link block in the center of the link as the crosshead moves through one stroke, the valve stem will be moved a distance equal to *twice the lap of the valve plus twice the lead.*

Thus,
$$\frac{A}{B} = \frac{\text{Stroke of Piston}}{2(\text{lap}+\text{lead})}.$$

RULE 12. *To determine travel of link block.* The required horizontal movement or travel of the point of the radius rod connection to the lap and lead lever for a given total valve travel must be determined. This movement is equal to the total travel of the valve *minus* (twice the lap plus twice the lead)—or that produced by the lap and lead lever, and may be expressed as follows:

The travel of the link block at full gear position is the movement of the point at which the radius rod is attached to the lever; and hence if the movement at the lever is calculated, the travel of the link block in full gear is obtained; from which the swing of the link, and the throw of the eccentric crank may be determined.

Let T = the travel of the radius rod connection point to the lever, or the
   link block travel in full gear;
   S = stroke of the piston;
   V = travel of the valve:
   P = twice the lap plus twice the lead = 2(lap+lead)
For inside admission valves:

$$T = \frac{S\sqrt{V^2 - P^2}}{S - P}.$$

That is, the link block travel at full gear is equal to the stroke of the engine
multiplied by the square root of the difference of the squares of the valve
travel and (twice the lap plus twice the lead); divided by the difference
of the piston stroke and (twice the lap plus twice the lead).
   For outside admission valves:

$$T = \frac{S\sqrt{V^2 - P^2}}{S + P}.$$

Which is the same as that for inside admission valves, except that the sum of
the piston stroke and (twice the lap plus twice the lead) is used when dividing.
   The swing of the lap and lead lever and also that of the link must be
equal on both sides of their central positions, and hence their swings on one
side are equal to one-half of their total swings.
   RULE 13. *Lengthening eccentric rod. Link block below link center when
running ahead. (Walschaert gear.)*
   In forward motion: Lengthening eccentric rod moves valve ahead.
   In backward motion: Lengthening eccentric rod moves valve back.
   If the link block is above the center of the link when running ahead, then,
in each case, the valve will be moved in the direction opposite to that stated
above. A change in the length of the eccentric rod results in a change in
the position of the valve, approximately in proportion to the relation
between the eccentric throw and valve travel.
   RULE 14. *Changes to radius rod and valve stem.* To move the valve
ahead, lengthen the radius rod or valve stem the amount desired.
   To move the valve back, shorten the radius rod or valve stem the amount
desired.
   Any change in the radius rod will cause approximately the same variation in the movement of the valve.
   RULE 15. *Checking the alterations made on the eccentric rod.* Place the
engine on either dead center. Move the link block throughout its entire

travel in the link. If the eccentric rod is of the correct length, the valve stem will not move during this operation. In a similar manner check the parts for the other dead centers.

Baker Locomotive Valve Gear. The following are general rules in connection with setting valves operated by the Baker gear. The Baker gear has a ratio of 4 to 1, that is, when in full gear, and the engine is on dead center, one inch variation in the eccentric rod produces one-fourth inch variation at the valve.

RULE 16. *Inside admission valves.*

Forward Motion (direct)

a Lengthening eccentric rod will shift the valve *ahead one-quarter* of the amount the rod is altered.

b Shortening the eccentric rod will shift the valve *back one-quarter* of the amount the rod is altered.

Backward Motion (indirect)

a Lengthening the eccentric rod will shift the valve *back one-quarter* of the amount the rod is altered.

b Shortening the eccentric rod will shift the valve *ahead one-quarter* of the amount the rod is altered.

RULE 17. *Outside admission valves.*

Forward Motion (indirect)

a Lengthening the eccentric rod will shift the valve *back one-quarter* of the amount the eccentric rod is altered.

b Shortening the eccentric rod will shift the valve *ahead one-quarter* of the amount the rod is altered.

Backward Motion (direct)

a Lengthening the eccentric rod will shift the valve *ahead one-quarter* of the amount the rod is altered.

b Shortening the eccentric rod will shift the valve *back one-quarter* of the amount the rod is altered.

RULE 18. *The alterations of the valve rod are always direct.* That is, to move the valve *ahead, lengthen* the valve rod the amount by which it is desired to shift the valve. To move the valve *back, shorten* the valve rod the amount by which it is desired to shift the position of the valve. This rule holds for both inside or outside admission valves, and when the engine is in either the forward or backward motion.

CHAPTER VII

SUMMARY

Having shown how the valve and valve gear may be studied, it may be well to summarize the facts which have already been separately pointed out.

There are but two general types of valves ordinarily used on locomotives, the flat, or D slide valve; and the cylindrical slide, or piston valve.

With the increase in cylinder dimensions and steam pressures, the D slide valve could not be given a proper length of port without becoming unduly large; and even if partly balanced it created an excessive amount of friction when moved over its seat. The piston valve has been introduced largely to overcome this difficulty, and has been very successfully operated, notwithstanding the fears expressed when it was first applied to a locomotive.

The shape of the piston valve facilitates designing for the high temperature required by the use of superheated steam, and with the present extensive use of superheated steam the piston valve has become the standard type of valve for all classes of locomotives.

The plain slide valve and piston valve do not differ in the manner of steam distribution except as to the size of the port and port opening, so that in case of Mallet compound locomotives where the low-pressure cylinders afford a long port for the slide valve, and from the fact that the high temperature of the superheated steam is confined to the high-pressure cylinders (where the piston valve is used), the slide valve has been generally employed on the low-pressure cylinders. Another reason for this arrangement is that the slide valve will lift when drifting and relieve excessive pressure produced by compression in the large low-pressure cylinder.

Various additional ports have been added to each type of valve, for the purpose of overcoming the disadvantages resulting from slow movement of the valve at admission and cut-off. Most of these improvements are on the principle of the Allen valve, which gives a double opening of the port when it is most needed.

The D slide valve is always arranged for outside admission. The piston valve may be arranged for either outside or inside admission. As already pointed out, the piston valve with inside admission has a number of advantages, prominent among which are the absence of live steam at the ends of the valve chamber where it is more readily condensed, and also the absence of high pressure upon the valve stem packing. With this arrangement the valve is more readily balanced. The inside admission piston valve also permits the steam passages to the cylinder to be made very short and direct. For these reasons the inside admission piston valve is preferred to the outside admission style and is used in nearly all cases.

As the valve controls the admission and discharge of steam to and from the cylinder, its motion is of the greatest importance, and cannot be studied too carefully. At this period in development of the locomotive, the valve gear question is one of extreme importance. While almost every other part has undergone great changes, valve gear design and efficiency have remained practically at a standstill.

Of the numerous patented motions of the past, each calculated to improve the functions of steam admission and exhaust with their resultant complications, only two gears, the Stephenson and Walschaert, have up to the present time been considered practicable by the majority of railroads.

It is common knowledge that these two types are not up to the desirable standard of efficiency, hence it is important to know whether or not any of the new devices now being exploited produce better results.

The following considerations relating to the principal valve gears which are discussed in the preceding pages may help in an analysis of their relative merits.

It is generally claimed that the Stephenson motion, when properly constructed and adjusted, will give a wide range of practically equal cut-offs at both ends of the stroke. This fact, with the variable lead feature (or increasing lead as the cut-off is shortened), undoubtedly explains the reason for its general use by American locomotive manufacturers. But with the modern growth in the size and capacity of all classes of locomotives, the Stephenson gear is not structurally and mechanically well adapted to the heavy construction required. In a design of Stephenson gear, which would be suitable to meet the requirements of the large locomotives of to-day, the frictional surfaces of the four eccentrics and straps would become excessive, and a source of constant trouble in lubrication and from uneven wear. Also, the fact that the links are supported on hangers from the reverse shaft arm makes it difficult to support the heavy links against the side thrust caused when running around curves. Again, the transferring of the motion from inside to outside of the frames by means of the rocker arms, usually employed with the Stephenson gear, throws the motion out of the direct path and causes strains in the members which require special construction in order to afford proper maintenance of these parts.

The Stephenson gear being almost entirely underneath the engine and between the frames, the large parts become crowded and difficult of access for proper inspection and oiling. As a result, this gear, especially for large size locomotives, will not stay in good condition for any considerable length of time. Hence, with the increase in size of locomotives, the designer has been forced to employ other types of valve gears and to sacrifice a better steam distribution for a more satisfactory construction, structurally and mechanically. He has turned to the Walschaert gear, a mechanism equally well proven by European manufacturers, with the result that the Walschaert valve gear has superseded the Stephenson link motion, and become the universal standard gear for large American locomotives. Having proved its utility on large locomotives, it is now being applied to the smaller sizes of locomotives.

The Walschaert gear being applied on the outside of the locomotive is entirely accessible for inspection, lubrication and maintenance. The eccentric motion, being taken from the crank-pin, eliminates the high surface velocities of the eccentric and strap; also, the construction is made so that all the motion is practically direct. The center line of the valve chamber, as a rule, is brought out in line with the eccentric crank and link.

The effect of the angularities in the Walschaert gear is practically compensated for by offsetting the link foot pin to produce equal travel of the link block on each side of the central position; and while the mechanism can be squared at one cut-off, say, the running cut-off position of the gear, the remaining positions will not produce equal results on account of the increasing and decreasing of the distortion as the block is moved a greater or less distance from the fixed point of the link.

The removal of the valve gear from between the driving wheels facilitates bracing the frames of the locomotive laterally, while with the Stephenson motion applied to heavy locomotives, the placing of proper crossties on the frames becomes extremely difficult.

The connections of the parts being made with hardened pins and bushings reduces the wear to a minimum, a feature of great importance in the maintenance of the gear. This fact is also true of the Baker gear. Both the Walschaert and Baker gears give constant lead for all positions of the reverse lever.

It is claimed that a reverse mechanism of the Marshall type, as used with the Baker gear, is superior to the link arrangements of the Stephenson and Walschaert gears, because of the elimination of the sliding link block. In the Baker reverse mechanism all the connections are positive, and naturally no slipping can occur. A study of this feature, Figs. 176 and 177, pages 165 and 170, will show that slipping occurs in a Walschaert gear mostly when the link block is in the upper half of the link. This is due to the opposing arcs of the link block and lift shaft arm. On the other hand, when the link block is in the lower half of the link, the slipping is hardly noticeable because the arcs under this condition are working in almost perfect unison. For this reason the Walschaert gear is usually designed to take the forward motion from the lower half of the link.

With the design employed in the Baker gear, the heavy shocks that are imparted directly to the reverse mechanism at high speed will, it is believed, cause the yoke to vibrate more or less, producing the same effect as a slipping of the link block; because any slight change in the pivot point of the reverse yoke will cause a relative change in the cut-off. To guard against this condition, hardened bushings and pins of the proper design may be provided so as to eliminate wear and lost motion.

In comparing the effects of the lap and lead lever as hung on the bell crank on the Baker gear with that in the Walschaert design, the steam distribution is found to be the same. This being so, it then becomes a question which is the better method from a mechanical standpoint. In the Baker gear the shocks of the crosshead movement acting on the lap and lead lever are absorbed by the bell crank, which causes the gear to be handled with greater difficulty, and increases the wear on the reverse bearing. In the Walschaert gear the lap and lead lever is supported from the valve stem crosshead, which relieves the reverse parts of the strain produced by the movement of the main crosshead. It is also more difficult to get a good connection to the lap and lead lever and valve stem when hung on the bell crank, as the valve is out of line with the center line of the gear frame. It is, therefore, necessary to offset the connections in some manner. This is not necessary with Walschaert arrangement of lap and lead lever.

If the Baker reverse mechanism is superior mechanically to the Walschaert, and the Walschaert method of handling the lap and lead lever is superior mechanically to the Baker method, a combination of the present Baker reverse arrangement with the Walschaert lap and lead lever arrangement, as shown in Fig. 205*A*, produces a mechanical combination which should prove advantageous even though no gain in steam distribution over the present arrangement is produced.

APPENDIX

THE STEAM ENGINE INDICATOR AND INDICATOR DIAGRAMS

The steam engine indicator is an instrument for drawing on paper a diagram which shows the action of the steam in the cylinder on one side of the piston during one complete revolution of the wheels.

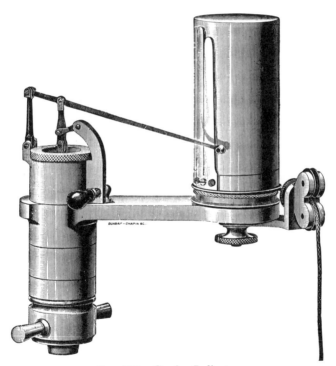

FIG. 265.—Crosby Indicator.

There are many designs of indicators, of which the Crosby, American-Thompson, Tabor and Star are very common. Figs. 265 and 266 illustrate the Crosby steam engine indicator. It is attached to the cylinder of the engine by means of a suitable cock shown in Fig. 267, and the thumb nut shown in Fig. 265. The drum string is attached by means of a suitable

reducing motion to the crosshead, which in turn gives the true motion of the
steam engine piston to the indicator.

The steam engine indicator was invented by James Watt, and was long
kept secret. The general principles on which the steam engine indicator is
based may be briefly stated. Referring to Fig. 266 (which shows the same
indicator as Fig. 265), the inside construction and locations of the various
parts may be seen.

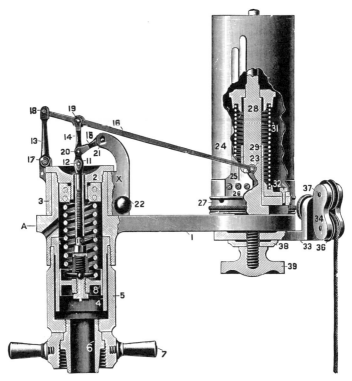

Fig. 266.—Cross-section of Crosby Indicator.

A piston 8 of carefully determined area is nicely fitted into a cylinder 4,
so that it will move up and down without much friction. The cylinder 4
is open at the bottom and fitted so that it may be attached to the cylinder
of a steam engine and have free communication with its interior, by which
arrangement the under side of the piston 8 is subjected to the varying pressure of the steam acting thereon. The upward movement of the piston,
due to the pressure of the steam in the cylinder, is resisted by a helical

spring of known strength. A piston rod 10 projects upward through the cylinder cap 2 and moves a lever 16 having at its free end a pencil point 23, whose vertical movement bears a constant ratio to that of the piston 8. A cylindrical drum covered with paper is attached to the cylinder proper of the indicator in such a manner that the pencil point may be brought in contact with its surface, and thus record any movement of either paper or pencil; the drum 24 is given a horizontal or rotary motion coincident with and bearing a constant ratio to the movement of the piston of the engine. It is moved in one direction by means of a cord attached to the crosshead and in the opposite direction by a spring 31 within itself.

When this mechanism is properly adjusted and free communication is opened with the cylinder of the steam engine, or locomotive in motion, it is evident that the pencil 23 is moved vertically by the varying pressure of steam under the piston 8, and the drum 24 is rotated by the reciprocating motion of the engine crosshead. If the pencil is held in contact with the moving paper, a figure or diagram will be traced representing the pressure of steam in the cylinder of the engine, the upper line showing the pressure urging the engine piston forward, and the lower line the pressure retarding its movement on the return stroke.

In order that the nature of the pressures may be more correctly interpreted, the line showing atmospheric pressure is drawn in its relative position. It will then appear whether the pressure of the steam at any part of the piston stroke is greater or less than that of the atmosphere.

THE INDICATOR DIAGRAM

An indicator diagram is the result of two movements; namely, a horizontal movement of the paper in exact correspondence with the movement of the engine piston and crosshead, and a vertical movement of the pencil in exact ratio to the pressure exerted in the cylinder of the engine; consequently, the diagram represents by its length the stroke of the piston of the engine on a reduced scale, and by its height at any point the pressure on the piston at the corresponding point in the stroke. The shape of the diagram depends altogether upon the manner in which the steam is admitted to and released from the cylinder of the engine. A diagram thus formed shows the pressure acting on one side of the engine piston only, during both the forward and return stroke. All of the changes of pressure may be properly located, studied, and measured. To show the corresponding pressures on the other side of the piston, another diagram must be taken from the other end of the cylinder. When the three-way cock shown in Fig. 267 is used, the diagrams from both ends are usually taken on the same paper, as shown in Fig. 268.

The names by which the various points and lines of an indicator diagram are designated are given in the following:

Referring to Fig. 269, the continuous line forming the figure or diagram

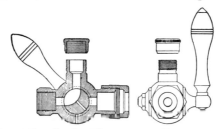

FIG. 267.—Crosby Three-way Indicator Cock.

CDEFGH is drawn by the indicator, and is the result of *one* indication (during one revolution) from *one side* of the piston of an engine. The straight line, *AB*, is also drawn by the indicator, but at a time when steam connection with the engine cylinder is closed, and both sides of the indicator piston 8 in Fig. 266 are subjected to atmospheric pressure only.

The Admission Line CD shows the rise in pressure due to the admission

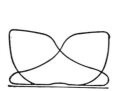

FIG. 268.—Indicator Cards from Both Ends of Cylinder.

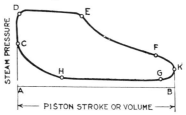

FIG. 269.—Good Indicator Card.

of steam to the cylinder by the opening of the steam port. If the steam is admitted quickly when the engine is about on the dead center this line will be nearly vertical.

The Steam Line DE is drawn when the steam port is open, and steam is admitted to the cylinder while the piston moves forward.

The Point of Cut-off E is the point where the admission of steam to the cylinder is stopped by the closing of the steam port.

The **Expansion Line EF** is a curved line, and shows the fall in pressure as the steam in the cylinder expands behind the moving piston of the engine.

The **Point of Release F** shows when the exhaust port opens.

The portion of the diagram from D to K represents the steam action forcing the piston of the engine along its stroke. At K the return stroke of the piston begins and the lower line of the diagram represents the action of the exhaust steam on the same side of the piston.

The **Back Pressure Line GH** shows the pressure against which the piston acts during its return stroke.

The **Point of Exhaust Closure, or Beginning of Compression H,** is the point where the exhaust port closes.

The **Compression Line HC** is a curved line and shows the rise in pressure due to the compression of the steam remaining in the cylinder after the exhaust port has closed.

The **Atmospheric Line AB** is a line drawn by the pencil of the indicator when its connection with the engine cylinder is closed and both sides of the piston of the indicator are open to the atmosphere. This line represents on the diagram the pressure of the atmosphere, or zero of the steam gauge, and becomes the base line from which the steam pressure may be measured.

Diagrams may be taken from each end of the cylinder separately on two pieces of paper, as shown in Figs. 270 and 271, or the two diagrams,

Fig. 270.—Indicator Card
Taken from Head End.

Fig. 271.—Indicator Card
Taken from Back End.

by using the three-way cocks, may be traced on the one paper, as shown in Fig. 268. The piping arrangement for the connection of the indicator with a three-way cock is shown in Fig. 272. It is evident from a study of this arrangement and the detail drawing of the three-way cock shown in Fig. 267, that by turning the handle of the cock first to one side, then to the other, the steam pressure in the engine cylinder is admitted to the indicator from one end at a time, and that the steam action at each end of the cylinder may be shown by the indicator in accordance with the position of the three-way cock.

When the handle of the cock is vertical, or straight up and down, the small passage through the valve of the cock will register with the small port at the bottom of the cock, leading to the atmosphere, so that the lower

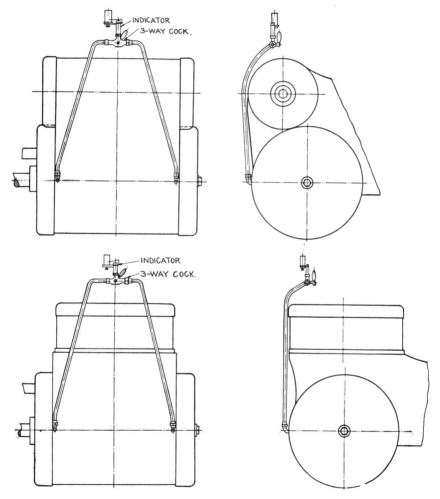

Fig. 272.—Diagram of Piping for Three-way Cock.

side of the indicator piston will be acted on by the pressure of the atmosphere only. This is the position of the three-way cock when it is desired to draw the atmospheric pressure line on the paper.

APPLICATION OF THE DIAGRAM

Determination of the action of the steam in the engine cylinder, and of the power developed at the time the diagram was taken, requires considerable experience in steam engine indication, and a discussion of the diagram as a means of showing what derangements exist in the valve motion and what remedies should be applied will not be given here.   However, it may be well to show how the indicator diagram is used in connection with the general method of computing the horse power.

Before taking up this discussion it will be well to fix clearly in mind certain important terms:

The Unit of Work is called the *Foot-Pound* and is the amount of work done in lifting one pound through a distance of *one foot*, or its equivalent.

The Horse Power is the standard used for measuring the rate at which work is performed in a steam engine.   Its value was originally determined by James Watt, from experiments made on London dray horses.   It is considerably above the power of an ordinary horse, and may be regarded as simply an arbitrary standard.

The Horse Power is equal to 33,000 foot-pounds of work exerted during one minute of time; that is, *one horse power* is developed when a weight of 33,000 *pounds* is raised through a distance of *one foot* in *one minute* of time, or its equivalent.

Mean effective pressure is the average pressure for the entire length of the piston stroke.   This is the pressure which moves the piston, and is measured between the upper and lower lines of the indicator diagram.   *Effective* has reference to the actual pressure of steam which is causing the piston of the engine to move, and *Mean* is that average pressure found by taking the steam pressure during one entire revolution, or for one forward and one return stroke of the piston.

The mean effective pressure may be obtained from the indicator diagram by determining the area enclosed by the diagram and then dividing this area expressed in square inches by the length of the diagram in inches, and multiplying by the number of pounds represented by *one inch* of height of the diagram, which is obtained by knowing the scale of the indicator spring.

The area of an indicator diagram may be obtained by the aid of an instrument called the planimeter; but it frequently becomes necessary to obtain the area without the use of a planimeter.   This may be accomplished by taking the average of a number of pressures measured between the *top* and *bottom* lines of the diagram at regular intervals along the length of the diagram.

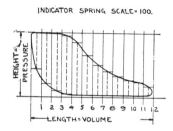

INDICATOR SPRING SCALE= 100.

HEIGHT = PRESSURE

1 2 3 4 5 6 7 8 9 10 11 12
LENGTH = VOLUME

FIG. 273.—Scaling M.E.P. from Diagram.

Fig. 273 illustrates the manner in which to lay off the diagram.

Divide the length of the diagram into any number of convenient spaces, say twelve, as shown in Fig. 273, then measure the heights or lengths of the vertical lines in each space; that is, measure the lengths of the dotted lines at the centers of each of the twelve spaces. The average of these heights is then determined by adding all of them together and dividing by the number of spaces. This result multiplied by the spring scale will give the mean effective pressure.

HORSE POWER OF LOCOMOTIVES

The general formula for ascertaining the horse power of a locomotive is as follows:

Ordinary locomotive having two cylinders.

$$\frac{P \times L \times A \times N}{33,000} = \text{H.P., in which}$$

$P =$ mean effective pressure in pounds per square inch (sometimes written M.E.P.), at the given speed;

$L =$ length of stroke of the piston measured in *feet;*

*$A =$ net area of the piston in square inches, equals the diameter (in inches) squared times 0.7854 minus area occupied by piston rod;

$N =$ number of strokes of the piston (four times the number of revolutions) per minute;

$H.P. =$ indicated horse power.

For example, let it be desired to determine the horse power of a locomotive which has been indicated, the diagrams giving a mean effective pressure, or M.E.P., of 150 pounds per square inch. The dimensions of the

_____
* If there is no extended piston rod the front end and back end H.P. must be calculated separately.

cylinder are 22 inches×28 inches, and the engine was running at a speed to have its drivers turn 180 revolutions per minute. Here P is equal to 150 pounds. The L is found by dividing 28 inches by 12 inches = 2.33 feet. The area A is 22 inches×22 inches×0.7854 = 380.13 square inches; and N is equal to 4×180 or 720 strokes per minute. (There are four working strokes of the two pistons for each revolution of the drivers.) Hence, by substituting these values in the general formula:

$$\text{H.P.} = \frac{150 \times 2.33 \times 380.13 \times 720}{33,000} :$$

$$\text{H.P.} = 2900.$$

For very close work it is necessary to deduct the area of the piston rod and figure each end separately.

TRACTIVE FORCE OF THE SINGLE EXPANSION LOCOMOTIVE

The single expansion locomotive is the ordinary two-cylinder type. It is often desired to ascertain the amount of tractive force, or hauling capacity, which a locomotive will develop. For this purpose the general formula as given below may be used. In this formula the mean effective pressure is usually taken as being either 85 percent or $\frac{4}{5}$ of the boiler pressure for running speeds not exceeding 10 miles per hour, and when it is not possible to indicate the cylinders. Thus:

$$T.F. = \frac{P \times d^2 \times S}{D} \text{ in which}$$

$T.F.$ = the tractive force in *pounds;*
 d = the diameter of the engine cylinder ($d^2 = d$ times d), in inches;
 P = mean effective pressure in pounds per square inch on the pistons;
 S = the stroke of the pistons *in inches;*
 D = the diameter of the driving wheels in inches.

For example: A locomotive working under a boiler pressure of 200 pounds per square inch has 24-inch×28-inch cylinders and 60-inch diameter drivers. The tractive force would be computed as follows: P is equal to $\frac{4}{5} \times 200 = 160$ pounds per square inch. Hence, substituting these values in the general tractive force formula, the tractive force is found to be:

$$T.F. = \frac{160 \times 24 \times 24 \times 28}{60} :$$

$T.F.$ = 43,200 pounds, at speeds not exceeding 10 miles per hour.

It is often convenient to determine the horse power developed by a locomotive in terms of the speed in miles per hour, and the following formula is arranged from the general horse power formula: Thus,

$$H.P. = \frac{P \times d^2 \times S \times (M.P.H)}{D \times 375} \text{ in which}$$

> $d =$ diameter of engine cylinder in square inches;
> $P =$ mean effective pressure in pounds per square inch at the given speed;
> $S =$ stroke of engine piston in inches;
> $M.P.H. =$ miles per hour at which locomotive is running;
> $D =$ diameter of drivers in inches;
> $H.P. =$ horse power.

The tractive force of a locomotive multiplied by the speed in miles per hour divided by 375 gives horse power.

For example: What is the horse power developed by the locomotive working under an $M.E.P.$ of 140 pounds per square inch, and having cylinders 22 inches $\times$ 28 inches, diameter of driving wheels 62 inches, and when running at a speed of 30 miles per hour?

Thus, $$H.P. = \frac{140 \times 22 \times 22 \times 28 \times 30}{62 \times 375}$$

$$H.P. = 2460.$$

It is usual practice in determining the mean effective pressure to be used in these formulæ to find an average value taken from a number of indicator diagrams of the two ends of both cylinders.

Fig. 274 illustrates four diagrams as taken from the right and left sides of a locomotive. The $M.E.P.$ is determined for each diagram by means of a planimeter, which finds the area in square inches, from which

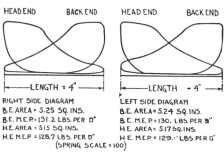

FIG. 274.—Four Cards, Right and Left Side.

values, knowing the spring scales used in the indicators, the mean effective pressure may be found.

Mean effective pressures:

$$* \text{Right Side } H.E. = \frac{5.15}{4} \times 100 = 128.7 \text{ pounds per square inch.}$$

$$\text{Right Side } B.E. = \frac{5.25}{4} \times 100 = 131.2 \text{ pounds per square inch.}$$

$$\text{Left Side } H.E. = \frac{5.17}{4} \times 100 = 129.0 \text{ pounds per square inch.}$$

$$\text{Left Side } B.E. = \frac{5.25}{4} \times 100 = 131.0 \text{ pounds per square inch.}$$

$$M.E.P. \text{ Total.} \qquad\qquad = 519.9 \text{ pounds per square inch.}$$

$$M.E.P. \text{ average} = \frac{519.9}{4} = 129.9 \text{ pounds per square inch.}$$

When the indicator diagrams are not taken, the calculation for the maximum mean effective pressure at slow speeds is found by multiplying the average boiler pressure by either 85 percent or $\frac{4}{5}$. Both values are commonly used, and give average results for speeds not exceeding 10 miles per hour.

TRACTIVE FORCE OF TWO=CYLINDER COMPOUND LOCOMOTIVES

For two-cylinder or cross-compound locomotives, assuming that the work done on the two sides is equal, it is only necessary in the calculations to consider the high-pressure cylinder. The formula is as follows:

$$\frac{\frac{2}{3}B \times d^2 \times S}{D} = T.F. \quad \text{(Total).}$$

TRACTIVE FORCE OF MALLET ARTICULATED COMPOUND LOCOMOTIVES

The formula given above for calculating the tractive force of a two-cylinder cross-compound locomotive is also applicable to the Mallet type, the result being multiplied by *two*, as the Mallet type has four cylinders.

The formula thus modified is as follows:

$$\frac{\frac{4}{3}B \times d^2 \times S}{D} = T.F.$$

* 5.15 = area of diagram,
    4 = length of diagram,
  100 = spring scale.

The notation used in the last two formulæ is the same, in which

B = boiler pressure in pounds per square inch;
d = diameter of high-pressure cylinder in inches;
S = length of stroke of piston in inches;
D = diameter of drivers in inches;
$T.F.$ = tractive force in pounds.

The constant given in these formulæ, with which the boiler pressure is multiplied, is for the general running conditions of the locomotive and is suitable for a speed not exceeding 10 miles per hour. The value of the tractive force thus obtained in pounds is that which the locomotive is capable of producing at slow speeds. As the speed of the locomotive increases the tractive force decreases, and for speeds exceeding 10 miles per hour the mean effective pressure should be specially determined by indication, or by use of proper speed factors sometimes given.

CLASSIFICATION OF LOCOMOTIVES
(Whyte's System)

Type.	Wheel Arrangement.	General Name.
0–4–0*	○○†	4 Wheel Shifter
0–6–0	○○○	6 Wheel Shifter
0–8–0	○○○○	8 Wheel Shifter
2–4–0	△ ○○	4 Coupled
2–6–0	△ ○○○	Mogul
2–8–0	△ ○○○○	Consolidation
2–10–0	△ ○○○○○	Decapod
2–12–0	△ ○○○○○○	Centipede
4–4–0	△ ○○○○	American Passenger
4–6–0	△ ○○○○○	10 Wheel
4–8–0	△ ○○○○○○	12 Wheel
4–10–0	△ ○○○○○○○	Mastodon
0–4–2	△ ○○○	
0–6–2	△ ○○○○	
0–8–2	△ ○○○○○	
0–4–4	△ ○○○○	Forney 4 Coupled
0–6–4	△ ○○○○○	Forney 6 Coupled
0–4–6	△ ○○○○○	
0–6–6	△ ○○○○○○	
2–4–2	△ ○○○○	Columbia
2–6–2	△ ○○○○○	Prairie
2–8–2	△ ○○○○○○	Mikado
2–10–2	△ ○○○○○○○	Santa Fe
2–4–4	△ ○○○○○	
2–6–4	△ ○○○○○○	
2–8–4	△ ○○○○○○○	
2–4–6	△ ○○○○○○	
2–6–6	△ ○○○○○○○	
4–2–2	△ ○○○○	Bicycle
4–4–2	△ ○○○○○	Atlantic
4–6–2	△ ○○○○○○	Pacific
4–8–2	△ ○○○○○○○	Mountain
4–4–4	△ ○○○○○○	Reading Baltic
4–6–4	△ ○○○○○○○	6 Coupled Double Ender
0–4–4–0	△ ○○ ○○	Mallet Articulated
0–6–6–0	△ ○○○ ○○○	Mallet Articulated
0–8–8–0	△ ○○○○ ○○○○	Mallet Articulated
2–4–4–0	△ ○○○ ○○	Mallet Articulated
2–6–6–0	△ ○○○○ ○○○	Mallet Articulated
2–8–8–0	△ ○○○○○ ○○○○	Mallet Articulated
2–4–4–2	△ ○○○ ○○○	Mallet Articulated
2–6–6–2	△ ○○○○ ○○○○	Mallet Articulated
2–8–8–2	△ ○○○○○ ○○○○○	Mallet Articulated
2–8–8–8–2	△ ○○○○○ ○○○○ ○○○○○	Articulated Triple Compound
2–8–8–8–8–2	△ ○○○○○ ○○○○ ○○○○ ○○○○○	Quadruplex

* First number designates number of wheels in leading truck.

Second number designates number of driving wheels.

Third number designates number of wheels in trailer.

†Explanation   △ ○○○○○○ – 4-6-2
                   1   2   3 4

(1) △ = Pilot
(2) ○○ = Truck
(3) ○○○ = Drivers
(4) ○ = Trailer

INDEX

Action of steam in cylinder, 3
    valve gear, 206–208
Admission, 8, 53, 58, 59, 258
    equalization of, 179
    inside, 25, 31, 46, 81, 91, 92, 94, 95, 101,
        112, 115, 116, 142, 148–151, 153,
        181, 183–186, 192–194, 223, 242,
        251
    line, 258
Advance, angle of, 88–89
Allen valve, 12–14, 17, 29, 250
    gear, 199
American balanced valve, 16–17
    Locomotive Co. power reverse, 135–140
Angle of advance, 88–89
Angularity of eccentric blades, 71–74, 157
    main rod, 63–71, 157
Arc of link, 74–76
Arm, rocker, 43–45, 47, 48, 80–82, 88, 90, 94
Atmospheric line, 259

Back end, 259
    pressure, 259
Backward motion, 35, 38–39, 211, 219, 222
Baker valve gear, 172–190, 237–242, 249,
    253
    diagram of, 180, 181
    parts of, 172, 175
    setting, 237–242, 249
Baker-Pilliod valve gear, 180, 181
Balanced area, 11, 15
    compound locomotive, 31–34
    valve, 16–17
Balancing, 11, 15–20, 21
    discs, 16
    rings, 16
    spring, 49
Bar, transmission, 43, 82
Bent rocker arm, 45, 81, 82

Block, link, 41, 42, 78, 107–108, 247
Bridges, 9, 27
Bridle, link, 42, 43, 66, 70, 71, 74–78,
    107–109
Brown, William S., 190
Bushing, 27

Chest, universal valve, 29–31
Classification of locomotives, 267
Clearance, 9
    exhaust, 7, 25, 26
Cock, indicator, 258–260
Combination lever, 100, 101, 110–116
Compound locomotive, 265
Compression, 8, 9, 54–56, 58, 59, 68, 69, 259
Connector, 101, 116, 157
Crank pin and piston positions, 50–82,
    142–156, 188
        Walschaert gear, 142–156
Crossed eccentric rods, 91, 94
Curves, 123, 124
Cut-off, 6, 8, 53, 54, 56–60, 68, 69, 217–222,
    237, 258
    equalization of, 166, 183, 221, 245

D slide-valve, 1–20
    proprotions, 9–11
    special forms, 12–20
Dead center, 52, 66, 213, 214, 223, 242
Diagram, indicator, 257–262
    piston positions, 203, 205
    valve, 200–210
Dimensions of valve, 200–210
Direct motion gear, 43, 46, 54
Discs, balancing, 16
Distortions, Stephenson gear, 66–82
    Walschaert gear, 106, 156–163, 228
Double admission, 12, 14

Eccentric, 36–39
　disadvantage of single, 100
　setting of, 86–95, 142–151, 168, 169, 184,
　　192, 193, 216, 237
　blade, 39, 40, 66, 67, 71–74, 91, 94, 157,
　　217, 226, 231, 232, 236, 239, 242, 244
　crank, 101, 104, 105
　rod. *See* Eccentric blade.
　Walschaert gear, 106, 248
　strap, 39–40
　throw, 38, 104
Eccentricity, 37–38
Equalization of admission, 179
　cut-off, 166, 183, 221, 245
Engine, three-cylinder, 196
Errors of link motion, 66–82
Evans, Oliver, 1
Events, valve, 8
Exhaust, 8, 54–56, 58, 60, 68, 69, 259
　clearance, 7, 25, 26
　closure, 8, 9, 54–56, 58, 59, 68, 69, 259
　lap, 7, 25, 26
Expansion, 5, 8, 54, 60, 259

Foot-pound, 261
Full forward gear, 52–57, 147–149, 188
　Walschaert motion, 142–151

Gooch stationary link, 198
Gridiron valve, 19

Hanger, link, 43
Head end, 259
Horse power, 261–263
Howe, William, 35
Hydro-pneumatic reverse gear, 128–131

Indicator, 255–257
　cock, 258–260
　diagram, 257–262
　piping, 260
Indirect motion, 43, 45, 54, 87–90, 94, 95,
　155
Inside admission, 25, 31, 46, 89, 91, 92,
　94, 95, 101, 112, 115, 116, 142, 148–151,
　153, 181, 183–186, 192–194, 223,
　242, 251
　lap, 7, 25, 26

John Bull engine, *frontispiece*
Joy valve gear, 194–196

Lap, 4–7, 86–87, 99, 209, 210, 212
　exhaust, 7, 25, 26
　and lead lever, Baker, 190
　　connector, 101, 116, 157
　　Walschaert, 100, 101, 110–116, 223,
　　　224, 230, 247
Lead, 50, 53, 55, 57, 59, 83–85, 86, 87, 99,
　101, 142, 156, 192, 198, 202, 208, 210,
　215–217, 225–229, 239, 243
Lever, lap and lead. *See* Lap and lead
　lever
　reverse, 43, 47–50, 107, 156, 168, 206–208,
　　218, 246
Lift shaft, 48, 49, 125
　spring, 48, 49, 125
Line on line, 5
Link, 40–43, 67, 98, 106–109
　arc, 74–76
　block, 41–42, 78, 107–108, 247
　bridle, 42, 43, 66, 70, 71, 74–78, 107–109
　　stud, 66, 70, 71, 74–78
　foot pin, 158–160
　Gooch, 198
　hanger, 43
　location of, 164
　motion, 35
　radius, 41, 42, 107, 110
　saddle, 43, 66, 70, 71, 74–78, 107–109
　stationary, 107
　swing of, 157
　union, 101, 116
Location of link, 164
Locomotive, compound, 265
Locomotives, classification, 267
Lost motion, 242

Mallet locomotive, 265
　valve gear, 236, 250
Marshall gear, 172–174, 177–180
Mean effective pressure, 261
Mellin power reverse gear, 135–140
Motion of valve, 79–95
Murdock, William, 36
Murray, Matthew, 1

Outside admission, 2, 25, 34, 75, 142, 145–
　148, 229–231
　lap, 5–7, 25, 26
Overbalance, 16
Overtravel, 10, 52

Packing rings, 27, 28
Pin, link foot, 158–160
Piping for indicator, 260
Piston, motion of, 60–66
  position diagram, 203, 205
  valve, 20–34, 112, 213, 250
    for balanced compounds, 31–34
    diameter of, 31
Planimeter, 261
Plate, pressure, 16
Port, 2, 9
Port marks, 211–213
  opening, 4
Power reverse, 128–141, 236
Pressure plate, 16

Quadrant, 48–50

Radial gear, 107, 172–196
Radius rod, 98, 101, 108–110, 115, 160–163, 227, 228, 248
  of link, 41–42, 107, 110
Ragonnet reverse gear, 131–134, 189
Reach rod, 48–49, 125–126
Release, 8, 54–56, 58, 60, 68, 69, 259
Reverse gear, hydro-pneumatic, 128–131
  Mellin, 135–140
  power, 128–141, 236
  Ragonnet, 131–134, 189
  Rushton, 140
  screw, 126–128, 189
  Young, 198
  lever, 43, 47–50, 107, 156, 168, 206–208, 218, 246
  shaft, 48, 49, 120–125
Reversible gear, 35, 38–39
Reversing, 85, 86, 155, 176, 182
Richardson balanced valve, 16
Rings, balancing, 16
  packing, 27, 28
Rocker arm, 43–45, 47, 48, 80–82, 88, 90, 94
  bent, 45, 81, 82
Rod, eccentric, 39, 40, 66, 67, 71–74, 91, 94, 157, 217, 226, 231, 232, 236, 239, 242, 244
  radius, 98, 101, 108–110, 115, 160–163, 227, 228, 248
  reach, 48–49, 125, 126
Rounding curves, 123–124

Rules for valve setting, 242–249
Running backward, 35, 38, 39, 211, 219, 222
  cut-off, 57–60, 151–154, 217
Rushton power reverse gear, 140

Saddle, link, 43, 66, 70, 71, 74–78, 107–109
Scotch yoke, 48, 63, 64
Screw reverse, 126–128, 189
Seal, 10
Seat, 2
  valve, 10, 26, 27
Setting, eccentric, 86–95, 142, 143, 151, 168, 169
  valves, 211–249
    Baker gear, 237–242, 249
    Stephenson gear, 215–222
    Walschaert gear, 223–237
Shaft, lift, 48–49, 125
  reverse, 48–49, 120–125
Shims, 39
Single eccentric, 100
Slip of link block, 78
Slot and roller support, 125
Southern valve gear, 190–194
Spring, lift, 48–49, 125
Springs of engine, 157
Squaring valves, 217–222
  Walschaert gear, 229
Standard gear, 43, 45, 46, 54
Starting valve, 34
Stationary link, 107
Steam action, 3
  engine indicator, 255–257
  lap, 5–7, 25, 26
  line, 258
  seal, 10
  superheated, 21, 22
Stem, valve, 22, 24, 46–48, 117–120
Stephenson gear, setting, 215–222
Stephenson, Robert, 35
  valve gear, 35–95, 251, 215–222
Strap, eccentric, 39, 40
Stud on link bridle, 66, 70, 71, 74–78
Summary, 250–253
Superheated steam, 21, 22
Swing of link, 157

Three-cylinder engine, 196
Throw of eccentric, 38, 104
Traction engine gear, 179–180

Tractive force, 263–265
Transmission bar, 43, 82
Travel, 1, 50, 59, 79, 80, 82, 83, 154, 155, 174, 179, 198, 206–208, 238

Underbalancing, 16
Union link, 101, 116
Universal valve chest, 29–31

Valve, Allen, 12–14, 17, 29, 250
  balanced, 16, 17
  D, 1–20
  gridiron, 19
  motion of, 79–95
  piston, 20–34, 112, 213, 250
  starting, 34
  Wilson, 14, 15, 17–20
Valve bushing, 27
  chest, universal, 29–31
  diagrams, 200–210
  dimensions, 200–210
  events, 8
  gear, 35
    action, 206–208
    Allen, 199
    Baker, 172–190, 253
    Baker-Pilliod, 180, 181
    Joy, 194–196
    Mallet, 236, 250
    Marshall, 172–174, 177–180

Valve gear, radial, 107, 172–196
    Southern, 190–194
    standard, 43, 45, 46, 54
    Stephenson, 35–95, 251
    traction engine, 179–180
    Walschaert, 22, 23, 96–171, 223–237
    Young, 196–198
  seat, 10, 26, 27
  setting, 211–249
  stem, 22, 24, 46–48, 117, 120
    crosshead, 117, 118
  travel. See Travel
  yoke, 46–48
Variable cut-off, Walschaert gear, 99

Walschaert gear, 22, 23, 96–171, 223–227
Walschaerts, Egide, 96
  advantage of, 144, 252
  elementary form, 97
  layout of, 163–171
  link, 98
  variable cut-off, 99
Watt, James, 1
Wilson valve, 14, 15, 17–20

Yoke, Scotch, 48, 63, 64
  valve, 46–48
Young reverse gear, 198
  valve gear, 196–198